SPRING FLORA
of
MINNESOTA

Including Common Cultivated Plants

By THOMAS MORLEY

MINNEAPOLIS • THE UNIVERSITY OF MINNESOTA PRESS
in association with the Department of Botany, University of Minnesota

CONTENTS

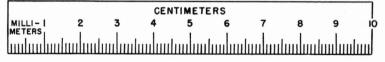

INTRODUCTION

With the retreat of winter and the coming of verdant spring there rises among the general public a surge of interest in the colorful world of plants, and at the same time formal classes in plant classification and identification begin in the schools, for this is the season when most such courses are given. The principal functions of a spring flora, then, are to provide a relatively inexpensive manual for student use, and to serve the public at a time of renewed interest.

Minnesota's floral spring might be said to begin in mid-March, when in early seasons the pasque flowers, quaking aspens, some maples, and perhaps other plants start to bloom, but few other flowers follow them until April. Then the hepaticas, bloodroots, trout lilies, and other early herbs become conspicuous, and many more of our trees and shrubs come into flower. From then on an ever-increasing procession of plants appears, till spring merges into summer in June. Spring in the state comes earliest in the south, in response to latitudinal climatic differences, so that a given wide-ranging plant may bloom two to three weeks later in the north than the south. Early springs start about a month sooner than late ones. Plants which appear at well separated intervals during an early spring may bloom much closer in time in a late spring, since then the season tends to become telescoped; thus it is that spring plants in general show more annual variation in blooming time than do summer ones.

The present book follows the general outline of the earlier Guide to the Spring Flowers of Minnesota, first written in 1908 and carried through four editions by F. E. Clements, C. O. Rosendahl, and F. K. Butters, then continued through an eighth edition of 1951 by Rosendahl and Butters only. In particular, the present inclusion of cultivated plants follows the precedent established with the third edition of the Guide. The Spring Flora is completely re-written, however, with the addition of species descriptions, distributions, and many species.

June 7 has been set as the arbitrary cut-off date for "spring"; only plants in bloom before then are included, with the exception of a very few that were added for special reasons. This date applies to a rather early season; in years of later springs the period covered might reach mid-June. Coverage of native and naturalized plants has been made as complete as possible, while for practical reasons only the more common cultivated ones are treated. Of the former there are 662 species, of the latter 194.

Families are arranged in the usual Englerian sequence, in conformance with other floras, but within the families the genera and species are alphabetically arranged. Information in the keys to species is not repeated in the specific descriptions that follow, for economy of space.

Plant distributions are described only within the state of Minnesota. In most instances these distributions are based entirely on the plant collections in the herbarium of the University of Minnesota at Minneapolis. Extensive as these collections are, they are by no means complete, and it has therefore been necessary in many cases to interpret ranges on the basis of scattered and apparently incomplete records. Consequently most of the ranges given here are subject to modification. The available reports on tree distribution prepared by the North Central Forest Experiment Station have been utilized, and the distributions of several species have been filled out through the use of field notes taken by Dr. E. V. Bakuzis and Dr. R. Waring, who kindly lent the notes to me. In addition, the maps in Olga Lakela's "A Flora of Northeastern Minnesota" were checked, as were a few other publications on local distributions.

3

The most important single source of information used in the preparation of this book has been the very fine herbarium at the University of Minnesota, mentioned above, without which very little worthwhile could have been done; I am indebted to its curator, Dr. G. B. Ownbey, for the free use of it, and to the many persons who contributed to it. I have also drawn heavily on major works in this field, in particular the eighth edition of Gray's Manual of Botany, by M. L. Fernald, the New Britton and Brown Illustrated Flora by H. A. Gleason and its condensed version, the Manual of Vascular Plants, by Gleason and A. Cronquist, and Trees and Shrubs of the Upper Midwest, by C. O. Rosendahl.

The nomenclature used herein is usually that of Fernald's book. Where it departs, his usage is given as a synonym, and similarly, where it differs from Gleason and Cronquist, their usage is given. Synonomy of the present book is usually limited to this.

SCIENTIFIC NAMES AND CLASSIFICATION

Those unfamiliar with scientific names will soon accustom themselves to their use and to the stepwise classification system of which they are a part. Individual plants resembling each other closely enough to be considered collectively as one "kind" of plant are designated as one species. More detailed considerations of the nature of species need not concern us here. Similar species are grouped together into genera (singular, genus). The scientific name is then given as the genus followed by the species. Thus our three native pines, White Pine, Red Pine, and Jack Pine, are named Pinus strobus, Pinus resinosa, and Pinus banksiana, respectively. Generic names start with a capital, specific names with a lower case letter except that in some cases it is permissible to capitalize the species name. The name of the author of the plant's name, usually abbreviated, follows the name itself when the fullest possible citation is used, as for example Pinus strobus L. (L. for Carolus Linnaeus) or Pinus resinosa Ait. (Ait. for William Aiton). Similar genera are grouped in turn into families, the family name usually being recognizable by the spelling of the Latin suffix, as in the Pinaceae, the pine family. Similar families are then grouped into orders, which generally are less well defined than families and which are not given herein. Orders are further assembled into still larger groups, and so on, the larger groups being separated from each other by more fundamental differences than the smaller. Additional categories representing levels of difference between these groups as well as below the species are available for use when desired.

The major groups included in this book are the gymnosperms and angiosperms. The angiosperms, the true flowering plants, are marked by the presence of a folded structure, the carpel, enclosing the ovules, by the usual presence of a perianth surrounding the reproductive parts, and by certain other characteristics; the gymnosperms lack these features. In practice we tell our native gymnosperms largely by their needle-like leaves, by the absence of a perianth, and by the presence of cones in most. Within the angiosperms are two great subdivisions, the monocotyledons and dicotyledons, each containing many families. The monocotyledons are characterized by the usually parallel leaf venation, the arrangement of the flower parts in 3's or 6's, the scattered vascular bundles and lack of vascular cambium in the stem, and the single leaf (cotyledon) of the embryo. The dicotyledons have usually branching leaf veins, flower parts in 4's or 5's particularly in the perianth, vascular bundles in a ring, vascular cambium, and two cotyledons. Exceptions can be found to all these characters. Families of monocotyledons in this book are those through the Orchidaceae; all the rest are dicotyledons.

4

KEYS AND THEIR USE

The most efficient way to identify the average unknown plant is by tracing it through the appropriate keys. Keys are simple elimination devices which will enable the user in a series of successive choices to eliminate all but the group to which the plant belongs. Two choices only are possible at each step in most keys, including those provided here. Starting at the upper left, the plant in hand is compared with the two contrasting statements headed "A"; the one best describing the plant is chosen, and the user then proceeds to the next pair of alternatives, immediately below and indented one step. Continue until a determination is reached. Keys to family, genus, and species are separate.

Genera marked with an asterisk are those for which all species native or naturalized to Minnesota are included in this Spring Flora. The other genera have some members which are excluded because of their later blooming time.

HELP WITH IDENTIFICATION

Plants may be sent for identification to the Herbarium at the Botany Department of the University of Minnesota. The specimens should be ample and should if possible include flowers or fruits, leaves, and stem, as well as roots when feasible. Each plant should be accompanied by information such as the locality and date of its collection, its habitat, and its size if it is too large to be taken whole. If the plant is cultivated this should be noted. Material may be sent fresh, wrapped with damp paper in a plastic bag and put in a box suitable for mailing, or it may be pressed and dried. To press it, place it inside a single page of newspaper folded once, spreading the leaves and other parts carefully to avoid crumpling or folding. Place the newspaper and contained specimen between drying materials such as large blotters or several more thicknesses of newspaper and apply pressure by boards and weights or by straps or ropes around two rectangles of plywood or the equivalent. The drying materials should be replaced about once a day by bone-dry fresh ones until the specimen is dry; the old materials may be dried in the sun or over heat for re-use.

ACKNOWLEDGEMENTS

I am indebted to Dr. A. O. Dahl for advice on cultivated plants; to Dr. M. Heimburger for information on Anemone; to Dr. R. A. Howard for determinations of cultivated plants, particularly Lonicera; to Mrs. Helen Irvine for information on the early-blooming grasses; to Mr. A. G. Johnson for advice on cultivated plants; to Mr. E. P. Kruschke for information on the Crataegus rotundifolia and C. macrosperma groups; to Dr. W. H. Lewis for information on Rosa carolina; to Dr. J. W. Moore, for general assistance; to Dr. G. B. Ownbey for useful suggestions; to Dr. S. J. Preece Jr. for information on Zygadenus; to Dr. L. H. Shinners for critical comments throughout; to Mrs. M. H. Smithberg for advice on cultivated plants and on Cornus; to Dr. L. C. Snyder for advice on cultivated plants; to Dr. O. A. Stevens for helpful criticisms; and to Dr. John W. Thieret for useful suggestions.

Finally, I gratefully acknowledge the financial assistance of the Junior F. Hayden Fund of the Department of Botany in meeting publication costs.

Minneapolis, 1968

VEGETATION TYPES OF MINNESOTA
THEIR APPROXIMATE BOUNDARIES UNDER NATURAL CONDITIONS

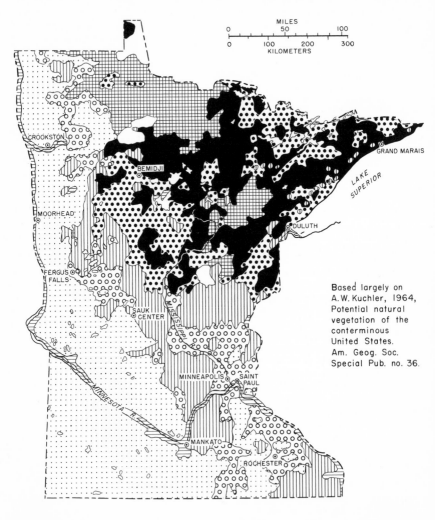

Based largely on
A. W. Kuchler, 1964,
Potential natural
vegetation of the
conterminous
United States.
Am. Geog. Soc.
Special Pub. no. 36.

Great Lakes spruce—fir
forest (Picea—Abies)

Great Lakes pine forest
(Pinus)

Conifer bog
(Larix—Picea—Thuja)

Maple—basswood forest
(Acer—Tilia)

Northern floodplains forest
(Populus—Salix—Ulmus)

Oak—savanna
(Quercus—Andropogon)

Bluestem prairie
(Andropogon—Panicum—
—Sorghastrum)

6

KEYS TO FAMILIES (and to genera and species in many cases)

PRELIMINARY KEY

A-Plants parasitic on the branches of conifers . . . . <u>Arceuthobium</u>, p.101
A-Plants terrestrial or aquatic.
  B-Woody plants: trees, shrubs, or woody vines or prostrate trailers.
    C-Gymnosperms: leaves needle-like, scale-like, or in one case fan-shaped with dichotomously branching veins (fig. 4), evergreen except in the Larches and <u>Ginkgo</u>; pollen and seed-bearing parts in separate clusters, the clusters never with petals; plants cone-bearing except in the Yews and <u>Ginkgo</u> (the cones small and berry-like in the Junipers) . . . . KEY 1, p. 8
    C-Angiosperms: leaves usually relatively broad, if needle-or scale-like then petals present, leaves never fan-shaped with dichotomously branching veins; pollen and seed-bearing parts in the same or separate clusters ("flowers"), often with petals; plants never bearing true cones.
      D-Leaves not yet developed.
        E-Leaf scars and leaf buds opposite . . . . KEY 2, p. 8
        E-Leaf scars and leaf buds alternate . . . . KEY 3, p. 8
      D-Leaves sufficiently developed to see their structure.
        F-Leaves compound . . . . KEY 4, p. 10
        F-Leaves simple.
          G-Leaves all or mostly opposite (if leaves densely clustered, note scars of previous leaves along the twig). . . KEY 5, p. 11
          G-Leaves all or mostly alternate.
            H-Shrubs or trees . . . . KEY 6, p. 12
            H-Prostrate trailers or twining or tendril-bearing vines . . . . KEY 7, p. 16
  B-Herbaceous plants (the above-ground stems relatively soft and mostly dying at the end of the growing season).
    I-Foliage leaves absent at least at flowering time; leaves sometimes represented by bracts or scales . . . . KEY 8, p. 16
    I-Foliage leaves present.
      J-Leaves all or at least some of them compound or cut 9/10 or more of the way to the midrib . . . . KEY 9, p. 17
      J-Leaves all simple (entire or cut less than 9/10 of the way to the midrib).
        K-Leaves parallel-veined, with 5 or more coarse to very fine lengthwise veins running from the base toward the apex; stem leaves alternate when present (rarely crowded to resemble a whorl); leaves never lobed . . . . . KEY 10, p. 20
        K-Leaves not parallel-veined, or with 3 lengthwise veins, alternate, opposite, or whorled when on the stem, entire to cleft.
          L-Flowers all in heads . . . . KEY 11, p. 21
          L-Flowers in various inflorescences or single, not all in heads.
            M-Flowers crowded tightly together with no space between in a single compact spike which is enclosed in a hooded structure open down one side . . . . . . <u>Symplocarpus</u>, p. 58
            M-Flowers otherwise.
              N-Perianth undifferentiated, either calyx-like or corolla-like or rarely none, usually of 1 whorl, if of 2 or more whorls the outer about like the inner in color, size, and shape . . . . KEY 12, p. 22
              N-Perianth differentiated, of both calyx and corolla, these distinctly different from each other.
                O-Petals separate to the base . . . . KEY 13, p. 24
                O-Petals fused at least at the base . . . . . . KEY 14, p. 25

KEY 1

Gymnosperms

A-Leaves fan-shaped with dichotomously branching veins (fig. 4)
 and no midrib . . . . Ginkgo, p. 35
A-Leaves linear, a midrib present.
 B-Leaves without a resinous odor when crushed, the fruit a
  single seed surrounded by a pinkish-red fleshy layer . . Taxus, p. 34
 B-Leaves with a resinous odor when crushed, the fruit either
  a small to large woody cone or a small bluish to brownish
  berry.
  C-Leaves alternate or in compact clusters, the fruit a woody
   cone with spirally arranged scales . . . . Pinaceae, p. 29
  C-Leaves opposite or whorled, the fruit either a small cone
   with opposite scales or a bluish to brownish berry
   . . . . Cupressaceae, p. 32

KEY 2

Woody angiosperms, leafless, leaf scars opposite

A-Cultivated shrubs with conspicuous yellow flowers; petals 4, fused
 below, 12-25 mm long; stamens 2 . . . . Forsythia, p. 215
A-Cultivated or native shrubs or trees, not as above, the flowers
 yellowish or not but the perianth either undifferentiated or the
 petals only 1.5-2.5 mm long and free and the stamens 4-12.
 B-Shrubs to small trees; buds and young twigs densely covered
  with tiny silvery to brownish-red peltate scales; stigma
  (when ovary present) entire; stamens (when present)
  perigynous . . . . Shepherdia p. 198
 B-Trees; buds and twigs not peltate-scaly; stigma (when
  present) 2-cleft; stamens (when present) hypogynous.
  C-Leaf scar a thin crescent containing usually 3 widely
   separate bundle scars; ovary (when present) prominently
   2-lobed, the stigmas 2, elongate; stamens (when
   present) 4-10; sepals 4 or 5. . . . . Acer, p. 186
  C-Leaf scar a thick crescent to a vertical ellipse containing
   very many nearly confluent bundle scars forming a U-
   shaped line; ovary (when present) unlobed, the stigma
   2-cleft but its branches not elongate; stamens (when
   present) 2 (rarely 3 or 4); sepals 4 or the calyx irregularly
   toothed or none . . . . Fraxinus, p. 215

KEY 3

Woody angiosperms, leafless, leaf scars alternate

A-Stamens absent (staminodes sometimes present), the plants
 dioecious (this section does not include monoecious plants
 whose staminate inflorescences have fallen to the ground).
 B-Stems thorny. . . . . Zanthoxylum, p. 181
 B-Stems thornless.

8

C-Shrubs to 1.5 m high; floral bracts, ovary, and usually
    the young twigs dotted with tiny golden resin-granules;
    catkins 5-10 mm long in flower . . . . Myricaceae, p. 91
C-Low to high shrubs or trees without resin dots (bud
    scales often resin-coated in Populus); catkins usually
    longer.
    D-Shrubs or trees without milky sap; floral bracts
        present; perianth cup-shaped and undivided or none;
        leaf scar with 3 or more bundle scars in a single
        lunate line. . . . . Salicaceae, p. 80
    D-Trees with milky sap; floral bracts none; perianth
        deeply 4-parted; bundle scars more than 3, not in
        single lunate line . . . . Morus, p. 100
A-Stamens present; plants dioecious, monoecious, or with bi-
    sexual flowers, when monoecious the inflorescences of two
    kinds, staminate and carpellate.
    E-Stems thorny.
        F-Stamens 4 or 5. . . . . Zanthoxylum, p. 181
        F-Stamens 15 or more. . . . . Rosaceae, p. 150
    E-Stems thornless.
        G-Flowers bisexual, never in catkins.
            H-Perianth of 1 whorl, calyx-like or corolla-like.
                I-Shrub; stamens perigynous; style 1 . . . . Dirca, p. 197
                I-Tree; stamens hypogynous; styles 2 . . . . Ulmaceae, p. 98
            H-Perianth of two whorls, calyx and corolla.
                J-Petals free to the base; stamens 15 or more . . Rosaceae, p. 150
                J-Petals fused below; stamens 10 . . . . Rhododendron, p. 210
        G-Flowers and inflorescences unisexual, at least the
            staminate flowers in catkins.
            K-Staminate flowers not subtended by bracts; each
                male flower with an obvious perianth of 4-8 tepals,
                visible without dissecting the catkin.
                L-Sap milky; staminate catkins often with short
                    branches toward the end; tepals and stamens
                    4; carpellate flowers, if present, with a 2-
                    parted style.. . . . . Morus, p. 100
                L-Sap not milky; staminate catkins unbranched;
                    tepals 3-7 (usually 6), stamens 3-12; carpellate
                    flowers, if present, with a 3-lobed stigma. . . . Quercus, p. 97
            K-Staminate flowers in the axils of bracts, sometimes
                fused to them; male flowers either with a flat or
                curled undivided perianth, or with a divided
                perianth hidden between the bracts, or the
                perianth none.
                M-Shrubs to 1.5 m high; floral bracts (at least below)
                    and usually the inflorescence axis and young twigs
                    dotted with tiny golden resin-granules; male cat-
                    kins 1-4 cm long, female (when present) 0.5-1 cm
                    long in flower . . . . Myricaceae, p. 91
                M-Low to high shrubs or trees; resin dots absent
                    (bud scales often resin-coated in Populus);
                    catkins short to long.
                    N-Bracts toothed, lobed, or fringed (all catkins
                      staminate). . . . . Populus, p. 80

N-Bracts (of staminate catkin) entire or slightly and
irregularly angled.
  O- Buds covered by one scale; catkins (staminate)
    ascending or spreading, rarely drooping,
    usually less than 7 times as long as wide
    (including stamens in width); stamens free
    from bract, exserted beyond it on prominent
    filaments; dioecious . . . . Salix, p. 82
  O-Bud scales several; staminate catkins pendu-
    lous, usually more than 7 times as long as
    wide; stamens adherent to bract or its stalk,
    remaining beneath the bract; monoecious,
    but female inflorescences often rare or
    inaccessible. . . . . Betulaceae, p. 93

KEY 4

Woody angiosperms, leaves compound

A-Leaves opposite (if leaves still densely clustered in early
  spring, note scars of previous leaves).
  B-Climber or trailer. . . . . Clematis, p. 115
  B- Shrub or tree.
    C-Leaves palmately compound with 5-7 leaflets . . . . Aesculus, p. 189
    C-Leaves pinnately compound or trifoliolate.
      D-Leaflets 3.
        E-Perianth of 1 whorl only; flowers unisexual. Acer negundo, p. 187
        E-Perianth of both calyx and corolla; flowers bisexual.
          F-Corolla yellow, of 4 petals fused at base . . . Forsythia, p. 215
          F-Corolla white, of 5 free petals. . . . . Staphylea, p. 186
      D-Leaflets 5-11.
        G-Corolla whitish, calyx often obsolete; flowers bisexual,
          ovary inferior; shrub or small tree . . . . . . Sambucus, p. 242
        G-Corolla none, calyx if present not whitish; flowers
          usually unisexual, ovary if present superior;
          polygamous or dioecious trees.
          H-Male flowers on elongating pendulous stalks, the
            stamens 4-8; ovary 2-lobed; leaf scar a thin crescent
            containing usually 3 widely separated bundle scars
            . . . . Acer negundo, p. 187
          H-Male flowers in dense compact racemes or panicles,
            the stamens 2 (rarely 3 or 4); ovary not lobed;
            leaf scar a thick crescent to a vertical ellipse
            containing numerous and almost confluent bundle
            scars forming a U-shaped line . . . . Fraxinus, p. 215
A-Leaves alternate.
  I-Leaflets 3.
    J-Prickly shrubs or trailers . . . . Rosaceae, p. 150
    J-Shrubs or vines without prickles.
      K-Erect shrub to 6 m high; leaflets with translucent
        dots. . . . . Ptelea, p. 181
      K-Low little-branched shrub 0.1-0.6 m high or a
        trailing or climbing shrub or vine; translucent
        dots none.

L-Lateral leaflets much smaller than the terminal one;
 flowers usually purple, rarely white . . . .
 . . . . Solanum dulcamara, p. 230
L-Leaflets all about the same size; flowers yellowish-
 green or white to pink.
 M-Leaflets 4-14 cm long, entire or coarsely and
 irregularly toothed with up to 7 teeth per side;
 flowers yellowish-green: POISON IVY. Rhus radicans, p. 184
 M-Leaflets 1-10 cm long, serrate, with 12 or more
 teeth per side if more than 4 cm long . . . . . . Rubus, p. 166
I-Leaflets 4 or more.
 N-Leaves twice compound.
 O-Trees; leaflets entire to crenulate . . . . Fabaceae, p. 170
 O-Shrub to 1.7 m high; leaflets mostly 3-5-lobed
 . . . . Paeonia suffruticosa, p. 123
 N-Leaves once compound.
 P-Trees with pendulous catkins of staminate flowers, the
 plants monoecious; female flowers few, with 2 or 4
 styles . . . . Juglandaceae, p. 91
 P-Low shrubs to trees, inflorescences never catkins,
 if somewhat resembling catkins then both petals and
 sepals present and the female flower with 1 style;
 flowers bisexual or unisexual.
 Q-Flowers conspicuously zygomorphic; petals 1 or 5,
 of different sizes and shapes when 5 . . . . . . Fabaceae, p. 170
 Q-Flowers radially symmetrical or nearly so; petals
 3-5, similar (sepals absent in Zanthoxylum).
 R-Stamens 15 or more . . . . Rosaceae, p. 150
 R-Stamens 0-10
 S-Inflorescence a spike or raceme; stamens 3-10
 when present.
 T-Tree; flowers 3.5-8 mm long . . . . . . Gleditsia, p. 174
 T-Shrub to 1 m high; flowers 20-30 mm long
 . . . . Dictamnus, p. 181
 S-Inflorescence a panicle or sessile umbel-like
 cluster; stamens 3-5 when present.
 U-Stems thorny. . . . . Zanthoxylum, p. 181
 U-Stems thornless. . . . . Rhus, p. 184

KEY 5

Woody angiosperms; leaves simple, opposite

A-Leaves prominently lobed or cleft.
 B-Petals free to the base or none (calyx present here and below).
 . . . . Acer, p. 186
 B-Petals present, fused at least at the base.
 C-Corolla yellow . . . . Forsythia, p. 215
 C-Corolla white to pink . . . . Viburnum, p. 243
A-Leaves not lobed or cleft.
 D-Perianth of one whorl only.
 E-Leaves silvery at least beneath from closely appressed
 tiny scales. . . . . Shepherdia, p. 198
 E-Leaves green on both sides.
 F-Perianth white to cream; leaves mostly entire, all
 opposite. . . . . Cornus, p. 204

F-Perianth greenish; leaves finely serrate, sometimes
    subopposite or partly alternate . . . . <u>Rhamnus</u> <u>cathartica</u>, p. 189
D-Perianth of two whorls, calyx and corolla.
  G-Petals fused at least at the very base.
    H-Stamens 10; ovary superior . . . . <u>Kalmia</u>, p. 209
    H-Stamens 0-5; ovary superior to inferior.
      I-Ovary superior, stamens 2. . . . . <u>Oleaceae</u>, p. 214
      I-Ovary 3/4 or more inferior; stamens 4 or 5
    . . . .<u>Caprifoliaceae</u>, p. 239
  G-Petals free to the base.
    J-Petals 10-30 mm long; stamens 20-40 . . . . . . <u>Philadelphus</u>, p. 145
    J-Petals 1.5-5 mm long; stamens 0-12.
      K-Flowers in a terminal raceme or panicle or panicle-
      like compound cyme.
        L-Leaves entire to rarely crenulate . . . .<u>Cornus</u>, p. 204
        L-Leaves conspicuously serrate . . . . <u>Acer</u>, p. 186
      K-Flowers axillary, single or in umbel-like clusters or
      cymes.
        M-Flowers single or in umbel-like clusters; stamens
        opposite the petals; usually some leaves alternate;
        flowers 4-merous. . . . . <u>Rhamnus</u> <u>cathartica</u>, p. 189
        M-Flowers in cymes; stamens alternate with the
        petals; leaves all opposite; flowers 4-5 merous
        . . . . <u>Euonymus</u>, p. 185

KEY 6

<u>Woody angiosperms; leaves simple, alternate; shrubs or trees</u>

A-Flowers in dense spherical heads 8-20 mm in diameter, the
  individual flowers small, crowded, pointing in all directions
  from center of head; heads male or female, both of the same
  form and both on the same tree . . . . <u>Platanus</u>, p. 149
A-Flowers not arranged as above.
  B-Stamens absent (staminodes sometimes present), all inflorescences alike (this section does not include monoecious
  plants whose staminate inflorescences have fallen to the
  ground).
    C-Flowers in axillary cymes or umbel-like clusters of 1 to
    ca. 15 flowers.
      D-Leaves silvery at least beneath from closely appressed
      tiny scales . . . .<u>Elaeagnus</u>, p. 197
      D-Leaves green on both sides.
        E-Leaves finely crenate to serrate; flowers with 4 or
        5 ovate or lanceolate greenish sepals 1.5-2 mm
        long; petals 4 or none, erect, greenish, 0.6 mm long
        . . . . <u>Rhamnus</u>, p.189
        E-Leaves entire or with a few teeth toward the leaf
        apex; flowers with 4-5 greenish minute deciduous
        subulate sepals, or these obsolete; petals
        spreading, linear-oblong, greenish-yellow to
        whitish-yellow, ca. 2 mm long . . . . . . <u>Nemopanthus</u>, p. 184
    C-Flowers in racemes, panicles, or catkins, usually
    more than 15.
      F-Flowers in erect lateral racemes or terminal
      racemes or panicles, the flowers well separated,
      both petals and sepals plainly visible.

G-Leaves unlobed, pinnately veined; flowers in
    terminal racemes or panicles . . . . Celastrus, p. 185
G-Leaves palmately lobed and veined; flowers in erect
    lateral racemes . . . . Ribes alpinum, p. 147
F-Flowers in compact roundish to elongate catkins, the
    more elongate ones sometimes with well separated
    flowers and pedicels up to 10 mm long; petals none.
    H-Shrubs to 1.5 m high, at least the upper leaf sur-
        face and the floral bracts with a scattering of
        tiny golden resin-granules, these often also
        present beneath the leaves and on the twigs;
        leaves fragrant when crushed; catkins 5-10 mm
        long in flower . . . . Myricaceae, p. 91
    H-Low to high shrubs or trees without resin dots (bud
        scales often resin-coated in Populus); leaves fragrant
        or not; catkins usually longer.
        I-Shrubs or trees without milky sap; leaves not lobed;
            floral bracts present; perianth cup-shaped and
            undivided or none; fruits dry, separate . . Salicaceae, p. 80
        I-Trees with milky sap; leaves sometimes irregularly
            3-5-lobed; floral bracts none; perianth deeply
            4-parted, its lobes becoming fused together and
            to the ovary; fruit a blackberry-like multiple
            fruit. . . . . Morus, p. 100
B-Stamens present, the inflorescences sometimes of two
    kinds, staminate and carpellate.
    J-Catkins present, at least the male flowers borne in
        them and sometimes the female also (flowers and
        inflorescences both unisexual; perianth of 1 whorl or
        none; all plants monoecious or dioecious).
        K-Staminate flowers not subtended by bracts; each male
            flower with an obvious perianth of 4-8 tepals, visible
            without dissecting the catkin.
            L-Sap milky; staminate catkins often with short branches
                toward the end; tepals and stamens 4; carpellate
                flowers, if present, with a 2-parted style; fruit a
                blackberry-like multiple fruit . . . . Morus, p. 100
            L-Sap not milky; staminate catkins unbranched; tepals
                3-7 (usually 6), stamens 3-12; carpellate flowers,
                if present, with a 3-lobed stigma; fruit an acorn
        . . . . Quercus, p. 97
        K-Staminate flowers in the axils of bracts, sometimes
            fused to them; male flowers either with a flat or
            curled undivided perianth or with a divided perianth
            hidden between the bracts, or the perianth none.
            M-Shrubs to 1.5 m high; at least the upper leaf surface
                and the floral bracts with a scattering of tiny golden
                resin-granules, these often also present beneath the
                leaves and on the twigs; leaves fragrant when crushed;
                male catkins 1-4 cm long, female (when present)
                0.5-1 cm long in flower; leaves sometimes deeply
                pinnately cut . . . . Myricaceae, p. 91
            M-Low to high shrubs or trees without resin dots (bud
                scales often resin-coated in Populus); leaves
                fragrant or not; catkins short to long; leaves not
                pinnately cut.

N-Bracts toothed, lobed, or fringed . . . . . . Populus, p. 80
N-Bracts (of staminate catkin) entire or slightly and
   irregularly angled.
   O-Catkins (staminate) ascending or spreading,
      rarely drooping, usually less than 7 times as
      long as wide (including stamens in measure-
      ments); stamens free from bract, exserted
      beyond it on prominent filaments; buds covered
      by one scale; dioecious . . . . Salix, p. 82
   O-Staminate catkins pendulous, usually more than
      7 times as long as wide; stamens adherent to
      bract or its stalk, remaining beneath the bract;
      bud scales several; monoecious, but the female
      inflorescences often rare or inaccessible
      . . . . Betulaceae, p. 93
J-Flowers never in catkins; if the inflorescence cylindric
   and spike-like both calyx and corolla present and the
   flowers bisexual; flowers usually bisexual, a few plants
   monoecious or dioecious.
   P-Perianth of 1 whorl, calyx-like or corolla-like.
      Q-Leaves silvery at least beneath from closely appressed
         tiny scales . . . . Elaeagnus, p. 197
      Q-Leaves green on both sides.
      R-Trees; leaf blades usually asymmetrical at base,
         serrate; stamens as many as the perianth divisions
         and opposite them; styles or style branches 2; fruit
         a 1-seeded samara or drupe . . . . Ulmaceae, p. 98
      R-Shrubs or small trees; leaf blades symmetrical at
         base, entire to serrate, if serrate the stamens
         alternate with the perianth divisions, the style
         3-4-cleft or the stigmas sessile, and the fruit a
         3-5-seeded drupe.
      S-Leaves crenate to serrate; perianth
         greenish . . . . Rhamnus, p. 189
      S-Leaves entire or with a few scattered teeth; perianth white
         to greenish-white, greenish-yellow, or pale yellow.
         T-Flowers white to cream, in terminal panicle-
            like cymes of many flowers . . . Cornus alternifolia, p. 205
         T-Flowers greenish-white, greenish-yellow, or
            pale yellow, in lateral clusters of 1-4.
         U-Flowers pale yellow, 6-11 mm long; stamens
            8 . . . . Dirca, p. 197
         U-Flowers greenish-white to greenish-yellow,
            1.5-3 mm long; stamens 4 or 5 . . Nemopanthus, p. 184
   P-Perianth of 2 or more whorls, usually but not always
      sharply differentiated into calyx and corolla.
      V-Petals fused at least at base . . . . Ericaceae, p. 206
      V-Petals (inner perianth whorl) free to base.
      W-Stamens more numerous than the petals (or the
         petals 10 or more). Check several flowers.
      X-Low shrub of sandy areas, the leaves 1-4 mm
         long . . . . Hudsonia, p. 192
      X-Shrubs to trees, leaves longer.

Y-Leaves entire, their edges rolled under, the
  lower leaf surface completely obscured by a
  covering of long tawny or rusty wool . . . . <u>Ledum</u>, p. 209
Y-Leaves not as above.
   Z-Corolla strongly bilaterally symmetrical;
    leaves 10-14 mm long . . . . <u>Caragana pygmaea</u>, p. 174
   Z-Corolla radially symmetrical; leaves larger.
    AA-Petals mostly 5 (10 or more in some
     cultivated forms), the stamens and petals
     perigynous or epigynous . . . . <u>Rosaceae</u>, p. 150
    AA-Petaloid perianth members 6-9; stamens
     and petals hypogynous . . . . . <u>Magnoliaceae</u>, p. 124
W-Stamens as many as the petals (petals 4-6).
  BB-Leaves coarsely to finely but consistently and
   distinctly toothed or lobed.
   CC-Petals shorter than the sepals.
    DD-Leaves all alternate or clustered, more or
     less palmately lobed and veined; stamens
     alternate with the petals . . . . <u>Ribes</u>, p. 146
    DD-Some of the leaves opposite; leaves never
     lobed, pinnately to somewhat palmately
     veined; stamens opposite the petals
     . . . . <u>Rhamnus cathartica</u>, p. 189
   CC-Petals longer than the sepals.
    EE-Petals white, 5-8 mm long; plants usually
     with scattered large thorns 2-5 cm long
     . . . . <u>Crataegus</u>, p. 154
    EE-Petals greenish-white to greenish-yellow,
     2-4 mm long; plants thornless.
     FF-Flowers in terminal raceme-like cymes
      or panicles . . . . <u>Celastrus</u>, p. 185
     FF-Flowers 1-4 in the leaf axils . . <u>Nemopanthus</u>, p. 184
  BB-Leaves entire or sometimes faintly and irreg-
   ularly crenulate.
   GG-Leaf edges rolled under, the lower leaf surface
    completely obscured by a covering of long
    tawny or rusty wool . . . . <u>Ledum</u>, p. 209
   GG-Leaves not as above.
   HH-Flowers in terminal panicle-like compound
    cymes . . . . <u>Cornus alternifolia</u>, p. 205
   HH-Flowers single or in umbel-like clusters
    along the stem.
    II-Spiny shrub; perianth parts 12-18 in all;
     stamens 6. . . . . <u>Berberis</u>, p. 123
    II-Spines none; perianth parts 8 or 10 in
     all; stamens 4 or 5.
     JJ-Petals shorter than the sepals, sometimes
      nearly equalling them; stamens opposite
      the petals. . . . . <u>Rhamnus frangula</u>, p. 190
     JJ-Petals longer than the sepals; stamens
      alternate with the petals . . . . <u>Nemopanthus</u>, p. 184

KEY 7

Woody angiosperms; leaves simple, alternate; vines or prostrate trailers

A-Leaves less than 2 cm long . . . . Ericaceae, p. 206
A-Leaves 2 cm long or longer.
  B-Leaf blades peltate near the margin . . . . Menispermum, p. 124
  B-Leaf blades not peltate.
    C-Vine with flowers in stalked umbels of 5 or more flowers;
      stems usually prickly on the lower and older parts . . Smilax, p. 67
    C-Habit various, flowers in crowded spikes, panicles,
      cymes or 1-3 in the leaf axils; stems smooth.
      D-Perianth ca. 4 cm long, strongly curved . . . . Aristolochia, p. 102
      D-Perianth 1.5 cm long or less, with radial symmetry.
        E-Flowers white to pink to purple; petals fused at
          least at base.
          F-Flowers pink to white; stamens 10; prostrate
            trailer . . . . Epigaea, p. 208
          F-Flowers usually purple, rarely white; stamens
            5; trailer or climber. . . . . Solanum dulcamara, p. 230
        E-Flowers yellowish-green; petals free at least at
          base, fused above in Vitis.
          G-Leaf blades cordate at base, mostly lobed . . . . . Vitis, p. 190
          G-Leaf blades acute at base, not lobed . . . . . . Celastrus, p. 185

KEY 8

Herbs, leafless

A-Flowers tightly crowded together with no space between in a
  single compact nearly round spike which is enclosed in a
  hooded structure open down one side . . . . Symplocarpus, p. 58
A-Flowers various, if in a dense spike the spike not enclosed.
  B-Perianth not petal-like in color and texture, often com-
    pletely hidden by subtending bracts, the perianth chaffy,
    scale-like, or bristle-like, all brownish to greenish
    when visible.
    C-Flowers each hidden behind a firm bract, the bracts
      ascending and overlapping in 1 or more compact spikes,
      no perianth of the usual sort visible, at most the styles
      and anthers exserted from behind t he bracts . . . Cyperaceae, p. 48
    C-Flowers not hidden behind individual bracts, re adily
      visible in an open inflorescence, the perianth of 6
      brownish to greenish segments . . . . Juncus, p. 59
  B-Perianth all or partly petal-like in color and texture and
    readily visible, not all brownish to greenish.
    D-Flowers in heads, each head surrounded by a close-
      fitting series of bracts . . . . Asteraceae, p. 247
    D-Flowers in various clusters, not in heads.
      E-Perianth parts 6, one very different from the others,
        the flowers bilaterally symmetrical. . . . . . . Orchidaceae, p. 75
      E-Perianth parts various, if 6 all nearly alike, the
        flowers radially or bilaterally symmetrical.
        F-Perianth parts totalling 8 or 10, differentiated into
          calyx and corolla, the petals free or fused.
          G-Petals free, sepals 3 . . . . Hudsonia, p. 192
          G-Petals fused, sepals 5 . . . . Orobanche, p. 236

F-Perianth parts 6, free, all nearly alike.
  H-Stamens 6 . . . . Liliaceae, p. 60
  H-Stamens 0-3.
    I-Stems aerial, much branched, bearing flowers
      3-6 mm long in ones or twos . . . . Asparagus, p. 62
    I-No aerial stem present, flowers appearing at
      the surface of the ground, much larger than
      above . . . . Crocus, p. 72

KEY 9

Herbs, leaves compound

A-Flowers in heads.
  B-Stem bearing a single pair of opposite leaves . . . . Adoxa, p. 245
  B-Stem leaves alternate or none.
    C-Leaves pinnately divided with 5 to many divisions. Asteraceae, p. 247
    C-Leaves with 3 leaflets . . . . Fabaceae, p. 170
A-Flowers not in heads.
  D-Flowers sessile, densely crowded with no space between
    around the base of an erect blunt-tipped stalk, the whole
    enclosed by a loosely encircling bract . . . . Arisaema, p. 57
  D-Flowers not as above.
    E-Perianth either calyx-like or corolla-like or rarely none,
      usually of 1 whorl, if of 2 or more whorls the outer parts
      about like the inner in color, size, and shape.
      F-Plant bearing a single nodding white flower in the fork
        between the two opposite palmately compound leaves
        . . . . Podophyllum, p. 124
      F-Plant not as above.
        G-Stamens 15 or more.
          H-Pistils 3 or more. . . . . Ranunculaceae, p. 111
          H-Pistil 1 or none.
            I-Leaves once or twice pinnately parted . Papaveraceae, p. 125
            I-Leaves 2 or more times ternately compound, with
              many separate leaflets . . . . Ranunculaceae, p. 111
        G-Stamens 0-8.
          J-Flowers in simple or compound umbels.
            K-Umbel 1, simple and terminal, arising from a
              single whorl of once palmately compound leaves
              . . . . Panax, p. 199
            K-Umbels various, leaves alternate or all basal.
              L-Ovary and styles missing from all flowers . Aralia, p. 199
              L-Ovary and styles present in at least some flowers.
                M-Styles 2 . . . . Apiaceae, p. 200
                M-Styles 4-6. . . . . Aralia, p. 199
          J-Flowers in racemes, panicles, or corymbs, or
            borne singly.
            N-Pistils several, separate and superior . . Thalictrum, p. 121
            N-Pistil 0 or 1, superior or inferior.
              O-Perianth parts 6 or 8, separate, the stamens
                as many . . . . Berberidaceae, p. 123
              O-Perianth of 4 free or 5 fused parts; stamens
                0-4.
                P-Stem leaves or bracts alternate. . . . . Lepidium, p. 140

P-Stem leaves or bracts opposite . . . . . <u>Valeriana</u>, p. 245
E-Perianth of both calyx and corolla, these distinctly differ-
    ent from each other.
  Q-Petals all fused at least at base.
    R-Leaves 3 or more times compound or cleft; corolla
      heart-shaped or 2-spurred at base . . . . <u>Dicentra</u>, p. 127
    R-Leaves basically once compound or cleft; corolla not
      heart-shaped or spurred at base.
      S-Corolla strongly bilaterally symmetrical.
        T-Divisions of the leaf 10 or more, connected by
          a web of tissue along the midrib, coarsely
          toothed; corolla 2-lipped; stamens 4 . . . <u>Pedicularis</u>, p. 233
        T-Leaflets 3 or more, fully distinct, entire or
          finely toothed; corolla pea-like; stamens 10
          . . . . <u>Fabaceae</u>, p. 170
      S-Corolla radially symmetrical.
        U-Leaflets 3, fully distinct, equal in size and shape
          or nearly so, entire to broadly crenate or notched
          at the apex.
          V-Leaflets obcordate, 5-23 mm long . . . . . . <u>Oxalis</u>, p. 179
          V-Leaflets elliptic to obovate, longer . . . <u>Menyanthes</u>, p. 218
        U-Leaves otherwise, the leaflets more numerous or
          not distinct or unequal in size and shape or
          sharply toothed.
          W-Stem leaves or bracts mostly opposite.
            X-Flowers sessile in terminal panicled cymes
            . . . . <u>Valeriana</u>, p. 245
            X-Flowers pedicelled, solitary opposite the
              leaves . . . . <u>Ellisia</u>, p. 220
          W-Stem leaves or bracts mostly alternate.
            Y-Style 3-cleft; larger leaves with 9-29 dis-
              tinct well-separated entire leaflets
              . . . . <u>Polemonium</u>, p. 220
            Y-Style entire or 2-cleft; larger leaves other-
              wise, mostly only cleft to near the midrib,
              divisions up to 13.
              Z-Style 2-cleft at tip; anthers opening by
                lengthwise slits . . . . <u>Hydrophyllaceae</u>, p. 220
              Z-Style entire; anthers opening by terminal
                pores or slits . . . . <u>Solanum</u>, p. 230
  Q-Petals all or at least half of them separate to the base.
    AA-Flower symmetry strongly bilateral, either the
      petals distinctly different in size and shape (often
      extended backward at base into a hollow spur) or
      only 1 in number.
      BB-Sepals (or calyx lobes) 2.
        CC-Leaves 2 or 3 times cleft into many divisions;
          stamens 6 . . . . <u>Fumariaceae</u>, p. 126
        CC-Leaves once compound, the leaflets 3-11;
          stamens 10 . . . . <u>Fabaceae</u>, p. 170
      BB-Sepals (or calyx lobes) 5.
        DD-No petals or sepals spurred.
          EE-Stamens all fused together or 1 of them free
          . . . . <u>Fabaceae</u>, p. 170
          EE-Stamens separate. . . . .<u>Dictamnus</u>, p. 181

DD-Either the lower petal or the upper sepal and
    petals extended backward at base into a hollow
    spur, short or long.
    FF-Lower petal spurred; leaves and flowers all
        basal . . . . Viola, p. 192
    FF-Upper sepal spurred, with spurs of the 2
        upper petals inside the sepal spur; leaves
        and flowers present on an erect stem. Delphinium, p. 116
AA-Flowers radially symmetrical or nearly so, the
  petals all similar, spurred or not, more than 1.
  GG-Sepals 2-4 (check several flowers).
    HH-Petals twice as many as the sepals (check
      several flowers).
      II-Leaves 2-parted; stamens 8. . . . . Jeffersonia, p. 124
      II-Leaves several to many times cleft or divided;
        stamens many.
        JJ-Juice colorless; leaves 2-3 times ternately
          compound, with separate leaflets; native
          . . . . Actaea, p. 112
        JJ-Juice white or yellow-orange; leaves 1-2
          times pinnately cleft; cultivated . Papaveraceae, p. 125
    HH-Petals as many as the sepals or other than above.
      KK-Petals 5-10. . . . . Ranunculaceae, p. 111
      KK-Petals 3 or 4.
        LL-Sepals and petals 3 each . . . . Floerkea, p. 183
        LL-Sepals and petals 4 each or in one case
          the sepals 3.
          MM-Stamens 2, 4, or 6 . . . . Brassicaceae, p. 128
          MM-Stamens 8 or more.
          NN-Leaflets 3 . . . . Polanisia, p. 143
          NN-Leaflets many . . . . Actaea, p. 112
  GG-Sepals 5 or more.
    OO-Plant bearing a single nodding white flower be-
      tween 2 opposite palmately compound leaves
      . . . . Podophyllum, p. 124
    OO-Plants not as above.
      PP-Stamens 15 or more.
        QQ-5 Sepal-like bracts alternating with the 5
          sepals. Rosaceae, p. 150
        QQ-Bracts of the calyx none.
          RR-Hypanthium present; stem leaves present,
            once compound. . . . . Rubus, p. 166
          RR-Hypanthium none; leaves often other than above.
          SS-Flower solitary and erect with 6-10
            crimson to purple petals 3-5 cm long
            . . . . Paeonia, p. 122
          SS-Flowers otherwise . . . . Ranunculaceae, p. 111
      PP-Stamens 0-10.
        TT-Filaments 10, anther-bearing or not, twice
          as many as the sepals and petals; ovary
          superior; flowers not greenish-yellow.
          UU-Leaves with 3 obcordate leaflets of equal
            size. . . . . Oxalis, p. 179
          UU-Leaves palmately or pinnately cleft or
            divided, the divisions more than 3.

VV-Leaves mostly opposite or all basal,
    palmately cleft or compound or pinnate-
    ly cleft or compound with deeply cleft
    leaflets. . . . . Geraniaceae, p. 179
VV-Leaves all alternate, pinnately com-
    pound with 9-11 ovate finely serrate
    leaflets . . . . Dictamnus, p. 181
TT-Filaments 0, 5, or 6, when present all
    anther-bearing and as many as the sepals
    and petals; ovary either fully inferior,
    none, or superior, if superior the sepals,
    petals, and stamens 6 each or the flowers
    greenish-yellow.
WW-Flowers in racemes or panicles; ovary
    superior.
    XX-Leaflets 3; sepals, petals, and stamens
        5 each: POISON IVY . . . . . Rhus radicans, p. 184
    XX-Leaflets many; sepals, petals, and
        stamens 6 each. . . . . .Caulophyllum, p. 123
WW-Flowers in simple or compound umbels;
    ovary inferior or none.
    YY-Umbel 1, simple and terminal, arising
        from the center of a single whorl of
        once palmately compound leaves . . .Panax, p. 199
    YY-Umbels various, the leaves alternate
        or all basal, palmate or pinnate.
    ZZ-Styles 2, the ovary and styles pre-
        sent in at least some flowers . .Apiaceae, p. 200
    ZZ-Styles 4-6 or the ovary and styles
        missing from all flowers . . . . . . Aralia, p. 199

KEY 10

Herbs; leaves simple, parallel-veined

A-Flowers each largely hidden behind a firm bract or between
    bracts, the bracts ascending and usually overlapping in one
    or more compact spikes, no perianth of the usual sort visible,
    at most the styles and anthers or sometimes hair-like
    bristles exserted from behind the bracts.
B-Stem cylindric, usually hollow between nodes, leaf sheaths
    usually split down one side, the flowers each held between
    two bracts, the stigmas plumose. . . . . Poaceae, p. 36
B-Stem usually triangular in section, usually pithy for its
    length, leaf sheaths fused around the stem; flowers each
    in the axil of a single bract except in Carex where an
    inner bract is fused around the female flower (fig. 66);
    stigmas not plumose. . . . . Cyperaceae, p. 48
A-Flowers not hidden behind individual bracts, readily visible,
    the inflorescence various, a typical perianth commonly visible.
C-Flowers crowded side by side with no space between in a
    very dense spike, the spike either subtended by a single
    large white bract, or set part way up a linear green stalk
    and thus appearing lateral . . . . Araceae, p. 57

C-Flowers not as above, if in a spike the spike terminal.
  D-Flowers in heads, each head surrounded by a close-
      fitting series of bracts . . . . <u>Asteraceae</u>, p. 247
  D-Flowers otherwise.
    E-One perianth part very different in form from the
      others, the flowers bilaterally symmetrical . <u>Orchidaceae</u>, p. 75
    E-Either all perianth parts similar or all petals and all
      sepals similar; symmetry radial or nearly so.
      F-Stem leaves distinctly opposite or whorled.
        G-Basal leaves abundant, the stem leaves opposite
          and much reduced in size. . . . . <u>Valeriana</u> edulis, p. 246
        G-Leaves otherwise, either all or partly whorled
          or only 2 per plant . . . . <u>Liliaceae</u>, p. 60
      F-Stem leaves alternate or the leaves all basal.
        H-Perianth of 4 sepals and a 4-lobed sympetalous
          corolla. . . . . <u>Plantago</u>, p. 236
        H-Perianth parts totalling 4 or 6, the inner whorl not
          fused of itself, sometimes fused with the outer
          whorl.
          I-Perianth brown, brownish-green, or greenish,
            1-5.5 mm long, the leaves narrowly linear.
            J-Flowers in few to many-flowered racemes, the
              3 or 6 carpels free or separating at maturity
              . . . . <u>Juncaginaceae</u>, p. 35
            J-Flowers in loosely branched cymes, the 3
              carpels fully fused . . . . <u>Juncaceae</u>, p. 59
          I-Perianth usually all or in part whitish or other-
            wise colored, if greenish the perianth parts
            longer or the leaves broader than above.
            K-Outer perianth parts green, inner ones rose
              to blue . . . . <u>Tradescantia</u>, p. 58
            K-Outer perianth parts not green; inner ones
              various.
              L-Ovary superior to 1/2 inferior; stamens 6
                or 4, as many as the perianth segments;
                if the ovary 1/2 inferior then the flowers
                whitish in open racemes or panicles
                (Zygadenus) . . . . <u>Liliaceae</u>, p. 60
              L-Ovary fully inferior; stamens 6 or 3, as
                many or half as many as the perianth seg-
                ments; inflorescence not as above.
                M-Stamens 6; leaves not laterally flattened
                  at base . . . . <u>Amaryllidaceae</u>, p. 70
                M-Stamens 3; leaves often folded double and
                  strongly flattened laterally at base, clasping
                  the stem . . . . <u>Iridaceae</u>, p. 72

KEY 11

Herbs; <u>leaves</u> <u>simple</u>, <u>not</u> <u>parallel-veined</u>; <u>flowers</u> <u>in</u> <u>heads</u>

A-Stem leaves opposite or whorled.
  B-Leaves crowded into an apparent single whorl
  . . . . <u>Cornus</u> <u>canadensis</u>, p. 205
  B-Leaves opposite, the pairs separated on the stem.

C-Perianth differentiated into a 2-cleft calyx and 5 free
    petals . . . . Portulaca, p. 105
C-Perianth undifferentiated, of 5 fused tepals . . . . . . Mirabilis, p. 104
A-Stem leaves alternate or leaves all basal.
  D-Flowers crowded tightly together with no space between in a
    single compact head or short spike which is enclosed in a
    hooded structure open down one side . . . . Symplocarpus, p. 58
  D-Flowers otherwise.
    E-Perianth parts all brown to green, 6 . . . . Juncus, p. 59
    E-Perianth in part colored otherwise, some parts in 5's.
      F-Peduncle enclosed just below the head by a sheathing
      bract; styles 5, ovary superior; calyx present,
      shallowly 5-lobed . . . . Armeria, p. 214
      F-Peduncle not so enclosed; style 1 with 2 branches,
      ovary inferior or pistil absent; calyx never 5-lobed,
      of very diverse forms, not resembling the usual
      calyx . . . . Asteraceae, p. 247

KEY 12

Herbs; leaves simple, not parallel-veined; flowers not in heads;
perianth undifferentiated

A-Spurges: "flowers" (actually tiny involucres, fig. 69) each with a
  cup-shaped "hypanthium" containing hairs, several stamens, and
  an ovary which becomes exserted on a stalk; style branches 3,
  each 2-cleft; juice milky . . . . Euphorbia, p. 182
A-Flowers not as above; juice colorless, orange, yellow, or white.
  B-Stem leaves (or bracts) all or mostly opposite or whorled.
    C-Leaves all or some of them palmately lobed.
      D-Flowers numerous in a terminal panicle . . . . . . Valeriana, p. 245
      D-Flowers 1 or several in an umbel-like cluster.
        E-Flowers 1-several, erect at anthesis; pistils several
        to many . . . . Ranunculaceae, p. 111
        E-Flower 1, pendulous; pistil 1 . . . . Podophyllum, p. 124
    C-Leaves entire, toothed, or pinnately lobed.
      F-Leaves whorled . . . . Galium, p. 237
      F-Leaves opposite.
        G-Perianth pink-purple, ca. 10 mm long . . . . . Mirabilis, p. 104
        G-Perianth greenish to whitish, sometimes tinged with
        yellow or purple, shorter.
          H-Basal leaves much larger than the stem leaves;
          flowers numerous in a terminal panicle; perianth
          parts fused; style 1 or none . . . . Valeriana, p. 245
          H-Basal leaves about equalling the stem leaves, or
          none; flowers 1-several, axillary or terminal;
          perianth parts free or somewhat fused; styles
          or style branches 2-5.
            I-Styles or style branches 3-5; ovary superior
            . . . . Caryophyllaceae, p. 106
            I-Styles 2; ovary 1/2 or more inferior. Chrysosplenium, p. 144
  B-Stem leaves (or bracts) alternate, or the leaves all basal
    and stem bracts none, or the plants aquatic with floating
    leaves.

J-Perianth parts or lobes 0, 3, or 4 (check several flowers).
   K-Perianth parts or lobes 0 or 3.
      L-Leaves all basal; flowers borne at ground level. . <u>Asarum</u>, p. 102
      L-2 leaves and 1 terminal flower borne on an aerial
        stem . . . . <u>Hydrastis</u>, p. 117
   K-Perianth parts or lobes 4.
      M-Stamens absent.
         N-Perianth rose-red to whitish; ovary fully inferior
         . . . . <u>Begonia</u>, p. 196
         N-Perianth greenish; ovary superior. . . . . . . <u>Parietaria</u>, p. 100
      M-Stamens present.
         O-Stamens many.
            P-Juice orange, yellow, or white; superior ovary
              conspicuous . . . . <u>Papaveraceae</u>, p. 125
            P-Juice colorless; ovary absent, or present in
              separate flowers and fully inferior . . . . . . <u>Begonia</u>, p. 196
         O-Stamens 2-6.
            Q-Leaves toothed . . . . <u>Lepidium</u>, p. 140
            Q-Leaves entire. . . . . <u>Parietaria</u>, p. 100
J-Perianth parts or lobes all or mostly 5 or more.
   R-Pistils several to many, separate and superior
   . . . . <u>Ranunculaceae</u>, p. 111
   R-Pistil 1 or none, superior or inferior.
      S-Leaves narrowly linear; perianth parts 6.
         T-Perianth parts yellow on the inner surface, 5-15
           mm long, separate; leaves all basal . . . . . . <u>Hypoxis</u>, p. 71
         T-Perianth parts greenish-white, greenish-yellow,
           greenish-brown, or brown, 2-5.5 mm long, if
           greenish-yellow then fused 2/3 or more of their
           length; stem leaves usually present.
            U-Leaves up to 15 mm long; flowers borne singly
              or in pairs, greenish-white or greenish-yellow
              . . . . <u>Asparagus</u>, p. 62
            U-Leaves longer; flowers in larger clusters, brown
              or greenish-brown. . . . . <u>Juncus</u>, p. 59
      S-Leaves lanceolate or broader; perianth parts 5-16.
         V-Stamens many.
            W-Terrestrial plants with toothed or lobed leaves
            . . . . <u>Papaveraceae</u>, p. 125
            W-Aquatic plants with floating heart-shaped leaves
              with entire or undulating margins. . . . . . . <u>Nuphar</u>, p. 111
         V-Stamens 0-9.
            X-Flowers all in axillary peduncled simple umbels
            . . . . <u>Smilax</u>, p. 67
            X-Flowers otherwise.
               Y-Stipules none; ovary 2/3 inferior; style 1;
                 stamens 5 . . . . <u>Comandra</u>, p. 101
               Y-Stipules present, in the form of a sheath sur-
                 rounding the stem at the base of the leaf; ovary
                 either superior with 2 or 3 styles or none;
                 stamens 0-9. . . . . <u>Polygonaceae</u>, p. 102

Herbs; leaves simple, not parallel-veined; flowers not in heads;
calyx and corolla present, the petals separate

A-Spurges: "flowers" (actually tiny involucres, fig. 69) each
    with a cup-shaped "hypanthium" containing hairs, several
    stamens, and an ovary which becomes exserted on a stalk;
    style branches 3, each 2-cleft; juice milky . . . . Euphorbia, p. 182
A-Flowers not as above; juice colorless, orange, yellow, or
    white.
    B-Corolla symmetry conspicuously bilateral, the lower petal
      either extended backward at its base to form a short hollow
      spur, or bearing a distinctive fringe near its tip, or elong-
      ate and 2-cleft.
      C-Lower petal spurred as described above; stamens 5 . . . Viola, p. 192
      C-Lower petal not spurred; stamens 1, 6, or 8.
        D-Leaves several to many, alternate . . . . Polygala, p. 182
        D-Leaves 2, opposite . . . . Listera, p. 79
    B-Corolla symmetry radial or nearly so, the petals not as above.
      E-Sepals 2 (check several flowers).
        F-Petals 2 (check several flowers). . . . . Begonia, p. 196
        F-Petals 4-16.
          G-Leaves toothed, cleft, or lobed, obovate to round in
            outline; juice red-orange, yellow, or white
            . . . . Papaveraceae, p. 125
          G-Leaves entire, linear to obovate; juice colorless
            . . . . Portulacaceae, p. 105
      E-Sepals 3 or more.
        H-Leaves all or mostly opposite or whorled.
          I-Leaves entire, sometimes slightly wavy-edged.
            J-Leaves 3 in a single whorl at top of stem . . . . Trillium, p. 68
            J-Leaves opposite, the pairs usually several to
              many . . . . Caryophyllaceae, p. 106
          I-Leaves distinctly toothed or lobed.
            K-Flowers pink to purple . . . . Geranium, p. 180
            K-Flowers white to whitish.
              L-Flowers in erect racemes . . . . . . Mitella diphylla, p. 145
              L-Flower single, nodding between 2 leaves
              . . . . Podophyllum, p. 124
        H-Leaves all or mostly alternate or the leaves all basal.
          M-Petals 3 or 4, as many as the sepals (check several
            flowers).
            N-Sepals and petals 3 each . . . . Polygonaceae, p. 102
            N-Sepals and petals 4 each.
              O-Stamens 4 or 6; ovary superior . . . . . Brassicaceae, p. 128
              O-Stamens 8; ovary fully inferior.
                P-Creeping plants of bogs and wet places, the
                  flowering branches sometimes erect; leaves
                  4-14 mm long . . . . Vaccinium, p. 210
                P-Erect plants of dry places; leaves 20-60 mm
                  long. Onagraceae, p. 198
         M-Petals mostly 5 or more, as many as or more than the sepals.
          Q-Trailing or climbing vine with leaves peltate near
            the margin; flowers in small panicles. . Menispermum, p. 124
          Q-Plants not vines, the leaves not peltate.

R-Leaves 1-4 mm long . . . . Hudsonia, p. 192
R-Leaves longer.
  S-Stamens all fused together by their filaments
  . . . . Malva, p. 191
  S-Stamens free.
    T-Pistils five to many, separate and superior
    . . . . Ranunculaceae, p. 111
    T-Pistils 1 or 2, superior or inferior.
      U-Stamens 5-10.
        V-Styles 2, on separate or united carpels
        . . . . Saxifragaceae, p. 143
        V-Style 1, pistil 1.
          W-Leaves mostly on the stem, inflorescence
          a series of small cymes, stamens 5
          . . . . Comandra, p. 101
          W-Leaves mostly basal, inflorescence a
          raceme, stamens 10 . . . . Pyrola, p. 209
      U-Stamens many.
        X-Leaves appearing inflated, conspicuously
        hollow for most of their length . Sarracenia, p. 143
        X-Leaves flat, not hollow.
          Y-Aquatic plant with floating heart-shaped
          leaves . . . . Nuphar, p. 111
          Y-Terrestrial plants with erect stems
          and aerial leaves.
            Z-Stem leaves 1-4 cm long; juice color-
            less . . . . Helianthemum, p. 191
            Z-Stem leaves none or 8-30 cm long;
            juice milky. . . . . Papaver, p. 125

KEY 14

Herbs; leaves simple, not parallel-veined; flowers not in heads;
calyx and corolla present, the petals fused

A-Milkweeds: flowers (fig. 70) in simple stalked umbels on leafy
  stems; sepals and petals folded back; stamens united around the
  ovaries and bearing from the base of the stamen column 5
  erect petal-like structures with their edges incurved at least
  below, from each of which arises in some species a slender
  pointed curved structure; juice milky . . . . Asclepias, p. 218
A-Inflorescence and flower characters various but not in above
  combination; juice colorless except in the Campanulaceae.
  B-Perianth consisting of 3 small free outer parts, 2 larger
    free intermediate parts, and 3 inner parts weakly or
    strongly fused, the lowermost of the inner ones folded
    lengthwise and bearing near its tip a fringe of 4 or more
    simple or branched linear structures . . . . Polygala, p. 182
  B-Perianth not as above.
    C-Stamens many, fused together by their filaments . . . . Malva, p. 191
    C-Stamens 10 or fewer, free or weakly united by their anthers.
      D-Ovary half to fully inferior or lacking, if lacking then
      the stamens 3 and epipetalous.
        E-Stem leaves alternate . . . . Campanulaceae, p. 246

E-Stem leaves opposite or whorled.
   F-Leaves whorled.....................Galium, p. 237
   F-Leaves opposite.
      G-Corolla 1-3.5 mm long; stamens 0 or 3 .. Valeriana, p. 245
      G-Corolla 5-17 mm long; stamens 4 or 5.
         H-Sepals and corolla lobes 4.........Rubiaceae, p. 237
         H-Sepals and corolla lobes 5.......Caprifoliaceae, p. 239
D-Ovary present and superior; stamens, if 3, free from
  the corolla.
  I-Stamens 8-10, twice as many as the corolla lobes
  ....Ericaceae, p. 206
  I-Stamens 2-5, as many as the corolla lobes or fewer.
    J-Corolla pink, regular, closely surrounding the ovary
      and constricted above it; stamens free from the
      corolla; ovule 1; leaves opposite and entire. Mirabilis, p. 104
    J-Corolla not with above combination of characters;
      stamens epipetalous; ovules 2 or more; leaves
      various.
      K-Either the flower symmetry distinctly bilateral
      or the corolla lobes fewer than 5; stamens 2 or 4.
        L-Leaves all basal; flowers in a spike on a bract-
          less peduncle; calyx and corolla lobes 4 each;
          corolla scarious with radial symmetry. .Plantago, p. 236
        L-Stem leaves present, if only as bracts on the
          peduncle; calyx and corolla lobes various, the
          corolla colored and petal-like, usually with
          bilateral symmetry.
          M-Ovary deeply 4-lobed, the lobes appearing
             as 4 nearly separate ovaries around the
             style base, a prominent nectary lobe some-
             times appearing as a 5th lobe; leaves
             opposite, stem square .... Lamiaceae, p. 226
          M-Ovary not conspicuously lobed; leaves alter-
             nate or opposite, stem occasionally square
             .... Scrophulariaceae, p. 230
      K-Flower symmetry radial or nearly so; calyx
      and corolla lobes 5 each; stamens 5.
        N-Ovary deeply 4-lobed, the lobes appearing as
          4 nearly separate ovaries around the style
          base.................... Boraginaceae, p. 221
        N-Ovary not deeply lobed.
          O-Style 2 or 3-cleft at tip; ovary respectively
            1-locular with parietal placentation or 3-
            locular with axile placentation.
            P-Leaves entire; style 3-cleft at tip
             .... Polemoniaceae, p. 218
            P-Leaves cleft to lobed; style 2-cleft at
             tip................ Hydrophyllaceae, p. 220
          O-Style undivided at tip; ovary 1 or 2 locular,
            the placentation respectively free central
            or axile.
            Q-Stem leaves opposite or whorled or the leaves
             all basal; placentation free-central; stamens
             opposite the corolla lobes .... Primulaceae, p. 212

Q-Stem leaves present and alternate; placentation axile; stamens alternate with the
   corolla lobes.
   R-Flowers in an erect terminal raceme of
      flowers each about 25 mm across; leaves
      never lobed . . . . Verbascum, p. 234
   R-Flowers borne singly or in branching
      clusters in or near the leaf axils, often
      smaller; leaves sometimes lobed
      . . . . Solanaceae, p. 228

KEY TO GENERA OR FAMILIES OF PLANTS WITH "DOUBLE" FLOWERS

(Flowers in which the number of petals is artificially increased beyond normal, often at the expense of stamens and pistils)

A-Trees or shrubs.
  B-Leaves opposite.
    C-Flowers in many-flowered panicles; petals fused; ovary superior
      or none . . . . Syringa, p. 216
    C-Flowers single or in few-flowered raceme-like or panicle-
      like clusters; petals free; ovary inferior . . . . . Philadelphus, p. 145
  B-Leaves alternate.
    D-Leaves compound.
      E-Stems prickly . . . . Rosa, p. 164
      E-Stems without prickles . . . . Paeonia, p. 122
    D-Leaves simple.
      F-Flowers perigynous, the ovary superior . . . . . . Rosaceae, p. 150
      F-Flowers epigynous, the ovary inferior. . . . . Pyrus, p. 162
A-Herbs.
  G-Petals spurred. . . . . Aquilegia, p. 115
  G-Petals not spurred.
    H-Perianth undifferentiated, all parts similar.
      I-Ovary inferior . . . . Narcissus, p. 71
      I-Ovary superior or none.
        J-Flowers 5-10 cm long, single (rarely 2 or 3) . . . . Tulipa, p. 69
        J-Flowers 2-3 cm long, in a raceme . . . . Hyacinthus, p. 64
    H-Perianth clearly differentiated into calyx and corolla.
      K-Sepals 2.
        L-Sepals falling as the flower opens; leaves lobed. . Papaver, p. 125
        L-Sepals persistent; leaves entire. . . . . Portulaca, p. 105
      K-Sepals 4 or 5.
        M-Sepals 4 . . . . Brassicaceae, p. 128
        M-Sepals 5.
          N-Sepals united into a tubular calyx; leaves opposite,
            simple, entire . . . . Dianthus, p. 108
          N-Sepals free; leaves alternate or all basal, usually
            toothed or compound.
            O-Petals yellow. . . . . Ranunculus, p. 117
            O-Petals red to white . . . . Paeonia, p. 122

GYMNOSPERMAE ----- GYMNOSPERMS

PINACEAE ----- PINE FAMILY

Monoecious trees or rarely shrubs; leaves spiral or densely clustered or fascicled, mostly evergreen; resin canals present; male or pollen cone consisting of an axis bearing many spirally arranged scale-like sporophylls; female cone consisting of an axis bearing spiralled scales each in the axil of a bract, the scale typically producing 2 naked ovules on its upper surface, the bracts at maturity varying from much shorter than to longer than the scales, often adnate to the scales; cone in fruit much enlarged, with hard dry parts.

A-Foliage leaves all or some of them in dense clusters or fascicles of 2-40.
  B-Leaves in fascicles of 2-5, evergreen.................PINUS
  B-Leaves partly spiral along the stem and partly in dense clusters
    of 20-40, deciduous............................. LARIX
A-Foliage leaves all spiral on the stem, none in dense clusters.
  C-Leaves on falling leaving a flat scar, flush with the twig surface
    on all sides; winter buds resinous; cones upright with scales
    that fall off at maturity.....................ABIES
  C-Leaf scars tilted up on the lower side or the leaf breaking off
    short of the twig surface leaving its base as a woody projection
    (sterigma, fig. 60); winter buds not resinous; cones pendent
    with persistent scales.
    D-Sterigmata standing out from the twig surface, 0.5-0.8 mm
      long, the leaves sessile on them; leaves more or less 4-angled,
      roughly diamond-shaped in section, commonly spreading
      upward and downward as well as to the sides from the twig. . PICEA
    D-Leaf scars merely tilted, or the sterigmata 0.2-0.5 mm long
      and bearing short-petioled leaves; leaves flat, tending to
      spread only horizontally.
      E-Leaves 8-13 mm long, their scars strongly tilted or raised
        on short sterigmata, the leaf bases decurrent; cones
        1.5-2.5 cm long; native...................... TSUGA
      E-Leaves 15-35 mm long, their scars moderately tilted, the
        leaf bases not decurrent; cones 4-8 cm long; cultivated
        .... PSEUDOTSUGA

ABIES ----- FIR [*]

Evergreen trees, the bark furrowed on older trunks, the unfurrowed bark with scattered raised "blisters" containing sap; leaves flat in ours, spirally attached but tending to spread only horizontally, on falling leaving flat round scars, the leaf bases not decurrent; cones upright, the scales and bracts falling from the persistent axis at maturity, the bracts longer to shorter than the scales. (The ancient Latin name.)

A-Leaves 1-2.7 cm long, dark green above, often slightly notched
  at tip; cones 5-10 cm long; native ....A. balsamea
A-Leaves 2.5-6 cm long, bluish-green above, rounded to acute at
  tip; cones 7-12 cm long; cultivated.................A. concolor

A. balsamea (L.) Mill. Balsam Fir. To 15 or 20 m high, the trunk to 50 cm in diameter; bracts of the cone usually concealed by the longer scales. Cool mesic to moist woods, Cook to Roseau Co., s. to ne. Otter Tail and ne. Chisago counties, with isolated stands in Pope and Fillmore counties.

A. concolor (Gord.) Hoopes. White Fir; cultivated. To 40 m high; bracts concealed. Mountains of w. North America.

LARIX ----- LARCH, TAMARACK *

Deciduous trees with scaly bark; leaves soft, needle-like, spirally arranged with decurrent bases on long rapidly grown shoots and in dense clusters on short slow-grown shoots on the older twigs and branches; cones small to medium-sized, the bracts usually visible although shorter than the scales; cones falling whole. (The classical Latin name.)

A-Cones 1-1.6 cm long; native . . . . L. laricina
A-Cones 2.5-4 cm long; cultivated . . . . L. decidua

L. decidua Mill. European Larch; cultivated. Tree to 12 m high or more; leaves 2.5-4 cm long. From Europe.

L. laricina (DuRoi) K. Koch. American or Black Larch; Tamarack. Tree to 35 m high; leaves 1.5-3 cm long. Bogs and swamps, occasionally on the upland in the north: Cook to Roseau Co., s. to Pennington, Otter Tail, Stearns, Carver, and Washington counties, with isolated stands in Rice and Houston counties.

PICEA ----- SPRUCE *

Evergreen trees with scaly bark; leaves in ours more or less 4-angled, spirally attached with decurrent bases, tending to project in all directions from the twig, each on falling leaving its woody base (sterigma, fig. 60) on the twig, the bases in ours 0.5-1.0 mm long, standing at angles of about 30-80° from the twig; cones pendent, long-persistent, falling whole; bracts shorter than and concealed by the scales. (L. name of some conifer, from pix, pitch.)

A-Branchlets conspicuously drooping; cones 9-20 cm long; cultivated
. . . . P. abies
A-Branchlets spreading more or less horizontally; cones 1.7-10 cm
   long; native or cultivated.
   B-Twigs minutely hairy; cones nearly round, 1.7-3 cm long; leaves
      5-15 mm long . . . . P. mariana
   B-Twigs glabrous; cones elongate, 3-10 cm long; leaves 8-30 mm long.
      C-Leaves 8-23 mm long, green to somewhat bluish, not unusually
         stiff and sharp; cones 3-5 cm long, the edges of the cone scales
         entire; native . . . . P. glauca
      C-Leaves 20-30 mm long, often conspicuously bluish at least on
         the new shoots, relatively stiff and sharp; cones 6-10 cm
         long, the edges of the cone scales irregularly notched; cul-
         tivated. . . . . P. pungens

P. abies Karst. Norway Spruce; cultivated. To 50 m high, usually with pendulous branchlets; twigs minutely pubescent; leaves 15-25 mm long; cone scales stiff with irregularly toothed margins. European.

P. glauca (Moench) Voss. White Spruce. To 25 m high or more. Cool mesic uplands, Cook to Kittson Co., s. to e. Pennington, e. Clay, Douglas, and Pine counties.

P. mariana (Mill.) B.S.P. Black Spruce. Mostly a small narrow tree 8-10 m high, rarely taller, dwarfed to 3-4 m in some swamps. Bogs, swamps, and cool slopes, Cook to e. Kittson Co., s. to e. Pennington, Becker, Kanabec, and n. Ramsey counties.

P. pungens Engelm. Colorado Blue Spruce; cultivated. To 50 m high, pyramidal in form. From the Rocky Mountains.

PINUS ----- PINE *

Evergreen trees or rarely shrubs; foliage leaves (except in seedlings) all in fascicles of 2-5 (1 per fascicle in the southwestern P. monophylla), each fascicle bound at the base by a sheath of bracts, the fascicles eventually falling as units; leaves needle-like, 2- or 3-sided; cones at various angles on the tree, persistent or eventually falling whole; bracts much shorter than the scales, not visible externally; ends of scales thickened where not over-lapped by the scale below in the closed cone, the thickened part called an apophysis (fig. 61), the apophysis with a small differentiated often rhombic and usually raised area, the umbo, the umbo often bearing a prickle. (The classical Latin name.)

A-Leaves in fascicles of 5. . . . . P. strobus
A-Leaves in fascicles of 2 or 3.
  B-Leaves usually in fascicles of 3, sometimes some fascicles of 2
    present on the same plant; cultivated. . . . . P. ponderosa
  B-Leaves in fascicles of 2; native or cultivated.
    C-Leaves 8-16 cm long, prevailingly more than 8 cm, the larger
      branches and upper trunk gray to brown or reddish-brown.
      D-Leaves slender and flexible, breaking with a snap; bark
        reddish on older trunks; native. . . . . P. resinosa
      D-Leaves relatively thick and stiff, giving way without a snap
        when broken; bark gray or faintly mottled with pinkish;
        cultivated . . . . P. nigra
    C-Leaves 2-8 (-9) cm long, if 8-9 cm then the larger branches
      and upper trunk red-orange to greenish-yellow.
      E-Plants usually dwarfed and shrubby, 1-4 m high; cultivated
      . . . . P. mugo
      E-Plants forming erect trees 4-20 m high; native or cultivated.
        F-Leaves 2-5.5 cm long, mostly straight, green to yellow-
          green; cones tilted slightly to strongly toward the branch
          tip; native . . . . P. banksiana
        F-Leaves 4.5-9 cm long, twisted, bluish or grayish-green;
          cones at right angles or turned back on the branches;
          cultivated . . . . P. sylvestris

P. banksiana Lamb. Jack Pine. Tree usually 5-12 m high; cones 3-5 cm long, somewhat curved, often remaining closed until opened by heat, often long-persistent on the tree; umbo lateral and spineless or nearly so. Mesic to dry mostly poor soils, Cook to Kittson Co., and s. to e. Mahnomen, Wadena, Morrison, Carlton, Anoka, and Chisago counties, with isolated stands in Wabasha, Winona, and Fillmore counties.

P. mugo Turra (P. montana Mill.). Swiss Mountain or Mugo Pine; cultivated. Shrub or small tree seldom over 3 or 4 mm high; leaves 3-8 cm long; cones 2-4 cm long, at right angles to the branch or tilted obliquely toward the branch tip; umbo lateral, gray, rough, sometimes with a short prickle. Mountains of central and s. Europe. Ours are mostly the low shrubby P. m. var. mugo.

P. nigra Arnold. Austrian Pine; cultivated. Tree to 25 m high; leaves 9-16 cm long; cones 5-9 cm long; umbo lateral, usually with a short prickle. S. Europe and Asia Minor. Ours are mostly P. n. var. nigra (P. n. var. austriaca (Hoess) Aschers. & Graebn.).

P. ponderosa Dougl. Western Yellow Pine; cultivated. To 50 m high; leaves 12-24 cm long; cones 7-15 cm long, the umbo lateral and bearing a prickle. W. North America. Ours are mostly P. p. var. scopulorum Engelm., a Rocky Mt. form which is relatively small throughout.

P. resinosa Ait. Red or Norway Pine. To 40 m high; leaves 8-15 cm long; cones 3-6 cm long, the umbo lateral and smooth. Mesic to dry soils, Cook to e. Roseau Co., s. to Clearwater, n. Morrison, Kanabec, and ne. Washington counties, with an isolated stand in n. Anoka Co.

P. strobus L. White Pine. Tree to 50 m high; leaves 5-10 cm long; cones 6-25 cm long, the umbo terminal on the scale, without a prickle. Mostly mesic soils, Cook to e. Roseau Co. and s. to e. Polk, Morrison, Sherburne, and Washington counties, and scattered to Winona, Olmsted, Mower, Fillmore, and Houston counties.

P. sylvestris L. Scotch Pine; cultivated. To 30 m high, seldom over 15 m in our area, the larger branches and upper trunk red-orange to greenish-yellow; cones 3-6 cm long, sometimes curved; umbo lateral and spineless or nearly so. Europe and w. Asia.

PSEUDOTSUGA ----- FALSE HEMLOCK

Evergreen trees with mostly smooth resinous bark when young, becoming deeply furrowed on old trees; leaves flat, spirally attached but tending to spread only horizontally, on falling leaving a scar raised on one edge, the leaf bases not decurrent; cones pendent, finally falling off the tree complete, each cone scale exceeded by a conspicuous 3-pointed bract. (Gr. pseudes, false, Japanese tsuga, hemlock.)

P. menziesii (Mirb.) Franco. Douglas Fir; cultivated. To 80 m high in its natural habitat, seldom over 12 m locally; leaves 15-35 mm long; cones 4-8 cm long. W. North America.

TSUGA ----- HEMLOCK [*]

Evergreen trees with rough bark; leaves small, flat, spirally attached but tending to spread only horizontally from the twig, each on falling leaving the woody leaf base on the twig, the base in ours 0.2-0.5 mm long, lying at angles of about 10-45° from the twig, decurrent; cones pendent, very small, falling whole; bracts much shorter than the thin scales. (Japanese tsuga, hemlock.)

T. canadensis (L.) Carr. Tree to 15 m high or more; leaves 8-13 mm long; cones 15-25 mm long, the ends of the scales minutely recurved. Mesic woods, rare in Minn., known only from St. Louis, Carlton, Pine, and Mille Lacs counties.

CUPRESSACEAE ----- CYPRESS FAMILY

Monoecious or dioecious trees or shrubs with opposite or whorled scale-like or needle-like evergreen leaves; resin canals present; male or pollen cone consisting of an axis bearing several opposite or whorled mostly

peltate sporophylls; female cone consisting of several opposite or whorled
scales, each scale with 1-12 ovules on its upper surface, the subtending
bracts of the scales either apparently missing or fully fused with the scale;
cones small, woody or fleshy and berry-like.

A-Twigs and the scale-like leaves on them strongly flattened; cones
    woody . . . . THUJA
A-Twigs not at all flattened, the leaves scale- or needle-like; cones
    fleshy and berry-like . . . . JUNIPERUS

JUNIPERUS ----- JUNIPER *

      Evergreen trees to low shrubs with shreddy fibrous bark; leaves
decussate or in whorls of 3; plants dioecious or rarely monoecious; cones
small, fleshy, berry-like, mostly bluish-black, consisting of several pairs
or whorls of minute fleshy scales adhering together. (The Latin name.)

A-Leaves all needle-like, all in whorls of 3.
  B-Leaves jointed at the base, the joint visible at first as a sharp
      constriction above and at the sides; native . . J. communis var. depressa
  B-Leaves not jointed at base, continuous onto the twig; cultivated.
    C-Low spreading shrub to 75 cm high . . . . J. procumbens
    C-Tree or tree-shaped shrub at least as high as wide. . J. chinensis
A-Leaves all or partly very short and scale-like, appressed to the
  twig, usually opposite or opposite and in 3's on the same plant.
  D-Prostrate, matted, creeping shrub. . . . . J. horizontalis
  D-Erect or ascending shrubs or trees, if low not creeping.
    E-Distance from the non-green "gland" on the outside of
      the scale leaf to the leaf tip mostly 3/4 to 1 1/4 the
      gland's length; fruit ripening the second year; male
      cones with 6 sporophylls; cultivated. . . . . J. scopulorum
    E-Gland mostly 1 1/2 to 3 times its length from the leaf
      tip; fruit ripening first or second year; male cones
      with 10 or more sporophylls; native or cultivated.
      F-Needle-leaves mostly opposite, in 3's only on leading twigs;
        scale leaves all acute; ripe berry blue-black, ripening the
        same year as ovule formation; native. . . . . J. virginiana
      F-Needle-leaves consistently both opposite and in 3's, some-
        times mostly in 3's; usually at least a few blunt or broadly
        acute scale leaves present near the point of growth initia-
        tion or renewal in the branchlet, or all scale leaves blunt;
        ripe berry brownish-purple, ripening the second year;
        cultivated. . . . . J. chinensis
J. chinensis L. Chinese Juniper; cultivated. China, Mongolia, Japan.
The most common form of this species in our area is J. c. cv. Pfitzeriana,
a broad-spreading shrub to 16 dm high with nodding branchlets and grayish-
green to bluish scale leaves.

J. communis var. depressa Pursh. Common, Ground, or Prostrate
Juniper. Low dense shrub ca. 1 m high; berries bluish. Bluffs, river bottoms, swamp margins, and other habitats, Cook to Lake of the Woods
Co., s. to Polk, Otter Tail, Morrison, Sherburne, Blue Earth, Fillmore,
and Houston counties.

J. horizontalis Moench. Creeping Juniper. Very low creeping shrub
often forming wide mats, often with erect branchlets up to 3 dm high, often
turning reddish in winter. Sandy and rocky places, uncommon in the state

but locally abundant, in Cook, Lake, n. St. Louis, Kittson, Polk, Otter Tail, Sherburne, Dakota, Goodhue, Winona, and Houston counties.

J. procumbens (Endl.) Sieb. & Zucc. (J. chinensis var procumbens Endl.). Cultivated. Leaves 6-8 mm long, each with 2 whitish-blue lines running downward from near the base. Cultivated in Japan, not known wild.

J. scopulorum Sarg. Rocky Mountain Juniper; cultivated. Tree to 12 m high; scale leaves mostly rather broadly acute; berry blue to purplish-brown. Rocky Mts. of w. N. America.

J. virginiana L. Red Cedar. In Minnesota a tree rarely over 10 m high; scale leaves mostly sharply acute to acuminate; foliage becoming reddish in winter; berry bluish. Dry gravelly or rocky soil, commonly on river bluffs, Houston to Martin Co. and n. to Big Stone, Becker, Cass, Aitkin, and Pine counties, and in s. St. Louis Co., the latter probably an introduction.

THUJA *

Evergreen trees or large shrubs with smooth bark eventually shredding; leaves very small, scale-like, decussately arranged, the whole twig flattened so that some leaves are flattened on the top and bottom and others folded on the edges of the twig; plants monoecious; cones very small, woody, consisting of a few pairs of decussate thin scales. (Gr. thyia, the ancient name of some resin-bearing evergreen.)

T. occidentalis L. White Cedar, Arbor Vitae. Tree to 20 m high, often remaining small in bogs. Usually in damp to wet places, rarely on dry ground or rocks, Cook to Roseau Co. and s. to Clearwater, Aitkin, and Anoka counties, with an isolated stand in Winona county.

TAXACEAE ----- YEW FAMILY

Evergreen monoecious or dioecious trees or shrubs; resin canals absent from leaves and wood, present in the bark; leaves flat, usually linear, spirally attached or rarely opposite; pollen cone consisting of an axis bearing spirally arranged sporophylls; ovules usually single and terminal on a branchlet, no female cone present, the seed wingless and surrounded by a soft fleshy tissue termed an "aril".

TAXUS ----- YEW *

Shrubs or small trees, dioecious or rarely monoecious; leaves spirally attached, without resinous odor, their bases decurrent; the aril typically a bright translucent red, open at the end. (The Latin name.)

A-Native straggling shrub ca. 1 m high; leaves 1-2.5 mm wide, the lengthwise pale green or yellow-green bands on the under side about as wide as the border strip between the band and the leaf edge . . . . T. canadensis
A-Cultivated shrub or small tree often more than 1 m high; leaves 2-3 mm wide, the yellow-green or yellowish bands on the under side about twice as wide as the border strip. . . . . T. cuspidata

T. canadensis Marsh. American Yew. Leaves turned to a horizontal position to make a flat spray; aril ca. 5 mm long, the seed ca. 4 mm long.

Cool mesic to damp woods, Cook to Lake of the Woods counties, s. to Mahnomen, Otter Tail, Aitkin, Anoka, Washington, Wabasha, Olmsted, Fillmore, and Houston counties.

T. cuspidata Sieb. & Zucc. Japanese Yew; cultivated. Leaves usually turning up to form a V-shaped trough; seed ca. 6 mm long. From Japan, Korea, and Manchuria.

GINKGOACEAE ----- GINKGO FAMILY

Deciduous dioecious trees; leaves alternate, fan shaped with dichotomously branching veins and no midrib; pollen produced in cone-like clusters consisting of an axis bearing numerous sporophylls; ovulate structure consisting of a naked stalk bearing at its summit a pair of ovules, each surrounded at its base with a collar-like growth; seeds drupe-like with an outer fleshy coat, a middle stony layer, and a thin inner papery layer. Only one genus.

GINKGO ----- MAIDENHAIR TREE

Characters of the family. (The Chinese name.)

G. biloba L. Cultivated tree to 40 m high, usually much less. From China and Japan.

ANGIOSPERMAE ----- ANGIOSPERMS; FLOWERING PLANTS

MONOCOTYLEDONS

JUNCAGINACEAE ----- ARROW GRASS FAMILY

Marsh herbs with narrow linear leaves, ours perennial; flowers in racemes or dense spikes, hypogynous, regular, bisexual (ours) or unisexual; perianth in ours of 2 similar whorls of 3 free parts; stamens as many as the perianth parts; carpels 3 or 6, free or weakly fused and separating at maturity.

A-Bracts present in the raceme; mature follicles widely spreading
. . . . SCHEUCHZERIA
A-Bracts absent from the raceme; follicles close together. . . TRIGLOCHIN

SCHEUCHZERIA *

Bog plants with narrow alternate leaves and short few-flowered bracted racemes; perianth of 2 similar whorls, stamens 6, carpels 3 and free, ovules and seeds 2 per carpel. (Johann Jacob and Johann Scheuchzer, Swiss botanists.)

S. palustris var. americana Fern. Plants 20-40 cm high; leaves grass-like with conspicuously enlarged sheaths; racemes 3-10 cm long, the lowest bract leaf-like, the others successively reduced. Cold sphagnum bogs and sedge mats, Cook to Clearwater Co., s. to Otter Tail, Pope, Hennepin, and Rice counties.

TRIGLOCHIN ----- ARROW GRASS

Marsh plants, the narrow sheathing leaves all basal; raceme long and bractless with many small greenish flowers; perianth of 1 or (in ours) 2 similar whorls, early deciduous; stamens 3 or 6; carpels 3 or 6, weakly fused until maturity, then separating from a rod-like central axis. (Gr. treis, three, and glochis, point.)

T. maritimum L. Plants 20-80 cm high; racemes 10-40 cm long. Marshes, boggy places, and shores, St. Louis to Kittson, Clay, Pope, Scott and Chisago counties and in Blue Earth Co.

POACEAE (GRAMINEAE) ----- GRASS FAMILY

Annual, biennial, or perennial herbs; stems round with mostly hollow internodes; leaves alternate, with a sheathing base (fig. 5), the margins of the sheath usually free from each other, often a small erect papery structure, the ligule, present at junction of sheath and blade; flowers in specialized inflorescence units, the spikelets (figs. 62-64), each typically consisting of a zig-zag axis, the rachilla, with a series of bracts placed along it alternately on opposite sides, the lower 2 bracts, the glumes, with no flowers in their axils, the succeeding ones, the lemmas, each with a second bract, the palea, in its axil, with a flower between each lemma and palea. Flowers bisexual, or in a few species all or some unisexual; flower consisting of usually 2 or 3 hypogynous stamens and a 1-ovuled ovary usually with 2 feathery stigmas, the perianth absent or consisting of usually 2 small translucent fleshy scales, the lodicules, next the lemma; fruit usually a caryopsis. Lemma, palea, and flower are termed a floret (fig. 65), the number of florets per spikelet varying from several to 1; flowers and other parts of the floret may be reduced or missing.

A-Inflorescence (arrangement of spikelets, not flowers) a single terminal
    spike, the spikelets or groups of spikelets arranged in 2 opposite
    lengthwise linear rows, this arrangement sometimes visible only
    when spikelets are stripped off to expose attachment places, in Hordeum
    the rachis often breaking easily into segments as when trying to remove
    spikelets.
  B-Both glumes absent or vestigial. . . . . HYSTRIX
  B-Both glumes present, though sometimes reduced to a pair
    of awns side by side in front of spikelet.
    C-Spikelets mostly 2 or 3 at each node, the glumes displaced
      to a side by side position.
      D-Internodes of spike 1-4.5 mm long, if more than 2 mm then the
        lemmas with awns 6-15 cm long or with 3-lobed appendages ca.
        8 mm long; axis sometimes breaking easily into segments. HORDEUM
      D-Internodes of spike 4.5-8 mm long; lemmas with awns 1.5-
        4.5 cm long; axis not easily breaking apart. . . . . HYSTRIX
    C-Spikelets single at each node (rarely a few nodes may bear
      2), glumes nearly opposite each other in the usual position
      except sometimes at base of spikelet.
      E-Midnerves of lemmas bearing a fringe of stiff divergent hairs
        0.2-0.5 mm long; glumes lance-linear or linear, usually
        with 1 nerve. . . . . SECALE
      E-Midnerves of lemmas glabrous; glumes lanceolate or
        ovate, usually with 3-7 nerves.

F-Glumes 1.5-3.2 mm wide, 3-7.5 times as long as
wide (excluding awns if present); perennials, native
and naturalized. . . . . AGROPYRON
F-Glumes 3.5-5.5 mm wide, 1.4-2 times as long as
wide; annuals; cultivated . . . . TRITICUM
A-Inflorescence not as above, if spike-like the spikelets arranged irregularly on all sides of the axis, the axis not breaking easily apart.
G-Lemma 1, the total number of primary bracts therefore 3.
H-Inflorescence cylindrical, dense, compact, and spike-like, the
pedicels and branches not visible till spikelets are pushed apart;
no branches over 10 mm long including spikelets.
I-Glumes with terminal awns up to 1 mm long, the lemma un-
awned. . . . . PHLEUM
I-Glumes unawned, the lemma awned near or below the middle
with an awn 1-8 mm long. . . . . ALOPECURUS
H-Inflorescence otherwise, if dense and spike-like then some
branches 15-50 mm long.
J-Awns 20 mm long or longer present on lemmas . . . . STIPA
J-Awns on lemmas up to 14 mm long or none.
K-Lemma finely pubescent on the back at least above; glumes
3.5-8.5 mm long.
L-Awns on lemmas 1-14 mm long; floret without 2 narrow
tufts of hairs as below . . . . ORYZOPSIS
L-Awns on lemmas none; floret with 2 narrow tufts of hairs
opposite each other at base, each tuft arising from a tiny
scale . . . . PHALARIS
K-Lemma glabrous; glumes 1.2-3.5 mm long.
M-Glumes with 3-5 nerves; lemma much harder than glumes,
bony when mature; spikelets 3-3.5 mm long . . . . . . MILIUM
M-Glumes with 1 nerve; lemma about like glumes or softer in
consistency; spikelets 1.2-2 mm long . . . . AGROSTIS
G-Lemmas 2 or more, total primary bracts therefore 4 or more,
sometimes varying greatly in size, shape, or texture.
N-Lemmas 2, the lower one (staminate or empty) resembling
a third glume in its strong nerves, texture, and color, the
terminal one being distinctly different in its obscure nerves,
hard or leathery texture, and often lighter color. . . . . . PANICUM
N-Lemmas 2 or more, not as above.
O-Sheath margins fused around the stem to make a tube
except at the summit (may split open in age) . . . . BROMUS
O-Sheaths open down one side (edges may overlap).
P-Longest glume less than 7/8 as long as the fully developed
spikelet.
Q-Upper glume widest above the middle, 3-4 times as
wide as the lower one . . . . SPHENOPHOLIS
Q-Upper glume widest below the middle, up to 2 times
as wide as the lower one.
R-Some or all lemmas 9 to 15-nerved at least above;
ligules fringed with minute hairs. . . . . DISTICHLIS
R-Lemmas with fewer nerves or none; ligules not
fringed with hairs.
S-Lemmas distinctly keeled from tip to base, not leathery,
with 1-5 strong nerves, either the lower margins or
nerves of the lemma or its very base bearing a mat
or tuft of cobwebby hairs. . . . . POA

S-Lemmas rounded on the back except sometimes at
the apex, leathery to horny, the nerves obscure,
glabrous to pubescent but not cobwebby as above
. . . . FESTUCA
P-Longest glume 7/8 as long as the fully developed spikelet
or longer.
T-Florets 3, the lower 2 present as 2 narrow hairy scales
1/3-1/2 as long as the 1 functioning floret . . . . . . PHALARIS
T-Florets 2 or 3, lower 2 not reduced as above.
U-Widest glume up to 2 mm wide; lemmas glabrous to
finely puberulent, the hairs scarcely visible.
V-Upper glume widest at or below the middle,
3. 2-5 mm long. . . . . KOELERIA
V-Upper glume widest distinctly above the
middle, 1. 4-2. 5 mm long. . . . . SPHENOPHOLIS
U-Widest glume 2. 5 mm wide or wider; lemmas glabrous or
some of them conspicuously hairy at least on the margins,
the hairs 0. 5-2 mm long.
W-Glumes about equal in size, 3. 5-6 mm long, translucent, brownish, bronze, or purple . . . . HIEROCHLOE
W-Glumes very unequal, the lowest about 4 mm long,
the upper 6-7 mm long including the awn-like
tip, glumes yellow-green. . . . . ANTHOXANTHUM

AGROPYRON ----- WHEAT GRASS

Annuals or usually perennials from creeping rhizomes, with flat or
inrolled blades usually auricled at base, ligule minute or none; spikelets in
spikes, 1 (rarely 2) at each joint of the rachis, placed flat-wise, 3-several
flowered, articulated above the glumes and between the lemmas except in a
few species in which the rachis breaks up with attached spikelets; glumes often
side by side at base but spreading to take their normal positions above, equal
or nearly so, usually nearly as long as the lemmas, 1-several nerved, often
awned; lemmas rounded on the back, 1-several nerved, blunt to acuminate,
awned or not. (Gr. agrios, wild, and pyros, wheat.)

A-Glumes oblong or lanceolate, with convexly curved margins; leaf
blades mostly 5-10 mm wide, flat. . . . . A. repens
A-Glumes abruptly narrowed near the middle, the upper part tapering
with nearly straight sides to a point; leaf blades mostly 2-4 mm
wide, often becoming inrolled when dry . . . . A. smithii

A. repens (L.) Beauv. Quack Grass. Leaf blades not tapering to a hard
sharp point; spikelets with 3-9 florets. Chiefly introduced from Europe but
apparently native along the n. Atlantic coast, becoming a widespread weed.
Throughout the state.

A. smithii Rydb. Leaf blades tapering to a hard sharp point; spikelets
with 6-13 florets. Native of the western plains, found sparingly e. to Freeborn,
Winona, Goodhue, Anoka, Crow Wing, Clearwater, and Roseau counties.

AGROSTIS ---- BENTGRASS

Annuals or perennials, usually tufted, with flat or inrolled leaf blades and membranous ligules; spikelets in narrow or open panicles, 1-flowered, articulated above the glumes; glumes about equal, narrow, acute or acuminate, 1-nerved; lemma acute to obtuse, shorter than to nearly equaling the glumes, rounded on the back, obscurely nerved, awned or awnless; palea short and delicate or absent. (Gr. agros, a field.)

A. hyemalis (Walt.) BSP. Perennial; panicle very diffuse and delicate; pedicels 0.3-2 mm long; spikelets 1.2-2 mm long; palea none or very minute and nerveless. Winona Co.; doubtfully in St. Louis and Lake of the Woods counties.

ALOPECURUS ----- FOXTAIL *

Low annuals or perennials with flat blades, ligules membranous, inflorescence a dense spike-like panicle; spikelets 1-flowered, flattened, jointed below the glumes; glumes 3-nerved, more or less fused at base; lemmas about as long as the glumes, blunt, 5-nerved, awned near or below the middle of the back; palea minute or none in ours. (Gr. alopex, fox, and oura, tail.) (The classical Latin name.)

A-Glumes 3.8-6 mm long, acute or acuminate, firm almost or quite
    to the tip . . . . A. pratensis
A-Glumes 1.6-2.8 mm long, obtuse or truncate and more or less
    notched.
    B-Awn exserted 0-1.6 mm, attached at or near the middle of the
        lemma, straight . . . . A. aequalis
    B-Awn exserted 2.5-3.8 mm, attached ca. half-way between base
        and middle of lemma, often bent near the glume tip . A. geniculatus

A. aequalis Sobol. Leaves 1-4 mm wide; panicle 3-5 mm thick; glumes 1.6-2.8 mm long. In mud or shallow water, throughout the state except for the se. corner.

A. geniculatus L. Leaves 1-4 mm wide; panicle 3-6 mm thick; glumes 2-2.5 mm long. Eurasian and perhaps circumboreal, perhaps native in our range; moist places on rocks, Pipestone, Cottonwood, Brown, and Chippewa counties.

A. pratensis L. Meadow Foxtail. Leaves 2-6 mm wide; panicle 4-8 mm thick; awn exserted 2-5 mm, often bent near the glume tip. Native of Eurasia, naturalized in moist meadows, fields , and waste places, recorded from Lake, St. Louis, Anoka, and Hennepin counties.

ANTHOXANTHUM ----- SWEET VERNAL GRASS *

Annuals or perennials with sweet-scented foliage, the leaf blades flat; spikelets in spike-like panicles, 1-flowered, articulated above the glumes; glumes very unequal, much exceeding the lemmas, the lower 1-nerved, the upper 3-nerved; lower 2 lemmas without flowers, the lower awned on the back near the apex, the upper awned near the base; the third and central lemma fertile, shorter than the others and enclosed by them, brown and shining at maturity. (Gr. anthos, flower, and xanthos, yellow.)

A. ovatum Lag. (A. puellii Lec. & Lam.; A. odoratum ssp. aristatum (Boiss.) Trab.). From Europe; ours a single specimen from Winona Co., of somewhat doubtful origin.

BROMUS ----- BROME GRASS

Annuals, biennials, or perennials with flat leaves; spikelets in panicles, 3-many flowered, eventually disarticulating above the glumes; glumes slightly unequal, shorter than the lemmas, 1-5-nerved; lemmas 5-9-nerved, mostly convex, 2-toothed at the apex, awnless or awned from between the teeth; stigmas below the summit of the ovary. (Gr. bromos, oats.)

A-Awn longer than the lemmas, 11-14 mm long . . . . B. tectorum
A-Awn shorter than the lemmas, to 3 mm long or none . . . . B. inermis

B. inermis Leyss. Hungarian or Smooth Brome;cultivated. Perennials 5-10 dm high; sheaths and blades glabrous, blades 6-15 mm wide. Used for forage and as a soil stabilizer, often escaped, throughout the state. European.

B. tectorum L. Downy Chess. Annuals 2-7 dm high; sheaths and blades pubescent, blades 2-5 mm wide. From s.Europe, widely established as a weed, mostly in the south, n. to s. St. Louis, Hubbard, and Clay counties.

DISTICHLIS ----- SALT GRASS, ALKALI GRASS *

Low dioecious perennials with usually overlapping sheaths and in-rolled leaf blades; ligule a truncated membrane fringed with minute hairs; spikelets in small panicles, flattened, 4-16-flowered; glumes unequal, keeled, obscurely nerved, shorter than the lemmas; lemmas smooth, some or all of them 9-15-nerved at least above. (Gr. distichos, two-ranked.)

D. stricta (Torr.) Rydb. Plants 2-4 dm high with numerous stiff in-rolled leaf blades mostly 5-10 cm long; spikelets 6-16-flowered, 12-20 mm long. Wet alkaline places, Pipestone to Kittson Co.

FESTUCA ----- FESCUE GRASS

Annuals or perennials with flat or inrolled leaf blades, in some species auricled at base; spikelets in panicles, 3-11-flowered, the rachilla disarticulating above the glumes; glumes unequal, usually shorter than the lemmas, the lower 1-nerved, the upper 3-nerved; lemmas rounded on the back, leathery to horny, obscurely 5-nerved, the apex usually awned, not toothed; stigmas at the summit of the ovary. (L. festuca, straw.)

A-Leaf blades 3-8 mm wide, flat . . . . F. obtusa
A-Leaf blades less than 3 mm wide, usually inrolled.
  B-Annuals, growing as single individuals or in small tufts of several
     individuals; root system slight; spikelets with 5-11 crowded
     florets obscuring the rachilla. . . . . F. octoflora
  B-Perennials, growing in large tufts of many individuals; root
     system copious; spikelets mostly with 4-7 uncrowded florets
     with rachilla internodes observable at maturity. . . . . F. ovina

F. obtusa Spreng. Perennials 6-12 dm high; panicle 15-30 cm long; spikelets 4-6 mm long, 3-5-flowered. Moist woods throughout most of the state, not recorded in a strip from Roseau through n.St. Louis to Cook Co.

F. octoflora Walt. Plants 1-4 dm high; panicle 3-10 cm long; spikelets 5-12 mm long, 6-10-flowered. Dry open soil, Houston to Rock Co. and n. to Stearns, Beltrami, and Washington counties.

F. ovina L. Sheep Fescue. Plants 1-5 dm high; panicle 1-10 cm long; spikelets 3-6-flowered. Dry open soil.

A-Panicle contracted, spike-like; anthers 1.2-1.7 mm long; spikelets 5-7 mm long; lemmas 3-5 mm long; native; Cook to Kittson Co., s. to Clearwater, ne.,Todd, e. Stearns, and Anoka counties
. . . . F. o. var. saximontana (Rydb.) Gl. (F. saximontana Rydb.).
A-Panicle loosely open, its branches divergent at anthesis; anthers 2.5-3.5 mm long; spikelets 7-10 mm long; lemmas 4.3-5.8 mm long; naturalized from Europe; Lake to Polk Co., s. to Ramsey and Faribault counties . . . . F. o. var. duriuscula (L.) Koch.

HIEROCHLOE ----- SWEET GRASS, SENECA GRASS, HOLY GRASS *

Fragrant perennial grasses; spikelets in panicles, 3-flowered, the two lower flowers staminate, the third bisexual with 2 stamens; glumes broad, thin and translucent, glabrous, shining; lemmas of staminate flowers conspicuously hairy at least on the margins, lemma of fertile floret shorter, all awnless. (Gr. hieros, sacred, and chloe, grass.)

H. odorata (L.) Beauv. Vanilla Grass, Indian Grass. Stems usually 3-6 dm high; panicle 5-10 cm long with widely spreading or somewhat drooping branches; glumes 3.5-6 mm long, the widest one 2.5 mm wide or wider. Moist soil, meadows, shores, or bog margins, throughout the state.

HORDEUM ----- BARLEY *

Annuals, biennials, or perennials with flat leaf blades and scarious truncate ligules; spikelets in a dense spike, usually 3 at each joint of the rachis, the rachis usually breaking into segments at maturity, each segment consisting of the triad of spikelets and a flattened internode; spikelets 1-flowered (rarely 2), the middle spikelet sessile and fertile, the lateral two pedicelled and usually staminate or abortive or sometimes each reduced to a bristle (all 3 fertile in some races of cultivated barley); glumes very narrow and elongate, awned or awnless, widened at base or not; lemma rounded on the back, 5-nerved, awned or appendaged. (The Latin name.)

A-1 or more florets at each joint more than 2 mm wide; rachis of spike continuous; auricles at base of blade well developed . . . . H. vulgare
A-Florets less than 2 mm wide, usually less than 1 mm; rachis of spike breaking easily into segments; auricles absent.
B-Awns 30-60 mm long . . . . H. jubatum
B-Awns 3-15 mm long . . . . H. pusillum

H. jubatum L. Squirreltail Grass, Foxtail Barley. Perennial; spike 5-10 cm long. Apparently native in the far ne. but a common weed in our range, throughout the state.

H. pusillum Nutt. Little Barley. Annual; spike 2-6 cm long, exserted or at first included in the upper sheath. Dry, sterile, or especially alkaline soil, Rock, Pipestone, and Brown counties.

<u>H</u>. vulgare L. Barley; cultivated. Annual; usually with awns 6-15 cm long but in one form awnless, the lemmas tipped instead with a 3-lobed appendage ca. 8 mm long. Occasionally escaped. Geographic origin uncertain.

HYSTRIX ----- BOTTLEBRUSH GRASS*

Perennials with flat leaves and short firm ligules; spikelets in spikes, 2-4 (rarely 1) at each joint of the rachis, 2-4-flowered, disarticulating above the glumes and between the lemmas; glumes usually reduced to short bristles or knobs or none; lemmas linear, rounded on the back, rigid, 5-nerved near the tip, drawn from there into a long awn; palea about as long as the body of the lemma. (Gr. hustrix, the hedgehog.)

<u>H</u>. patula Moench. Leaf blades 8-13 mm wide; spike 5-12 cm long; spikelets usually in pairs; glumes variable in development even on the same plant; lemmas 8-11 mm long with awns 1.5-4.5 cm long. Woods, throughout most of the state, not recorded in Cook, Kittson, and a few other counties.

KOELERIA*

Perennials or annuals with narrow blades and shining spike-like panicles; spikelets 2-4-flowered, disarticulating above the glumes; glumes nearly as long as or as long as the lemmas, somewhat unequal, the lower 1-nerved, the upper 3-5-nerved; lemmas rounded on the back, with papery margins, obscurely 5-nerved, awned or awnless. (Named for the German botanist G. L. Koeler.)

<u>K</u>. macrantha (Ledeb.) Spreng. (K. cristata (L.) Pers.). Junegrass, Crested Hair Grass. Stems tufted, 3-6 dm high; spike-like panicles 5-12 cm long, silvery yellow-green; spikelets mostly 3.5-5 mm long. Characteristic element of dry prairies, sandy areas, or open woods, western, e. to Houston, Anoka, Crow Wing, s. Beltrami, and Kittson counties, and in s. St. Louis Co.

MILIUM ----- MILLET-GRASS*

Erect perennials with flat leaf blades; ligule membranous; spikelets in a widely branched panicle, 1-flowered, articulated above the glumes; glumes alike, ovate or elliptic, nearly flat; lemma about as long as the glumes, awnless, nerveless, elliptic, rounded on the back, smooth, the edges inrolled, firm, white, and shining at maturity. (L. milium, millet.)

<u>M</u>. effusum L. Principal leaf blades 10-18 mm wide; panicle 10-30 cm long. Rich woods, mostly calcareous, thickets and glades, Lake to Lake of the Woods Co., s. to Clearwater, Wadena, Scott, Waseca, and Winona counties.

ORYZOPSIS ----- MOUNTAIN RICE, RICE GRASS

Tufted perennials with flat or inrolled leaf blades, ligule membranous or none; spikelets in very narrow to open panicles or racemes, 1-flowered, articulated above the glumes; glumes rather broad, acute to acuminate, awnless; lemma about equaling the glumes, becoming hardened and sometimes black in fruit, rounded, with a terminal straight or twisted awn readily broken from the lemma. (Gr. oryza, rice, opsis, appearance.)

A-Glumes 3.5-4 mm long, awn 0.5-2 mm long . . . . O. pungens
A-Glumes 5-8 mm long, awn 6-14 mm long. . . . . O. asperifolia

O. asperifolia Michx. Leaf blades, at least the basal ones, 5-10 mm wide, flat or partly inrolled; inflorescence a raceme or seldom-branched panicle. Moist to dry upland woods, Cook to Kittson Co., s. to Clay, Otter Tail, Stearns, Hennepin, Olmsted, and Winona counties.

O. pungens (Torr.) Hitchc. Leaf blades 1-2 mm wide, often inrolled; inflorescence a panicle. Dry, rocky or sandy soil, Cook to Roseau Co., s. to Clearwater, Crow Wing, Hennepin, and Fillmore counties.

PANICUM ----- PANIC GRASS

Annuals or perennials; leaves often rather broad, ligules various (usually of hairs); spikelets (fig. 63) in panicles or spike-like racemes, not flattened, each consisting of 2 glumes (the lower often much shorter than the upper), a lower "sterile" lemma which subtends a staminate or abortive flower and which resembles the upper glume, and an upper "fertile" lemma enclosing with its palea a bisexual flower, this lemma and palea hardened, usually white or pale and smooth and nerveless, often shining. (Ancient Latin name of the millet.)

A-Many leaves of plant 20 times as long as wide; early leaves narrow, 2-6 mm wide.
　B-Leaf blades mostly 5-8 cm long, densely pubescent on one or both sides; internodes of stem not greatly shortened, stem leaves and later the axillary leaves well distributed along stem; spikelets pubescent . . . . P. wilcoxianum
　B-Leaf blades mostly 10-30 cm long, glabrous or pilose; internodes greatly shortened, the stem leaves and later the axillary ones usually crowded at base of stem; spikelets glabrous or pubescent.
　　C-2nd glume and sterile lemma extending 0.5-1.5 mm beyond apex of fertile floret; spikelets 3-3.8 mm long. . . . P. depauperatum
　　C-2nd glume and sterile lemma not longer than apex of fertile floret; spikelets 2.1-3.5 mm long.
　　　D-Spikelets 2.1-3.0 mm long, 1.0-1.3 mm wide; stems in large tufts . . . . P. linearifolium
　　　D-Spikelets 2.7-3.5 mm long, 1.4-1.7 mm wide; stems mostly few in a tuft or single . . . . P. perlongum
A-Leaves all less than 20 times as long as wide, narrow or broad; early leaves 2-30 mm wide.
　E-Spikelets 1.3-2.6 mm long.
　　F-Spikelets 2.4-2.6 mm long.
　　　G-Leaf blades along the stem 2-6 mm wide, 13-19 times as long as wide; leaf sheaths mostly overlapping . . . P. wilcoxianum
　　　G-Leaf blades 5-10 mm wide, 7-12 times as long as wide; sheaths shorter than the internodes . . . . P. villosissimum
　　F-Spikelets less than 2.4 mm long.
　　　H-First glume irregularly truncated or rounded or very broadly rounded-acute, 0.2-0.5 mm, rarely to 0.7 mm long, less than two fifths, usually less than a third as long as the spikelet; spikelets 1.3-1.9 mm long . . . . P. lanuginosum

43

H-First glume regularly acute to acuminate, either 0.7-1.4 mm
    long or a third to a half as long as the spikelet; spikelets
    1.7-2.6 mm long.
  I-Spikelets 2.0-2.6 mm long; well-grown leaf blades 6-13 mm
    wide; fruit about 2 mm long and half as wide . . P. villosissimum
  I-Spikelets 1.7-2.0 mm long; well-grown leaf blades 4-7 mm
    wide; fruit about 1.5 mm long and two thirds as wide
    . . . . P. praecocius
E-Spikelets more than 2.6 mm long.
  J-Leaf blades 10-30 mm wide, deeply heart-shaped at base,
    the lobes clasping the stem. . . . . P. latifolium
  J-Leaf blades 2-14 mm wide, tapering or rounded at
    base.
   K-Spikelets 2.7-3 mm long.
    L-Spikelets 1.5 mm wide or wider, sparsely pilose to glabrous;
      leaves elliptic, 6-12 mm wide; plants 20-50 cm tall
      . . . . P. oligosanthes var. scribnerianum
    L-Spikelets less than 1.5 mm wide, copiously pubescent; leaves
      narrowly linear, 2-6 mm wide; plants 10-25 cm tall
      . . . . P. wilcoxianum
   K-Spikelets more than 3 mm long.
    M-Leaf blades pubescent on upper surface at least on
      apical half; spikelets pilose with hairs usually 0.5 mm
      long or longer . . . . P. leibergii
    M-Leaf blades glabrous or rarely sparsely pilose above;
      spikelets either glabrous or with hairs not more than
      0.3 mm long . . . . P. oligosanthes var. scribnerianum

P. depauperatum Muhl. Leaf blades 8-15 cm long, 2-5 mm wide, glabrous
to long-pilose; spikelets 3.0-3.8 mm long, glabrous or minutely pubescent.
Dry or sandy soil, usually in open woods, Lake and St. Louis counties,
Beltrami to Norman Co., Wadena, Hennepin, Goodhue, and Wabasha counties.

P. lanuginosum Ell. Leaf blades 4-12 cm long, 5-12 mm wide, glabrous
or pubescent on either or both sides, ligule occasionally with hairs up to 5
mm long; spikelets 1.3-1.9 mm long, finely pubescent. Dry or moist sterile
open soil, thickets and thin woodlands, throughout the state except for the
extreme se. corner.

P. latifolium L. Larger leaf blades usually 10-16 cm long, 10-30 mm
wide, glabrous or nearly so on both sides, the edges fringed with hairs at
the cordate base; spikelets 3.0-3.7 mm long, pubescent. Rich open woods
and thickets, Houston and Fillmore to Scott and Chisago counties.

P. leibergii (Vasey) Scribn. Larger leaf blades 7-11 cm long, 7-12 mm
wide, hirsute on both sides, to nearly glabrous above, more or less ciliate;
ligule a band of hairs less than 2 mm long; spikelets 3.1-4.0 mm long,
hirsute with hairs 0.5-1 mm long. Prairies, meadows, and open woods,
Houston to Rock Co., n. to Ramsey, Kanabec, Hubbard, and Kittson counties.

P. linearifolium Scribn. Leaf blades usually 10-20 cm long, 2-5 mm
wide, glabrous to sparsely pilose; spikelets 2.1-3.0 mm long, 1.0-1.3 mm
wide, glabrous to pilose. Appears not clearly distinguished from P. perlongum.

P. linearifolium Scribn. Leaf blades usually 10-20 cm long, 2-5 mm
wide, glabrous to sparsely pilose; pedicel of subterminal spikelet of each
panicle branch usually longer than its spikelet; spikelets 2.1-3.0 mm long,
1.0-1.3 mm wide, glabrous to pilose. Appears not clearly distinguished
from P. perlongum.

Dry or stony soil, open woods and banks, Cook to Lake of the Woods Co., s. to Norman, Clay, Benton, Anoka, Blue Earth, and Winona counties.

P. oligosanthes var. scribnerianum (Nash) Fern. Larger leaf blades 6-12 cm long, 6-12 mm wide, glabrous or rarely sparsely pilose above, glabrous to pubescent beneath, usually ciliate, and long hairy at base, the ligule a band of hairs 1-2 mm long; spikelets 2.7-4 mm long, glabrous to sparsely hirsute. Dry or moist often sandy soil in prairies and open woods, Houston to Rock Co., n. to Chisago, Crow Wing, and Kittson counties.

P. perlongum Nash. Leaf blades 8-25 cm long, 2-5 mm wide, long-pilose; pedicel of subterminal spikelet of each panicle branch shorter than its spikelet; spikelets 2.7-3.5 mm long, 1.4-1.7 mm wide, minutely pubescent. Appears not clearly distinguished from P. linearifolium. Dry soil, usually in prairies, Houston to Nobles and Pipestone counties, n. to Washington, Kanabec, Crow Wing, Clearwater, and Kittson counties.

P. praecocius Hitchc. & Chase. Leaf blades 4-8 cm long, 4-7 mm wide, long-pilose on both sides, ligule occasionally with hairs up to 5 mm long; spikelets 1.7-2.0 mm long, finely pubescent. Dry prairies, clearings, and open woods, Houston to Pipestone Co., n. to s. St. Louis, Crow Wing, Clearwater, and Kittson counties.

P. villosissimum Nash. Leaf blades 5-10 cm long, 6-13 mm wide, more or less pilose on both sides, ligules occasionally with hairs up to 5 mm long; spikelets 2.0-2.6 mm long, finely pubescent, the first glume 0.7-1.4 mm long. Dry, especially sandy soil, prairies and open woods, Houston and Fillmore counties, n. to Dakota, Anoka, and Sherburne counties.

P. wilcoxianum Vasey. Leaf blades 4-8 cm long, 2-6 mm wide, from hirsute on both sides to nearly glabrous above, ligule a band of hairs about 1 mm long; spikelets 2.5-3.0 mm long, pilose, first glume 0.7-1.4 mm long. Dry prairies and thin woods, Houston to Pipestone Co., n. to Washington, Morrison, Red Lake, and Kittson counties.

PHALARIS ----- CANARY GRASS, RIBBON GRASS

Annuals or perennials with flat ribbon-like leaves, the ligules large and membranous; spikelets in dense panicles with 1 functioning terminal floret and two sterile lemmas below the floret on opposite sides in the form of 2 narrow scales 1/3-1/2 as long as the floret; glumes about equal, keeled, usually winged along the midnerve; fertile lemma becoming hardened, often shining. (Gr. phalaris, a kind of grass.)

P. arundinacea L. Reed Canary Grass. Stout erect grass 10-15 dm high, principal leaf blades 10-30 cm long, 10-15 mm wide, sometimes striped with white; glumes 4-6.5 mm long; sterile lemmas very small and tufted with long hairs. Stream banks, lake shores, marshes, and moist ground, throughout the state.

PHLEUM *

Annuals or perennials, ligule elongate, leaves flat, inflorescence a dense spike-like panicle; spikelets 1-flowered, flattened, jointed above the glumes; glumes 3-nerved; lemma much shorter than the glumes, thin, 3-5-nerved, awnless. (Gr. phleos, a kind of reed.)

P. pratense L. Timothy; cultivated. Grown for hay and pasture, often escaped from cultivation throughout the state. From Europe.

POA ----- MEADOW GRASS, SPEARGRASS

Annuals or perennials, usually tufted or sod-forming, with flat narrow leaves ending in a boat-shaped tip; spikelets in panicles, flattened, 2-6-flowered; glumes 1-3-nerved, keeled, awnless; lemmas 1-5-nerved, usually distinctly keeled from tip to base, awnless, usually either the lower margins or lower nerves or the very base bearing a mat or tuft of cobwebby hairs; upper florets reduced, the rachilla not extended beyond the uppermost. (Gr. poa, grass.)

A-Stems strongly flattened with 2 sharp edges, the nodes elliptic in section; lemmas with 1 or 3 nerves distinct, the lateral nerves obscure; stems from long running rhizomes. . . . . P. compressa
A-Stems rounded or slightly compressed, the nodes round in section; larger lemmas with 5 distinct nerves at least in the upper half; stems from rhizomes or not.
  B-Cobwebby hairs lacking from the callus (the very base of the floret, visible when floret is removed); annuals, often prostrate . . . P. annua
  B-Cobwebby hairs present on the callus; perennials.
    C-Backs of lemmas glabrous on the 5 nerves . . . . P. saltuensis
    C-Backs of lemmas pubescent on 1 or more nerves.
      D-Lemmas 2.5-3.5 mm long; lower branches of panicle in whorls of 3-5 at a node; rhizomes present . . . . P. pratensis
      D-Lemmas 3.5-4.5 mm long; lower branches of panicle mostly in pairs or 3's at a node; rhizomes absent . . . . P. wolfii

P. annua L. Speargrass, Annual Bluegrass. Annual; spikelets 3-5 mm long; lemmas 2.4-3.4 mm long, more or less cobwebby or pubescent on the nerves. Widespread in moist soil, often a lawn weed, throughout the state. Introduced from Eurasia.

P. compressa L. Canada Bluegrass, Wiregrass. Perennial; spikelets 3.5-6 mm long; lemmas 2-2.8 mm long. Open, usually dry places, especially in acid soil, throughout the state. Introduced from Europe.

P. pratensis L. Kentucky Bluegrass, June Grass. Leaf blades 2-5 mm wide; spikelets 3-6 mm long; lemmas 2.5-3.5 mm long. Moist or dry soil, avoiding acid soils and heavy shade, throughout the state. Apparently native in the north and in Canada but introduced elsewhere, the introductions evidently from Europe.

P. saltuensis Fern. & Wieg. Leaf blades 2-5 mm wide; spikelets 3.5-5.5 mm long; lemmas 2.4-3.9 mm long. Woods and clearings, Cook to St. Louis Co.

P. wolfii Scribn. Leaf blades 1-2 mm wide; spikelets 4-6 mm long; lemmas 3-4.5 mm long. Moist woods, s. Lake Co. and Houston Co.

SECALE ----- RYE

Mostly annuals with flat leaves; spikelets in spikes, 1 at each joint of the rachis, usually 2-flowered, eventually disarticulating above the glumes; glumes narrow, rigid, sharp pointed, shorter than the lemmas; lemmas broader, sharply and asymmetrically keeled, 5-nerved, tapering into a long awn, the keel and exposed margins with a comb of sharp teeth. (The Latin name.)

S. cereale L. Rye; cultivated. Annual; spikes 8-15 cm long or sometimes smaller, awns 3-8 cm long. Often escaped to waste ground, probably not persisting. Cultigen, thought to be derived from ancestors in southwest Asia.

SPHENOPHOLIS ----- WEDGE GRASS

Perennials with usually flat leaves; spikelets in panicles, 2-3-flowered, disarticulating both below the glumes and below the upper lemma; rachilla prolonged beyond the uppermost floret; glumes very unequal, the lower narrow, linear or linear-oblong, 1-nerved, the upper broad, obovate, 3-5-nerved; lemmas obscurely nerved, awnless, about equalling or slightly longer than the glumes, obscurely nerved, awnless or rarely with a straight awn below the summit. (Gr. sphen, a wedge, and pholis, scale.)

S. obtusata (Michx.) Scribn. Panicle dense, 5-15 cm long; spikelets 2-3 mm long. Moist or dry soil, prairies and borders of woods, Houston to Rock Co., n. to Hennepin, Clearwater, and Polk counties, and in s. St. Louis Co.

STIPA ----- PORCUPINE GRASS, FEATHERGRASS,
SPEARGRASS, NEEDLEGRASS *

Coarse perennial grasses with inrolled leaves; spikelets in a panicle, 1-flowered, articulated above the glumes; glumes narrow, acute or bristle-pointed, the lower 3-nerved, the upper 5-nerved; lemmas shorter than or equalling the glumes, inrolled and rounded, becoming hardened, obscurely nerved or nerveless, bearing a tuft of hairs at the very base and a long terminal awn which is usually twice bent near the middle; the lower one or two segments twisted. (Gr. stupe, tow.)

A-Awn of floret 2-3.5 cm long, the floret 4.5-6 mm long; glumes
    8-12 mm long including awns. . . . . S. viridula
A-Awn of floret 10-20 cm long, the floret 9-21 mm long; glumes
    17-42 mm long including awns.
    B-Floret 9-13 mm long not including its awn; glumes(17-)21-30mm
      long. . . . . S. comata
    B-Floret 18-21 mm long not including its awn; glumes 28-42 mm
      long. . . . . S. spartea

S. comata Trin. & Rupr. Needle-and-thread Grass. Sheaths glabrous or nearly so; ligule 3-4 mm long. Dry plains and prairies, Pipestone to Kittson Co., e. to Redwood, Ramsey, and Stearns counties, with one collection from a filled area in Duluth.

S. spartea Trin. Porcupine Grass, Speargrass. Sheaths glabrous; ligules of upper leaves 4-6 mm long, of the lower much shorter. Mesic to dry western prairies, e. to Houston, Chisago, Crow Wing, Beltrami, and Kittson counties, with an isolated locality in St. Louis Co.

S. viridula Trin. Feather Bunchgrass; Green Needlegrass. Sheaths more or less hairy at margins and summit; ligule less than 1 mm long. Dry plains and prairies, Pipestone to Kittson Co., e. to Martin and Stearns counties.

TRITICUM ----- WHEAT

Annuals with flat leaf blades; spikelets in a spike, 1 at each joint of the rachis, placed with the edges of the lemmas next the rachis, 2-5-flowered, disarticulating above the glumes and between the florets or continuous; rachis disarticulating or not; glumes stiff, 3-several-nerved, the apex short-toothed or with 1 or more awns; lemmas broad, very asymmetric, many-nerved, abruptly pointed or awned. (The Latin name.)

T. aestivum L. Wheat; cultivated. Leaf blades 5-15 mm wide; spikes mostly 5-12 cm long; spikelets broad, glabrous or pubescent, long-awned to awnless; glumes 3.5-5.5 mm wide, 1.4-2 times as long as wide (excluding awns when present). Origin uncertain.

CYPERACEAE ----- SEDGE FAMILY

Grass- or rush-like herbs, the stems usually pith-filled, often tri-angular; leaves spiral or all basal, with sheathing bases, the sheaths fused around the stem, the blades narrow or sometimes absent; flowers bisexual or unisexual, in small spikes, these single or clustered, each consisting of an axis bearing a series of bracts, the bracts spiralled or rarely alternate on opposite sides; flowers present in the axils of most or all of the bracts, in a few genera the female flowers surrounded by an additional subtending bract known as a perigynium when fully fused around the flower; perianth none or of bristles or scales or both; stamens 1-3 (-6), hypogynous; ovary 1-locular with 1 erect ovule; style 2- or 3-cleft, the branches not feathery; fruit an achene or nutlet.

A-Ovary enclosed in a sac, the perigynium, the style at anthesis pro-
    truding through the terminal opening; flowers unisexual . . . . CAREX
A-Ovary not enclosed as above; flowers bisexual.
  B-Base of the style conspicuously swollen, persistent on the fruit as
    a "tubercle". . . . . ELEOCHARIS
  B-Base of the style not swollen, deciduous from the fruit.
    C-Pistil surrounded at base by 1-6 bristles . . . . SCIRPUS
    C-Pistil surrounded at base by very numerous bristles or hairs
    . . . . ERIOPHORUM

CAREX ----- SEDGE

Grass-like perennials with usually 3-ranked leaves, monoecious (rarely dioecious); flowers in spikes, each in the axil of a bract known as a scale, without perianth, the staminate and pistillate flowers either in differ-ent spikes or in different parts of the same spike in monoecious plants; staminate flowers consisting of 2-3 stamens; pistillate flowers consisting of a lens-shaped or 3-angled ovary with a 2- or 3- branched style, the ovary surrounded by a sac-like perigynium (fig. 66) with the style protruding from the small terminal opening; fruit an achene, remaining surrounded by the perigynium. (The ancient Latin name.)

A large genus, in which ripe fruit is necessary for the determination of many species. The 29 species included here are plants which usually have fully ripe fruit by the first week of June; they constitute about 23% of our Carex flora.

A-Spike one on each stem.
  B-Style branches 2; achenes lens-shaped or plano-convex . C. gynocrates
  B-Style branches 3; achenes triangular to round in cross section.
    C-Spikes either staminate or pistillate . . . . C. umbellata
    C-Spikes pistillate at base, staminate at summit.
      D-Lowest pistillate scale not foliaceous, about equalling or a
      little longer than the perigynium; perigynium with a beak
      0.3-0.5 mm long . . . . C. filifolia
      D-Lowest pistillate scale foliaceous, much exceeding the
      perigynium; beak 0.7-3.0 mm long.
        E-Beak 2-3 mm long, perigynia 4.5-6 mm long . . . . . . C. backii
        E-Beak 0.7-1.0 mm long, perigynia 3.5-5 mm long. . C. saximontana

‍-Spikes 2 or more on each stem.
  F-Style branches 2; achenes lens-shaped or plano-convex.
    G-Inflorescence compound, at least the lowest node bearing a branch
      with 2 or more spikes.
      H-Perigynia without nerves or very obscurely nerved; at least the
        lower spikes 12-45 mm apart . . . . C. sparganioides
      H-Perigynia distinctly 3-11-nerved at least on the outer face;
        spikes closely aggregated or separated up to 18 mm.
        I-Perigynia 1-1.8 mm wide, 2-4 times as long as wide . . C. stipata
        I-Perigynia 2.2-3.2 mm wide, 1.3-1.9 times as long as wide
        . . . . C. muhlenbergii
    G-Inflorescence simple, the spikes single at each node.
      J-Spikes with the staminate flowers at the base when both sexes
        present, sometimes the terminal spike all staminate.
        K-Perigynia 1-2 mm wide, unwinged. . . . . C. interior
        K-Perigynia 2.1-3 mm wide, with thin wing-edges . . . . . C. brevior
      J-Spikes with the staminate flowers at the tip when both sexes
        present, sometimes some or most spikes all staminate.
        L-Perigynia 4.2-6 mm long, distinctly nerved.
          M-Beak of perigynium 0.8-1.2 mm long, 1/5-1/4 the length of
            the perigynium. . . . . C. muhlenbergii
          M-Beak of perigynium 1.5-3 mm long, 2/5-1/3 the length of
            the perigynium. . . . . C. foenea
        L-Perigynia 2.2-4 mm long, if over 3.6 mm then nerveless or
          only obscurely nerved near the base.
          N-Spikes closely set together in the inflorescence, all over-
            lapping; perigynia golden brown to blackish; flowering
            stems arising singly or few together from a slender
            rhizome. . . . . C. eleocharis
          N-At least the lower spikes well separated, not over-
            lapping, 5-45 mm apart; perigynia greenish to yellow-
            green; flowering stems tufted, rhizomes either none or
            very short.
            O-Leaf blades 1-3 mm wide; leaf sheaths not as below. . C. rosea
            O-Leaf blades 4-10 mm wide; leaf sheaths often with cross-
              veins or minute bumps linking the lengthwise veins on
              the back near the junction of sheath and blade. . C. sparganioides
  F-Style branches 3; achenes 3-angled to nearly round in cross section.
    P-Blades of the bracts or leaves subtending the lower pistillate
      spikes no longer than their sheaths, often much shorter or none,
      no blades over 12 mm long; pistillate scales not as below.
      Q-Staminate spikes or the spikes with the most staminate flowers
        with peduncles 7-70 mm long, if less than 12 mm then the
        longest bract sheath 9 mm long or longer and purple-brown.
        R-Leaf blades 10-25 mm wide . . . . C. plantaginea
        R-Leaf blades 2-4 mm wide.
          S-Pistillate scales conspicuously and abruptly cuspidate
          . . . . C. pedunculata
          S-Pistillate scales rounded to acute . . . . C. richardsonii
      Q-Staminate spikes sessile or with peduncles up to 11 mm long,
        if more than 5 mm then the longest bract sheath less than
        4 mm long and not purple-brown.
        T-Perigynia 1.5-2.2 mm long, with beaks 0.2 mm long . C. eburnea
        T-Perigynia 2.2-4.7 mm long, with beaks 0.4-1.7 mm long.
          U-Stems all elongate; inflorescences all normally with the
            terminal spike staminate, none of them hidden and
            merely pistillate . . . . C. pensylvanica

U-Stems of various lengths, the longer ones with staminate
or both staminate and pistillate spikes, the shorter ones
only pistillate, always some of the latter 0-4 cm above
ground level and usually more or less hidden among
the leaf bases . . . . C. umbellata
P-Either the blades of the bracts or leaves subtending the lower pistillate spikes longer than their sheaths, usually much longer and
much more than 12 mm long, or bracts absent and the pistillate
scales resembling them, green and exceeding the spikes.
V-Pistillate scales several times as long as the perigynia, to
3 cm long, green throughout, dilated at base and mostly
concealing the perigynia.
W-Beak 2-3 mm long, perigynia 4.5-6 mm long . . . . . . C. backii
W-Beak 0.7-1.0 mm long, perigynia 3.5-5 mm long
. . . . C. saximontana
V-Pistillate scales at most but slightly exceeding the perigynia,
not green throughout.
X-Perigynia pubescent, at least around base of beak.
Y-Stems and leaves pubescent. . . . . C. hirtifolia
Y-Stems and leaves glabrous.
Z-Stems of various lengths, the longer ones with staminate
or both staminate and pistillate spikes, the shorter ones
only pistillate, always some of the latter 0-4 cm above
ground level and usually more or less hidden among the
leaf bases . . . . C. umbellata
Z-Stems all elongate; inflorescences all normally with
the terminal spike staminate, none of them hidden and
merely pistillate.
AA-Body of perigynium subglobose, about as long and
thick as wide; scales about equalling to longer than
the perigynia. C. pensylvanica
AA-Body of perigynium ellipsoid to obovoid, distinctly
longer than wide, usually wider than thick; scales
2/3-7/8 as long as the perigynia. . . . . C. peckii
X-Perigynia glabrous.
BB-Leaf blades hairy. . . . . C. castanea
BB-Leaf blades glabrous to scabrous.
CC-Perigynia with only 2 distinct nerves or ribs.
DD-Bract subtending the lower pistillate spike 70-200
mm long . . . . C. sprengelii
DD-Bract subtending the lower pistillate spike 3-25
mm long. . . . . C. umbellata
CC-Perigynia with 7-50 nerves, sometimes 2-4 more
prominent than the others.
EE-Staminate spikes 2-4.
FF-Perigynia with 7-11 nerves. . . . . C. rostrata
FF-Perigynia with 16-22 nerves . . . . C. lacustris
EE-Staminate spike single.
GG-Staminate spike peduncled, its base usually raised
above the top of the upper pistillate spike; bracts
of the pistillate spikes reaching at most to the tip
of the staminate spike; pistillate scales 1.5-2.6 mm
wide, 1-nerved, usually conspicuously marked on
either side of the green midnerve with purplish-
brown . . . . C. meadii

GG-Staminate spike sessile or short-stalked, its
    base usually below the top of the uppermost pistillate
    spike; 1 or more bracts well exceeding the staminate
    spike; pistillate scales 0.8-3 mm wide, if wider than
    1.9 mm the lower ones 3-nerved; midnerve greenish,
    the sides whitish to pale brown.
    HH-Pistillate scales 2-3 mm wide, 3.6-5 mm long, the
        lower ones in the spike 3-nerved. . . . . . C. turgida
    HH-Pistillate scales 0.8-1.9 mm wide, 1.9-7 mm
        long, 1-nerved.
        II-Perigynia roundish in section, ellipsoid, the
            base rounded to the attachment; pistillate
            scales 0.8-1.8 mm wide, 1.9-2.6 mm long
            . . . . C. granularis
        II-Perigynia 3-angled in section with rounded
            angles, obovoid, the base drawn out with a
            straight or incurved taper; pistillate scales
            1-1.9 mm wide, 1.9-7 mm long (including
            awn).
            JJ-Larger leaves of the fertile shoots 2-7 mm
                wide, of the sterile shoots 3-9 mm wide;
                pistillate scales mostly with a central tooth
                or awn 0.2-5 mm long, rarely toothless
                . . . . C. laxiflora
            JJ-Larger leaves of the fertile shoots 9-19
                mm wide, of the sterile shoots 11-38 mm
                wide; pistillate scales mostly truncate to
                acute, rarely with a tooth 0.2 mm long
                . . . . C. albursina

C. albursina Sheldon. Tufted; bract of uppermost pistillate spike short
and much exceeded by bract of next spike below; perigynia 2.7-4.2 mm long,
beakless or with a short beak, 18-30-nerved. Moist to mesic woods, especially on slopes, Houston and Fillmore to Brown and Washington counties.
Often regarded as a variety of C. laxiflora.

C. backii Boott. Densely tufted, the slender stems much overtopped by the
leaves; leaf blades 3-6 mm wide; pistillate scales green, to 3 cm long, the
lowest 3-6 mm wide, dilated at base and mostly concealing the perigynia;
staminate part of spike 2-4 mm long, inconspicuous, overtopped or concealed
by the uppermost perigynium; perigynia ellipsoid-ovoid, empty at summit.
Dry rocky or sandy soil, recorded from Lake, St. Louis, Hubbard, Clearwater,
and Chisago counties.

C. brevior (Dew.) Mack. Leaves 1-4 mm wide; spikes 3-8, ovoid to subglobose; perigynia broad-ovate to roundish, 3.4-4.6 mm long. Mesic to dry open
places, Houston to Rock, Kittson, and Chisago counties, and in St. Louis Co.

C. castanea Wahl. Tufted, purple-tinged at base; leaf blades 2.5-7.5 mm
wide; spikes slender-peduncled, spreading or drooping; lower bracts of pistillate spikes with short sheaths and short narrow blades, the upper usually
bladeless; perigynia lanceolate, 3.8-5.8 mm long, obscurely 3-angled, with
2 strong nerves and about 13 smaller more or less incomplete ones, and with
a beak ca. 1/3 the length of the body. Swamps, bogs, and wet meadows, Cook
to Koochiching, Itasca, and Carlton counties.

C. eburnea Boott. Densely tufted, from long rhizomes; leaf blades involute, 0.5 mm wide or less; pistillate spikes 2-6-flowered, on long erect
peduncles overtopping the sessile staminate spike; pistillate scales much
shorter than the perigynia; perigynia obovoid, few-nerved, glabrous, 3-

angled in section. Calcareous soil, Houston to Lyon Co., n. to Washington and Hennepin counties and in Carlton and Clay counties.

C. eleocharis Bailey (C. stenophylla var. enervis (Mey.) Kukenth.). Leaf blades 1-2 mm wide; spikes 5-6, closely aggregated, usually scarcely distinguishable, ovoid, 4-6 mm long; pistillate scales acute; perigynia 1-8 per spike, ovate, 2.5-3.6 mm long, more than half as wide, nerveless or nerved, the short beak 1/3 as long as the body. Dry plains and bluffs, Rock to Kittson Co., e. to Otter Tail, w. Stearns, w. Blue Earth, and Martin counties.

C. filifolia Nutt. Densely tufted; leaf blades to 0.7 mm wide; upper 1/2 or 2/3 of spike staminate; perigynia puberulent at least above, 2.5-3.7 mm long, more or less obovoid. Dry plains and hills, Pipestone to Otter Tail, Becker, and Clay counties.

C. foenea Willd. (C. siccata Dew.). Stems scattered, on creeping rhizomes; leaf blades 1-3 mm wide; spikes 4-14, staminate at the tip or all staminate, the terminal spike staminate at tip and with a few closely appressed staminate spikes at its base which may simulate a staminate base to the terminal spike; pistillate scales acute; perigynia 4.6-6 mm long, plano-convex, many-nerved, with narrow greenish edges, tapering to a beak 2/5 the length of the perigynium. Dry open soil. St. Louis to Polk, ne. Becker, ne. Todd, Dakota, Wabasha, and Fillmore counties.

C. granularis Muhl. (C. haleana Olney). Tufted, from very short rhizomes; leaf blades to 10 mm wide; bract of the uppermost pistillate spike usually short and much exceeded by the bract of the next spike below; perigynia 2.2-3.2 mm long, with beaks 0.2-0.3 mm long, 16-20 nerved. Damp meadows, shores, bottomlands, or woods, chiefly in calcareous regions, probably throughout the state, unrecorded from many counties.

C. gynocrates Wormsk. Stems few from filiform creeping stolons and rhizomes; leaf blades ca. 0.5 mm wide; spike 5-15 mm long; perigynia widely spreading, shining, oblong-ovate, 3-3.5 mm long, half as wide, nerved on both sides, with the beak ca. 0.5 mm long. Sphagnum bogs and peaty soils, St. Louis to Clearwater and Becker counties and in Anoka and Hennepin counties.

C. hirtifolia Mackenzie. Loosely tufted; leaves 3-7 mm wide; bract of lowest pistillate spike sheathless; pistillate scales obovate; perigynia 3-angled, hairy, nerveless, the obovoid body 2.6-3.5 mm long, abruptly rounded into a slender beak 0.8-1.3 mm long. Mesic woods and meadows, Houston, Olmsted, Ramsey, and Chisago counties.

C. interior Bailey. Densely tufted; leaf blades 1-2 mm wide; spikes 2-4 (-6), next each other or widely separated, subglobose with wide spreading perigynia; pistillate scales ca. 1/2 as long as perigynia, with rounded apexes; perigynia 2.2-3.6 mm long, many-nerved or nerveless, the beak ca. 1/4 as long. Swamps, bogs, and wet meadows, throughout the state.

C. lacustris Willd. Main leaves 5-13 mm wide; pistillate spikes 2-4, 3-10 cm long; perigynia lance-ovoid, glabrous, 4.7-7.3 mm long. Wet places, Lake to Roseau, Clearwater, Pope, Waseca, and Houston counties.

C. laxiflora Lam. Tufted; bract of uppermost pistillate spike usually short and much exceeded by the bract of the next spike below; perigynia 2.8-4.5 mm long, 18-30-nerved, beakless or with a short beak, the beak usually bent sharply to one side. Woods, bottomlands, thickets, and meadows.

A-Pistillate spikes dense and crowded, all the perigynia overlapping; Houston to Pipestone Co., n. to Chisago, Aitkin, Clearwater, and Kittson counties, and in St. Louis Co. . . . .
. . . . C. l. var. blanda (Dewey) Boott (C. blanda Dew.).

A-Pistillate spikes elongate, at least the lowest perigynia separated by
   internodes of about their own length; Cook and St. Louis counties
   . . . . . . C. 1. var. ormostachya (Wieg.) Gl. (C. ormostachya Wieg.).

   C. meadii Dewey. Tufted from long rhizomes; most stem-leaves near
the base, 3-7 mm wide; pistillate scales 1.5-2.6 mm wide, 2-3.8 mm long;
perigynia obovoid, 3.1-4 mm long including a beak 0-0.5 mm long, obscurely
3-angled, 16-22-nerved. Meadows, prairies, and depressions, Houston to
Rock Co., n. to Anoka, Hennepin, Renville, Swift, Mahnomen, and Kittson
counties.

   C. muhlenbergii Schk. Tufted; leaf blades 2-4 mm wide; spikes closely
aggregated, all overlapping, staminate at the tip, sometimes a few small
staminate ones present; pistillate scales ovate, acute to awned, 3/4 as long
as the perigynia or longer; perigynia 4.2-4.8 mm long, plano-convex, 5-11-
nerved on the convex side and often on the plane side, abruptly acuminate to
a beak 0.8-1.2 mm long, 1/5-1/4 the length of the perigynium. Dry sandy
soil, Houston to Washington and Anoka counties.

   C. peckii Howe (C. nigromarginata var. elliptica (Boott) Gl.). Loosely
tufted; leaf blades 1.5-3 mm wide; pistillate spikes closely grouped, sessile,
4-8 mm long; staminate spike 5-10 mm long; perigynia 2.7-4.1 mm long.
Dry rocky slopes and woods, Cook to Kittson Co., s. as far as Winona,
Blue Earth, and Lyon counties.

   C. pedunculata Muhl. Leaves mostly basal, 2-3 mm wide; spikes 4-5,
6-15 mm long, staminate spikes usually pistillate at base, pistillate spikes
often with a few terminal staminate flowers; pistillate scales purple-brown on
the sides, mostly a bit longer than the perigynia; perigynia obovoid, 3.5-5
mm long, 3-angled, thinly hairy to glabrate, minutely beaked. Mesic woods,
usually in calcareous soil, Cook to Clearwater, Clay, Stearns, Hennepin,
Goodhue, and Houston counties, and in Blue Earth Co.

   C. pensylvanica Lam. Pennsylvania Sedge. Tufted from long or short
rhizomes; leaf blades 1-3 mm wide; staminate spike 8-20 mm long, pistillate
spikes 3-12 mm long, sessile; pistillate scales nearly equaling to exceeding
perigynia, reddish-purple to pale brown; perigynia 2.2-4.5 mm long.
A-Lower sheaths of sterile shoots bladeless; perigynia 2.2-3.3 mm long,
   1-1.5 mm thick; open dry soil or mesic woods, probably throughout
   the state, not recorded from Cook and Lake counties and several
   others . . . . C. p. var. pensylvanica.
A-Lower sheaths of the sterile shoots bearing blades; perigynia 2.7-
   4.5 mm long, 1.5-2.2 mm thick; prairies and openings, Houston
   to Rock Co., n. to Washington, Anoka, Morrison, Otter Tail,
   Polk, and Kittson counties, and in s. St. Louis Co.
   . . . . C. p. var. digyna Boeckl. (C. heliophila Mackenz.).

   C. plantaginea Lam. Tufted, tinged with red-purple at base and on sheaths;
leaves of fertile stems reduced to bladeless or nearly bladeless sheaths;
bracts of pistillate spikes with short scale-like blades on long sheaths; perigynia glabrous to slightly scabrous, 3.7-4.9 mm long, 3-angled. Mesic woods,
collected only in Hennepin and Winona counties.

   C. richardsonii R. Br. Leaves mostly basal, 1.5-2.5 mm wide; spikes
3-4, 10-20 mm long; pistillate scales longer and wider than the perigynia,
purple-brown on the sides; perigynia obovoid, 2.5-3.5 mm long, obscurely
3-angled, thinly puberulent. Dry or rocky upland woods and prairies, St.
Louis to Roseau, Clearwater, and Crow Wing counties.

   C. rosea Schk. Densely tufted, very slender; spikes 4-8, subglobose,
the upper often closely aggregated; pistillate scales round-ovate to nearly

acute, shorter than the perigynium body; perigynia lance-ovate, 2.6-4 mm long, nerveless or obscurely nerved near the base, tapering to a beak 1/4 the length of the perigynium. Woods and thickets, probably throughout the state, unrecorded from many counties.

C. rostrata Stokes. Beaked Sedge. Tufted; principal leaf blades 5-10 mm wide; staminate spikes 2-4; pistillate spikes 2-5, usually well separated, dense, 4-10 cm long, 10-15 mm in diam.; pistillate scales lanceolate; perigynia wide-spreading or reflexed, ovoid, 4-8 mm long, acuminate into a beak ca. 1/4 the length of the body; style contorted just above the base. Wet places and shallow water, throughout the state, more common northeastward.

C. saximontana Mackenzie. Similar to C. backii but paler, the perigynia obovoid, tightly filled by the achene, plus differences in the key. Dry woods and thickets, Pipestone, Renville, Blue Earth, and Hennepin counties, and Clay, Becker, Clearwater, and Kittson counties.

C. sparganioides Muhl. Tufted; spikes 5-9, in ours at least the lower well separated, 12-45 mm apart, subglobose or ovoid; bracts of spikes none or shorter than the cluster; scales ovate, acute to cuspidate; perigynia ovate or lance-ovate, 2.8-3.6 mm long, nerveless or nearly so, acuminate into a beak 1/4-1/3 the length of the perigynium. Mesic woods, Houston, Ramsey, Wright, and Chisago counties.

C. sprengelii Dewey. Tufted from long rhizomes; leaf blades 2-4 mm wide; staminate spikes 1-3; pistillate spikes 2-4, widely separate, on slender peduncles; pistillate scales lanceolate, nearly or as long as the perigynia; perigynia 4.5-7.6 mm long, 2-nerved, shining. Alluvial thickets and shores or open or rocky woods, throughout the state except for Cook, Lake, and perhaps a few other counties.

C. stipata Muhl. Densely tufted; main leaf blades 3-8 mm wide; inflorescence dense, ovoid, 3-10 cm long; some or all spikes staminate at apex; scales 1/2-3/4 as long as the perigynia; perigynia lance-ovoid, plano-convex, 4-6 mm long, strongly 3-11-nerved on the convex side, 3-5-nerved on the plane side, acuminate into a beak 1/2 the length of the perigynium. Swampy woods and wet meadows, throughout the state except sw. of a line through Martin and Clay counties.

C. turgida (Fern.) Moore (C. amphibola var. turgida Fern.). In loose or dense clumps; main leaf blades 4-10 mm wide; bract of uppermost pistillate spike usually nearly equalling to exceeding the bract of the next spike below; perigynia 4-5.5 mm long, oblong-cylindric, roundish in section, beakless, 24-48 nerved, the nerves sometimes impressed instead of raised. Mesic woods, bottomlands, and meadows, Houston to Martin Co., w. and n. to Murray, Lac Qui Parle, Sibley, and Ramsey counties.

C. umbellata Schk. Densely tufted, forming mats; leaves 1-5 mm wide; the longer spike-bearing shoots themselves 0.5-4 cm long, each bearing 2-4 spikes that appear terminal on the shoot, 1-3 of the spikes pistillate, 4-10 mm long, on short peduncles, 1 of them staminate, 5-13 mm long, on a longer peduncle, the staminate spike sometimes accompanied by 1 (rarely 2) pistillate ones with peduncles 1-4 mm long placed 0-11 mm below the staminate spike; the shorter spike-bearing shoots only pistillate, always some of them 0-4 cm above ground level, usually more or less hidden among the leaf bases; pistillate scales ovate or obovate, about as wide and long as the perigynia, acute to short-cuspidate; perigynium body pubescent or glabrous, obovoid, 1.6-2.8 mm long, with 2 nerves very prominent above that extend up the edges of the prominent bidentate beak, the whole perigynium 2.2-4.7 mm long. Dry sandy or rocky soil, Cook to Clearwater Co., s. to Dakota and Houston counties. Sometimes subdivided into 3 varieties as follows:

A-Leaves hard, very scabrous, the broader ones 2.5-5 mm wide; pistillate
scales lance-ovate, long-tapering; perigynia glabrous or nearly so,
3.2-4.7 mm long, with ellipsoid or ellipsoid-obovoid bodies, the beak
1.0-2.5 mm long; Cook to Pine Co. and in Dakota and Wabasha
counties. . . . . C. u. var. tonsa Fern. (C. tonsa (Fern.) Bickn.).
A-Leaves relatively soft, 1.5-2.5 (-3) mm wide; pistillate scales lance-
ovate to broadly ovate or ovate-oblong; perigynia pubescent, 2.2-4.7
mm long, the beak 0.5-1.7 mm long.
    B-Pistillate scales lance-ovate, tapering to long or acuminate tips;
    perigynia as in var. tonsa but the beak 0.9-1.7 mm long; Cook
    to Clearwater to Dakota Co. . . . . C. u. var. umbellata.
    B-Pistillate scales broadly ovate or ovate-oblong, with short acute
    tips; perigynia 2.2-3.3 mm long, with globose-ovoid bodies, the
    beak 0.5-1 mm long; Cook to St. Louis Co. and Goodhue to
    Houston Co.. . . . .C. u. var. brevirostris Boott (C. abdita Bickn.).

ELEOCHARIS ----- SPIKE RUSH

Annual or perennial rush-like herbs of water or wet places, often
from long rhizomes; leaves bladeless, reduced to sheaths on the cylindrical
or triangular stems, each stem bearing a single terminal spike; flowers
bisexual; perianth of 3-6 (rarely -12) bristles; stamens 1-3; style 2-3-cleft
with an expanded base (tubercle) usually enlarged at maturity and persisting
on the lens-shaped or 3-angled achene. (Gr. helos, marsh, and charis,
grace.) Some species of Eleocharis bloom in late spring but do not have the
fruit necessary for proper identification till summer, and are therefore
omitted.

E. palustris (L.) R. & S. (E. smallii Britt.). Tufted perennial from
rhizomes; style 2-cleft, achene lens-shaped; sterile scales at base of spike
2 or 3. Marshes and shallow waters, throughout the state except for the se.
corner, Goodhue to Mower Co. and southeastward.

ERIOPHORUM ----- COTTON GRASS

Perennial rush-like or grass-like herbs, the stems with 1-several
terminal spikes, these when more than 1 subtended by 1 or more leaf-like
bracts; flowers bisexual; perianth of very numerous smooth hairs becoming
very long in fruit; stamens 1-3; style 3-cleft, not expanded at base, completely deciduous at maturity; achene sharply 3-angled, surrounded by the
persistent bristles. (Gr. erion, wool, phora, bearing.)

A-Spike single on each stem.
    B-Stems several to many, forming dense tufts or clumps; empty bracts
    at base of spike mostly 10-15 . . . . E. spissum
    B-Stems single or few together; empty basal bracts mostly 7 or
    fewer . . . . E. chamissonis
A-Spikes 2 or more on each stem.
    C-Leaf-like bract 1 (the lowest of the bracts), erect, not exceeding
    the highest spike, the other bracts reduced to bladeless sheaths
    . . . . E. gracile
    C-Leaf-like bracts 2 or 3, shorter than or exceeding the inflorescence.
        D-Leaf sheaths green; bracts of the spike with a prominent mid-
        nerve to the tip. . . . . E. viridi-carinatum
        D-Leaf sheaths with a dark top; bracts of the spike with a midnerve
        not extending to the very thin papery tip . . . . E. angustifolium

E. angustifolium Honckeny. Basal leaves present, the wider blades to 8 mm wide; stems 1-2 mm thick at top; spikes on peduncles to 5 cm long; hairs white. Bogs throughout most of the state, not recorded s. of a line through Dakota, Blue Earth, and Pipestone counties.

E. chamissonis C. A. Mey. Basal leaves present; blades 1-3 mm wide; stem with 1 or 2 bladeless sheaths, the upper near the middle; hairs reddish-brown to white. Wet meadows, marshes, and bogs, St. Louis, Hubbard, Clearwater, Hennepin, and Chisago counties.

E. gracile Koch. Basal leaves absent; blades 1-2 mm wide; stems less than 1 mm thick at top; peduncles of spikes to 3 cm long; hairs white or sordid. Bogs and swamps, St. Louis to Clearwater Co., and Chisago to Blue Earth and Waseca counties.

E. spissum Fern. Basal leaves present; blades about 1 mm wide; stem with 1 or 2 bladeless sheaths; hairs usually white. Bogs and wet soil, Cook to Lake of the Woods Co., s. to Clearwater, Aitkin, and Anoka counties, and in Blue Earth Co.

E. viridi-carinatum (Englm.) Fern. Basal leaves present, 2-5 mm wide; flowering stems 1-2 mm thick at top; peduncles to 5 cm long; hairs white to very pale brown. Swamps, bogs, and wet meadows, St. Louis to Clearwater, Becker, and Crow Wing counties, and in Anoka, Hennepin, and Goodhue counties.

SCIRPUS ----- BULRUSH, CLUBRUSH

Annual or perennial rush-like or grass-like herbs, the stems with 1-many spikes in a single simple or compound inflorescence subtended by 0-several bracts; flowers bisexual; perianth of 1-6 bristles; stamens 2-3; style 2-3-cleft, not expanded at base but sometimes deciduous shortly above the base leaving a slender tip on the achene; achene lens-shaped or 3-angled. (L. scirpus, bulrush.)

A-Spike single and terminal, bract consisting merely of the slightly
    modified lowest scale of the spike . . . . S. clintonii
A-Spikes more than one, with 1 or more prominent bracts.
    B-Bracts 3-5, spreading . . . . S. fluviatilis
    B-Bract 1, erect, often appearing as a continuation of the stem.
        C-Stem sharply 3-angled, spikes 2-8 . . . . S. americanus
        C-Stem round in section, spikes many . . . . S. validus

S. americanus Pers. Three-square, Sword-grass, Chair-maker's Rush. Bract 3-13 cm long, appearing as a continuation of the stem; spikes 6-12 mm long. Shores and shallow water especially on sandy soil, St. Louis to Mahnomen, Pipestone, and Waseca counties.

S. clintonii Gray. Stem 3-angled; bract equalling or shorter than the spike; spike 3-5 mm long. Dry woods, Kittson, Clearwater, Stearns, Anoka, Hennepin, and Ramsey counties.

S. fluviatilis (Torr.) Gray. River Bulrush. Stem 3-angled; bracts flat, elongate; spikes 10-30 mm long. Marshes and shallow fresh water, especially river banks, throughout most of the state, unrecorded in many counties.

S. validus Vahl. Softstem Bulrush, Great Bulrush. Bract 1-9 cm long; spikes 5-10 mm long. Swamps, shores, and shallow water, throughout the state except for Cook and a few other counties.

ARACEAE ----- ARUM FAMILY

Perennial herbs (ours) or occasionally woody; leaves alternate or all basal; flowers small, bisexual or unisexual, closely aggregated over all or part of a thick axis (the spadix, fig. 67) forming a dense spike or head usually subtended by a large leaf-like or colored bract (the spathe); if flowers unisexual the plants monoecious (rarely dioecious); perianth of 4-6 tepals or none; stamens 2-8, hypogynous, opposite the tepals when these are present; ovary superior but sometimes more or less embedded in the axis, 1-4-locular; ovules several per locule; placentation variable; fruit a berry.

A-Leaves compound, the leaflets 3-17. . . . . ARISAEMA
A-Leaves simple.
   B-Leaves and spathe linear, grass-like . . . . ACORUS
   B-Leaves and spathe ovate or wider.
      C-Veins of the leaf curved and parallel, not forming a network . . CALLA
      C-Veins of the leaf branching and joining to form a network
      . . . . SYMPLOCARPUS

ACORUS ----- SWEET FLAG *

Perennial aromatic herbs from stout rhizomes with linear erect elongate leaves, the spadix diverging laterally from a 3-angled scape, the erect spathe appearing to be a continuation of the stem; flowers bisexual; tepals 6; stamens 6; ovary 2-3-locular; ovules pendulous. (Ancient Latin name of an aromatic plant.)

A. calamus L. Leaves to 2 m long, 5-25 mm wide; spadix 5-10 cm long; plant with a citronella-like fragrance in all parts. Swamps and shallow water, throughout the state, not recorded in a few counties.

ARISAEMA ----- JACK-IN-THE-PULPIT, DRAGON-ROOT *

Perennial herbs with 1 or 2 large once compound leaves, monoecious or dioecious; flowers covering only the basal part of the elongate spadix, the spadix subtended and partly surrounded by a hood-like green or brown spathe; perianth none; male flowers usually above the female when both present, consisting of 2-5 stamens; female flowers consisting of a 1-locular ovary with 1-several erect ovules; spadix in fruit a cluster of globose red berries. (Gr. aris, a kind of arum, and haema, blood.)

A-Leaflets 3; spathe arched over the blunt spadix . . . . A. triphyllum
A-Leaflets 5-17; spadix long-protruded from the spathe . . . . A. dracontium

A. dracontium (L.) Schott. Dragon-root, Green Dragon. Leaf usually 1; spathe green, 3-6 cm long; spadix exserted 5-10 cm beyond the spathe. Damp woods, Houston, Winona, and Dakota counties.

A. triphyllum (L.) Schott. Jack-in-the-Pulpit, Indian Turnip. Leaves usually 2; spathe green to purple-striped, its tube 3-7 cm long, not exceeded by the spadix. Two varieties in our range:

A-Spathe-tube smooth or obscurely fluted with broad flanges at top; found usually in moist but not wet locations along water courses; generally distributed throughout the state . . . .
  . . . . A. t. var. triphyllum (A. atrorubens (Ait.) Blume).

A-Spathe-tube with very prominent white flutings or ridges, with narrow
   or moderately broad flanges at top; found in wet boggy places; found
   so far only in Koochiching, Itasca, and Isanti counties.............
   .... A. t. var. stewardsonii (Britt.) Stevens.

CALLA ----- WATER ARUM*

Perennial herb of swamps and shallow water with heart-shaped basal
leaves; spathe white; flowers on all parts of the spadix, bisexual or the upper
staminate; perianth none; stamens 6; ovary 1-locular with several erect
ovules; fruiting spadix a cluster of red berries. A single species. (Ancient
Latin name of an unknown plant.)

C. palustris L. Spathe 3-6 cm long, prolonged into an inrolled tip. From
Cook to Lake of the Woods Co., s. to Polk, e. Stearns, Hennepin, and
Chisago counties, and in s. Le Sueur Co.

SYMPLOCARPUS ----- SKUNK CABBAGE

Perennial ill-smelling herb, the flowers appearing early, the leaves
later; leaves basal, broadly ovate, net-veined; flowers on all parts of the
spadix, forming an almost spherical cluster which is mostly enclosed by the
hood-shaped reddish-brown spathe; flowers bisexual; perianth of 4 tepals;
stamens 4; ovary 1-locular with 1 suspended ovule, sunken in the spadix;
fruit multiple. A single species. (Gr. symploke, connection, karpos, fruit.)

S. foetidus (L.) Nutt. Leaves to 6 dm long; spathe at ground level,
8-15 cm long. Swamps and muddy ground, Houston and Fillmore counties,
n. to Kanabec and s. Pine counties and in se. St. Louis and sw. Lake counties.

COMMELINACEAE ----- SPIDERWORT FAMILY

Annual or perennial herbs, often succulent, with mucilaginous sap;
leaves alternate, entire, lengthwise-veined and dilated to form a tubular
sheath around the stem at base; flowers mostly cymose or rarely solitary,
regular (ours) or zygomorphic, bisexual or rarely polygamous; sepals 3,
free; petals 3, free (ours) or fused; stamens 6 or fewer, hypogynous; ovary
(2-) 3-locular; ovules 1 to few per locule, the placentation axile; style 1;
fruit usually a loculicidal capsule.

TRADESCANTIA ----- SPIDERWORT*

Perennials with alternate linear to lanceolate leaves; flowers in
umbel-like cymes subtended by elongate foliaceous bracts (except 1 species);
flowers bisexual with radial symmetry; sepals green; petals free, blue to
pink, rarely white, quickly withering; stamens 6, usually with hairy filaments; ovary 2-3-locular, style slender, stigma capitate; fruit a few-seeded
capsule. (Named for J. Tradescant, English gardener.)

A-Sepals glabrous or pubescent at base or apex only, without globular-
   tipped ("glandular") hairs .... T. ohiensis
A-Sepals sparsely to densely pubescent with glandular hairs or both
   glandular and non-glandular ones.

B-Sepals and pedicels densely villous with both glandular and non-
  glandular hairs usually 1-1.5 mm long; sepals (8-) 10-14 mm
  long . . . . T. bracteata
B-Sepals and pedicels sparsely pubescent with glandular hairs only,
  these usually about 0.5 mm long; sepals 6-10 mm long . T. occidentalis

T. bracteata Small. Larger leaves 5-15 mm wide; bracts often longer
and wider than the leaves; sepals obtuse to subacute; petals 15-20 mm long.
Prairies, Rock to Fillmore and Winona counties, n. and w. to Washington,
Morrison, Otter Tail, and sw. Norman counties.

T. occidentalis (Britt.) Smyth. Leaves 3-10 mm wide; bracts similar to
leaves; sepals acute to acuminate; petals 10-16 mm long. Dry prairies and
plains, Wabasha to Scott and Hennepin counties, Anoka and Chisago to
Morrison and Crow Wing counties, and Clay to Polk Co.

T. ohiensis Raf. Leaves 7-15 mm wide; sepals usually 8-12 mm long,
often red-margined; petals 10-20 mm long. Meadows, thickets, and relatively moist prairies, Houston, Fillmore, and Winona counties.

JUNCACEAE ----- RUSH FAMILY

Ours annual or perennial herbs resembling sedges and grasses;
leaves mostly basal, alternate on the stem, with sheathing bases, the
blades flattened, cylindrical and narrow, or none; flowers regular, bisexual or unisexual; perianth of two similar whorls of small stiff green or
brown free members, 3 in each whorl; stamens 6 or 3, hypogynous; ovary
1- or 3-locular; fruit a loculicidal 3-valved capsule.

A-Plants glabrous; edges of leaf sheath free; ovules and seeds several to many. . . . . JUNCUS
A-Plants more or less hairy; sheaths tubular; ovules and seeds 3 . . LUZULA

JUNCUS ----- RUSH

Glabrous annuals or perennials; leaves round in section or flat, or
sometimes the blades absent, sheaths open; edges of leaf sheath free; flowers few to many in a compact to loosely branched cyme; stamens 6 or 3;
ovary 1-locular or 3-locular by inward growth of the parietal placentas;
ovules and seeds several to many. (L. juncus, rush.)

A-Sheaths at base of stem without blades; involucral leaf erect, resemb-
  ling a continuation of the stem, the inflorescence appearing lateral
  . . . . J. balticus
A-Sheaths at base of stem or some of them with blades; inflorescence
  appearing terminal.
  B-Outer perianth segments 2.3-3.5 mm long, inner 1.9-3.4 mm long
  . . . . J. greenei
  B-Outer perianth segments 3.7-5.4 mm long, inner 3.4-5.3 mm long
  . . . . J. dudleyi

J. balticus Willd. Basal sheaths up to 15 cm long; involucral leaf up
to 18 cm long; perianth segments 3-4.8 mm long. Shores and wet places,
probably throughout the state, not recorded se. of a line from Dakota to
Martin Co. nor in Cook nor several other counties.

J. dudleyi Wieg. Leaves basal, flat but narrow; involucral leaf 4-11 cm
long; perianth segments longer than the capsule. Moist or dry soil, throughout the state.

J. greenei Oakes & Tuckerm. Basal leaves filiform, nearly cylindrical, deeply channeled; involucral leaves 2-15 cm long; perianth segments shorter than the capsule. Moist to dry mostly sandy soil, Goodhue, Anoka, Todd, and Pine to St. Louis counties.

LUZULA ----- WOOD RUSH

Perennials with narrow, flat, more or less pubescent leaves often inrolled toward the tip; sheaths tubular; flowers in umbel-like or spike-like usually compound inflorescences; stamens 6; ovary 1-locular with 3 ovules attached near the bottom. (Diminutive of L. lux, light.)

A-Inflorescence umbel-like, the branches mostly 1-flowered, less often
    with 2 or more flowers . . . . L. acuminata var. acuminata
A-Inflorescence of 2-12 spike-like or head-like clusters on long or
    short branches umbel-like or not . . . . . . L. campestris var. multiflora

L. acuminata Raf. var. acuminata. Leaves to 10 mm wide; perianth segments 2.6-4.3 mm long; seed body ca. 1 mm long with a pale terminal appendage nearly as long. Moist or dry open woods, meadows and hillsides, Cook to Beltrami Co., s. to Otter Tail, Todd, and Ramsey counties, and in Rice and Winona counties.

L. campestris var. multiflora (Retz.) Celak. (L. multiflora (Retz.) Lejeune). Leaves to 7 mm wide; perianth segments 2-3.7 mm long; seed body 1-1.3 mm long with a basal appendage 0.4-0.5 mm long. Fields, meadows, and open woods, Houston and Fillmore counties n. to Ramsey, e. Stearns, Aitkin, St. Louis, and Cook counties, Cass to Clearwater Co., and in Kittson Co.

LILIACEAE ----- LILY FAMILY

Herbs, vines, or woody plants; leaf arrangement various; flowers usually bisexual, regular or nearly so; perianth usually conspicuous, usually 6-parted in 2 whorls of 3, the segments free or less often fused, the outer and inner whorls usually alike or occasionally differentiated; stamens as many as the perianth segments, usually hypogynous or adnate to the perianth; ovary usually 3-locular with axile placentation, usually superior; fruit a capsule or berry. The conservative interpretation of this family is followed here in order to agree with the usage of the major manuals of the region.

A-Flowers or flower clusters borne laterally, at the nodes along the
  main stem or its branches.
  B-Leaves reduced to minute scarious scales, with clusters of needle-
    like branchlets 8-15 mm long in their axils . . . . ASPARAGUS
  B-Leaves flat and green, of normal size.
    C-Leaves petioled, often with tendril-tipped stipules; flowers in
      umbels; perianth segments free . . . . SMILAX
    C-Leaves sessile or clasping, without tendrils or stipules, if
      flowers in umbels then the perianth segments fused.
      D-Perianth tubular, 6-lobed . . . . POLYGONATUM
      D-Perianth segments free to base.
        E-Flowers straw colored to yellow, 13-45 mm long. . . .UVULARIA
        E-Flowers greenish to cream to purple, 4-12 mm long
        . . . . STREPTOPUS

A-Flowers or flower clusters terminal on leafy or leafless stems.
  F-Flowers solitary.
    G-Leaves in a single whorl of 3 at summit of stem . . . . . . TRILLIUM
    G-Leaves alternate or basal.
      H-Flowers erect; cultivated . . . . TULIPA
      H-Flowers turned down, from horizontal to nodding; native or
        cultivated.
        I-Leaves 2, near ground level . . . . ERYTHRONIUM
        I-Leaves 3 or more, well elevated on the stem.
          J-Perianth segments 2-7 mm wide, cream to yellow-
            orange; native . . . . UVULARIA
          J-Perianth segments 11-22 mm wide, mottled or white;
            cultivated . . . . FRITILLARIA
  F-Flowers few to many, in clusters.
    K-Leaves all or some attached along the flowering stem (basal
      leaves sometimes present).
      L-Perianth segments 11-35 mm wide; cultivated.
        M-Flowers erect; perianth segments without nectar glands . TULIPA
        M-Flowers nodding; perianth segments each with a near-
          basal nectar gland on the inner face . . . . FRITILLARIA
      L-Perianth segments 7 mm wide or less; native.
        N-Leaves narrowly linear, to 12 mm wide . . . . ZYGADENUS
        N-Leaves lanceolate or broader, 10-100 mm wide.
          O-Flowers 2 or 3, perianth segments 13-45 mm long . UVULARIA
          O-Flowers many, perianth segments 1.5-6 mm long.
            P-Perianth segments 6 . . . . SMILACINA
            P-Perianth segments 4 . . . . MAIANTHEMUM
    K-Leaves all basal or nearly so, sometimes absent at flowering
      time (in Convallaria appearing as if borne on a separate stalk
      attached part way up the flowering stem but actually attached
      deep down).
      Q-Flowers 50-100 mm long; cultivated . . . . HEMEROCALLIS
      Q-Flowers 3-38 mm long; native or cultivated.
        R-Flowers in umbels.
          S-Plants when crushed with odor of onion or garlic; umbel
            subtended by 2 or 3 scarious bracts . . . . ALLIUM
          S-Plants without such odor; umbel without bracts . . CLINTONIA
        R-Flowers in spikes, racemes, or panicles.
          T-Perianth segments separate to their attachments below
            or on the ovary (or lightly cohering for about 1/10 their
            length in Scilla); native or cultivated.
            U-Flowers 8-60, white or whitish; near-basal stem
              leaves present; native . . . . ZYGADENUS
            U-Flowers 1-4, blue or white; leaves all basal;
              cultivated. . . . . SCILLA
          T-Perianth segments plainly fused into a tube for 1/6 or
            more of their length; cultivated.
            V-Perianth segments fused for 1/6-1/4 their length
            . . . . CHIONODOXA
            V-Perianth segments fused for more than 1/3 their length.
              W-Flowers 20-38 mm long . . . . HYACINTHUS
              W-Flowers 2.5-9 mm long.
                X-Leaves linear, to 12 mm wide . . . . MUSCARI
                X-Leaves oblong-oval, 20-75 mm wide . . . CONVALLARIA

ALLIUM ----- ONION

Biennial or perennial from a bulb, with odor of onion or garlic; leaves alternate or usually all basal, mostly narrow; flowers in bracted umbels, white to pink or purple, bisexual; perianth segments 6, free; stamens 6, hypogynous; ovary 3-locular; ovules 1 or 2 per locule; style 1, stigma simple or slightly 3-lobed; fruit a loculicidal capsule. A genus that may more properly belong in the Amaryllidaceae, owing to its bracted umbel. (L. _allium_, garlic.)

A-Stem and leaves thick and hollow; cultivated . . . . <u>A</u>. fistulosum
A-Stem and leaves slender, not hollow; native.
   B-Flowers mostly or all replaced by bulblets; ovary
     unappendaged . . . . <u>A</u>. canadense
   B-Flowers not replaced by bulblets; ovary bearing 6
     short, erect, sub-terminal appendages. . . . . <u>A</u>. textile

<u>A</u>. canadense L. Wild Onion, Wild Garlic. Leaves 2-7 mm wide; bracts broadly ovate, acuminate; umbels bearing bulblets only or with 2-15 flowers also; bulblets to 1 cm long. Moist or dry open woods and prairies, Rock to Houston Co., n. to Washington, Stearns, and Big Stone counties, and in Clay Co.

<u>A</u>. fistulosum L. Welsh Onion, Spring Onion; cultivated. Bulbous base little thicker than the stem; leaves about equaling the stem. Leaves used for seasoning. Occasionally persisting or escaping around fields. From Asia.

<u>A</u>. textile A. Nels. & Macbr. Leaves 1-3 mm wide; bracts ovate; bulblets none; each lobe of ovary bearing 2 short erect projections on the back just below the summit. Dry prairies, Pipestone to Polk Co., e. to Stevens, Swift, and Chippewa counties.

ASPARAGUS*

Branching perennials with alternate scale-like true leaves and needle-like or flat branchlets in their axils; flowers in the axils of the true leaves, small, bisexual or unisexual; perianth segments 6, free or fused; stamens 6, attached to base of perianth; ovary superior, 3-locular with 2 ovules per locule; style 1 with 3 short stigmas; fruit a berry. (The ancient Greek name.)

<u>A</u>. officinalis L. Asparagus; cultivated. Dioecious; branchlets simulating leaves thread-like or needle-like, 8-15 mm long; flowers greenish-white, 3-6 mm long, fruit red. From Europe, often escaped to disturbed ground, recorded scattered from Pipestone to Houston counties, n. to s. St. Louis, Clearwater, and Kittson counties.

CHIONODOXA ----- GLORY-OF-THE-SNOW

Small perennial herbs with bulbs and basal linear to oblanceolate leaves; flowers few in a short raceme, bisexual, mostly blue (with red and white color forms); perianth segments 6, similar, fused at base into a bell-shaped tube 1/6-1/3 their length; stamens 6, attached to the tube; ovary superior, 3-locular with many ovules; style short, stigma capitate; fruit a capsule. (Gr. chion, snow, _doxa_, glory.)

<u>C</u>. luciliae Boiss. Cultivated. Perianth segments 13-25 mm long, blue to white, often with blue center and white edges, or in one form pink; ovary blue-violet. From Asia Minor.

CLINTONIA *

Perennial herbs from rhizomes with 2-5 broad basal leaves surrounding a leafless stem bearing a few-flowered umbel of bisexual flowers, bracts of the umbel inconspicuous or none; perianth bell-shaped, its segments 6, similar, free; stamens 6, each attached to the base of a perianth segment; ovary superior, 2- to 3-locular with 2 or more ovules per locule; style 1, stigma obscurely 3-lobed; fruit a blue or black berry. (Named for DeWitt Clinton.)

C. borealis (Ait.) Raf. Bluebead Lily, Corn-lily. Leaves oblong to elliptic to obovate, to 30 cm long; umbel 3-8-flowered, sometimes with a few additional flowers below it on the peduncle; perianth segments greenish-yellow, 12-25 mm long; fruit blue (rarely white), ca. 8 mm in diameter. Moist woods and wooded bogs, Cook to e. Roseau Co., s. to Mahnomen, ne. Todd, n. Anoka, and Chisago counties.

CONVALLARIA ----- LILY OF THE VALLEY

Perennial herbs from rhizomes, with 2 or 3 nearly basal broad leaves; flowers racemose on a leafless stem, bisexual; perianth bell-shaped, its 6 segments united for most of their length; stamens 6, attached to the base of the perianth; ovary superior, 3-locular, ovules several per locule; style 1, stigma obscurely lobed; fruit a berry. (L. convallis, a closed valley.)

C. majalis L. Cultivated. Leaves to 20 cm long, their petioles cylindrical with the lower one enclosing the others and appearing as a stalk attached part way up the flowering stem, actually attached deep down; flowers white or tinged rose, fragrant, 6-9 mm long; fruit red. Occasionally escaped near gardens. From n. Eurasia.

ERYTHRONIUM ----- DOG-TOOTH VIOLET, ADDER'S TONGUE, TROUT LILY *

Perennial from a deep solid corm, sterile plants with 1 leaf, fertile with 2 nearly opposite ones at or near ground level, leaves often mottled; flowers bisexual, single (in ours) on a leafless stem, turned to a horizontal or lower position; perianth segments 6, separate; stamens 6, hypogynous; ovary 3-locular with several to many ovules, style 1, stigmas 3 or 1 and 3-lobed; fruit a capsule. (From Gr. erythros, red, for the purplish-flowered European species.)

A-Perianth segments 8-14 mm long, pinkish-white; stem producing a
    lateral offshoot just below the leaves, none from the corm. E. propullans
A-Perianth segments 20-45 mm long, white, pinkish-white, or yellow;
    offshoots if present arising from the corm.
  B-Perianth white or whitish; stigmas separate and outwardly curved
  . . . . E. albidum
  B-Perianth yellow; stigmas not separate . . . . E. americanum

E. albidum Nutt. White Dog-tooth Violet, etc. Sterile plants numerous; perianth normally white, varying to light pink often tinted with green, blue, or purple externally, yellow at base within. Mesic to moist woods and thickets, Houston to Freeborn Co., n. and w. to Blue Earth, Morrison, and St. Louis counties, and scattered to Murray, Renville, and Clay counties.

E. americanum Ker. Yellow Dog-tooth Violet, etc. Sterile plants many; perianth normally yellow, often spotted toward the base within or darker without.

Rich soil in woods, bottom lands, and meadows, s. St. Louis, Carlton, and
Goodhue to Winona counties.

E. propullans Gray. Dwarf or Minnesota Dog-tooth Violet, etc. Plant
reproducing vegetatively by the single offshoot below the leaves; most plants
blooming; perianth occasionally with fewer than 6 segments. Rich soil in
woods; known only from Minnesota, in Goodhue and Rice counties; rare,
should not be collected.

FRITILLARIA ----- FRITILLARY

Perennials from bulbs with erect leafy stems, leaves alternate or
whorled; flowers solitary or in racemes or umbels, nodding, bisexual;
perianth segments 6, separate, often mottled, with a near-basal nectar
gland on the inner face; stamens 6, attached to the base of the perianth
segments; ovary superior, 3-locular with many ovules; style 1, stigma
3-lobed; fruit a loculicidal capsule. (L. fritillus, a dice box.)

A-Flowers several, beneath a crown of leaves . . . . F. imperialis
A-Flower solitary, at summit of stem . . . . F. meleagris

F. imperialis L. Crown Imperial; cultivated. Leaves many, scattered
or in whorl-like groups, linear, often more than 25 mm wide; flowers ill-
smelling, purplish, brick-red or orange. From the Himalayas and Iran.

F. meleagris L. Snakes-head, Checkered Lily; cultivated. Leaves 3-6,
alternate, linear to oblong-lanceolate, 2-8 mm wide; flowers normally 1,
rarely 2 or 3, checkered and veined with purplish or maroon, or white.
From Europe and sw. Asia.

HEMEROCALLIS ----- DAY LILY

Perennial from fleshy roots and tubers; leaves numerous, basal,
linear; flowers in a cluster on a leafless stem, bisexual, each flower lasting
one day; perianth funnel-shaped, its 6 segments fused below into a short
tube; stamens 6, attached at top of tube; ovary superior, 3-locular with many
ovules; style 1, stigma capitate; fruit a loculicidal capsule. (Gr. hemera,
day, kallos, beauty.)

A-Stems to 6 dm high, shorter than or as long as the leaves;
    flowers 2-4, yellow-orange. . . . . H. dumortieri
A-Stems 8-12 dm high, exceeding the leaves; flowers 5-9,
    yellow . . . . H. lilio-asphodelus

H. dumortieri Morr. Narrow Dwarf Day Lily; cultivated. Inflorescence
compact; flowers fragrant, 5-7 cm long; perianth tube 8 mm or less long;
inner perianth lobes with membranous edges, their veins more or less
joined. From Siberia and Japan. Many cultivars are grown.

H. lilio-asphodelus L. (H. flava L.). Common Yellow Day Lily; cultivated. Inflorescence open; flowers fragrant, 7.5-10 cm long; perianth
tube 15-35 mm long; inner lobes not membranous on the edges, the veins
not running together. From e. Siberia and Japan./ Many cultivars are grown.

HYACINTHUS ----- HYACINTH

Perennials with bulbs and narrow basal leaves; flowers in a terminal
raceme, erect or pendulous, fragrant, red, blue, white, to yellowish; bisexua

erianth bell-shaped, its 6 segments united for over 1/3 their length; stamens
attached to the tube, included in it; ovary superior, 3-locular, style 1,
igma capitate; fruit a loculicidal capsule. (Gr. hyakinthos, a youth from
hose blood sprang this flower.)

H. orientalis L. Common Hyacinth; cultivated. Stem 15-45 cm high;
aves 25 mm or more wide; flowers 20-38 mm long, purple, pink, white,
: pale yellow. From Greece to Syria and Asia Minor.

MAIANTHEMUM ----- FALSE LILY OF THE VALLEY, MAYFLOWER *

Low perennial herbs from slender rhizomes, sterile plants with 1
asal leaf, fertile plants with a stem bearing a few alternate sessile or
etioled leaves; flowers in a terminal raceme, small, white, bisexual;
erianth segments 4, separate, spreading; stamens 4, hypogynous; ovary
-locular, ovules 2 per locule; style 1, stigma 2-cleft; fruit a berry.
.. Maius, May, Gr. anthemon, a flower.)

M. canadense Desf. Canada Mayflower; Wild Lily of the Valley. Leaves
sually 2, occasionally 1 or 3, ovate to ovate-oblong, 3-10 cm long, cordate
t base; raceme 2-5 cm long; flowers fragrant, 4-6 mm wide; berry pale
ed. Mesic woods. Two partially separated varieties can be recognized:

-Leaves glabrous beneath or nearly so, entire or minutely crenulate;
    lower leaf blade 3-6 cm long, its petiole 1.5-6 mm long; Cook to
    Lake of the Woods Co., s. to Clearwater, Kanabec, Hennepin,
    and Wabasha counties . . . . M. c. var. canadense.
-Leaves pubescent beneath, fringed with hairs on the edges; lower
    leaf blade 4.5-10 cm long, its petiole 2.5-10 mm long; flowering
    later than var. canadense; Cook to Kittson Co., s. to Clay,
    Pope, McLeod, ne. Blue Earth, and Houston counties, and
    in Lac Qui Parle Co. . . . . M. c. var. interius Fern.

MUSCARI ----- GRAPE HYACINTH

Perennials from bulbs, with narrow basal leaves; flowers small, blue
: white, nodding, in a terminal spike-like raceme or panicle on a leafless
em, bisexual; perianth segments 6, fused for most of their length; stamens
attached to the perianth; ovary superior, 3-locular, style 1, stigma 3-
bed; fruit a loculicidal capsule. (L. name referring to the musky odor of
)me species.)

M. armeniacum Leicht. Cultivated. Leaves shorter to longer than stem; ped-
:els (1.5-) 4-6 mm long; flowers blue or white, 5-6.5 mm long. From sw. Asia.

M. botryoides Mill. Cultivated. Leaves shorter than to equalling the stem; ped-
:els 0.5-3.5 mm long; flowers blue or white, 2.5-5 mm long. From s. Europe.

POLYGONATUM ----- SOLOMON'S SEAL *

Perennial herbs from rhizomes (stem scars on rhizomes resembling
eal imprints, thus the common name), stem erect or arching with many
ternate leaves and short axillary umbels of 1-15 flowers; flowers white to
:eenish or yellow, bisexual; perianth tubular, its 6 segments fused for
ost of their length; stamens 6, attached to the perianth; ovary superior,
-locular with many ovules; style 1, stigma capitate, obscurely 3-lobed;
uit a dark blue or black berry. (Gr. polys, many, and gonu, knee, re-
rring to the many-jointed rhizome.)

65

A-Leaves glabrous on the veins beneath . . . . P. biflorum
A-Leaves pubescent on the veins beneath . . . . P. pubescens

P. biflorum (Walt.) Ell. (incl. P. commutatum (Schult. f.) A. Dietr. and
P. canaliculatum (Muhl.) Pursh). Stem 4-12 dm high; leaves with 1-19 prominent nerves beneath; peduncles slender or flattened, 1-15-flowered; flowers
mostly greenish-white, 13-20 mm long; filaments strongly flattened. A polyploid complex of diploid, tetraploid, and hexaploid strains, the plants varying
considerably in size and number of flowers but not clearly separable into
different taxonomic groups. Mesic woods, thickets, and roadsides, Houston
to Rock Co., n. to Chisago, Cass, Lake of the Woods, and Kittson counties.

P. pubescens (Willd.) Pursh. Stem 5-9 dm high; leaves with 3-9 prominent
nerves beneath; peduncles slender, 1-2 (-4) -flowered; flowers yellowish-
green, 7-13 mm long; filaments not flattened. Mesic woods and thickets,
Cook to Lake of the Woods Co., s. to Otter Tail, Pope, Benton, Hennepin,
and Winona counties.

SCILLA ----- SQUILL

Perennial herbs with bulbs and narrow basal leaves; flowers small,
blue to purple to white, in a terminal raceme on a leafless stem, bisexual;
perianth bell-shaped to wide-spreading, its 6 segments separate or lightly
cohering at base for ca. 1/10 their length; stamens 6, attached to the perianth;
ovary superior, 3-locular; style 1, stigma 1; fruit a loculicidal capsule.
(The ancient Gr. and L. name.)

S. sibirica Haw. Cultivated. Leaves mostly 2-4; flowers 1-4, mostly
horizontal to nodding, deep blue (other color forms exist); perianth wide-
spreading, its segments 12-22 mm long. From Russia and sw. Asia.

SMILACINA ----- FALSE SOLOMON'S SEAL*

Perennial herbs from long creeping rhizomes; stems unbranched,
erect or sloping, with few to many alternate, sessile or nearly sessile
leaves; flowers small, white, in a terminal raceme or panicle, bisexual;
perianth segments 6, separate, spreading; stamens 6, hypogynous; ovary
3-locular, ovules 2 per locule; style 1, stigma obscurely 3-lobed; fruit
a red berry. (Diminutive of Smilax.)

A-Flowers in a panicle . . . . S. racemosa
A-Flowers in a raceme.
    B-Leaves 6 or more; peduncle 2-10 (-14) mm long; leaves
        minutely hairy beneath. S. stellata
    B-Leaves 1-4; peduncle 17-50 mm long; leaves glabrous . . S. trifolia

S. racemosa (L.) Desf. Leaves elliptic, finely hairy beneath; flowers
3-5 mm wide; fruit red, dotted with purple. Rich soil in mesic to moist
woods, throughout the state excepting perhaps a few extreme southern and
northwestern counties.

S. stellata (L.) Desf. Star-flowered False Solomon's Seal. Leaves
lanceolate or lance-oblong; flowers 6-11 mm wide; fruit at first green with
blackish stripes, turning uniformly dark red. Mesic, especially gravelly
and sandy soil of woods, clearings, and shores, throughout the state except
for Cook and Lake counties.

S. trifolia (L.) Desf. Three-leaved False Solomon's Seal. Leaves elliptic to narrowly ovate or lanceolate; flowers 3-8 mm wide; fruit dark red. Wet woods and sphagnum bogs, Cook to Koochiching, Clearwater, Morrison, and Hennepin counties.

SMILAX *

Dioecious perennial herbs or shrubs mostly climbing by tendrils terminating the stipules; leaves alternate, broad, with lengthwise primary nerves and a network of veins between them; flowers small, yellow or greenish-yellow, often ill-smelling, in axillary stalked umbels; perianth segments 6, similar, separate; stamens 6; staminodes of the female flower hypogynous; ovary 3-locular, ovules 1 or 2 per locule; style none or very short, stigmas 1 or 3; fruit a blue or black berry. (Ancient Gr. name of obscure meaning.)

A-Stem woody, generally with prickles . . . . S. hispida
A-Stem herbaceous, without prickles.
  B-Peduncles borne chiefly from axils of foliage leaves; plants climbing
      by tendrils borne from axils of most of the middle and upper leaves,
      the stem greatly elongating . . . . S. herbacea
  B-Peduncles some or all borne from axils of bladeless bracts below
      the leaves; plants erect or nearly so, up to 1 m high, without
      tendrils or with tendrils from a few upper leaves only . . . S. ecirrata

S. ecirrata (Engelm.) S. Wats. Flowers carrion-scented; umbels with up to 25 flowers. Rich soil of mesic woods, Houston to Martin Co., n. to Pope, s. Clearwater, and St. Louis counties.

S. herbacea L. Carrion Flower. Flowers carrion-scented; umbels with 20-100 or more flowers. Moist to mesic soil of open woods, thickets, roadsides.

A-Leaves glabrous beneath, the lower side pale and somewhat glaucous;
     lateral leaf margins convex to the rounded or cuspidate tip; peduncles
     5-8 times as long as the subtending petioles; fruit dark blue, glaucous;
     Faribault, Waseca, Kanabec, St. Louis, Lake, and Wilkin counties.
    . . . . S. h. var. herbacea.
A-Leaves puberulent on the veins beneath.
  B-Leaves bright green and shining beneath, distinctly short-
     acuminate; peduncles 5-10 times as long as the subtending
     petioles; fruit black, the surface not whitened or blued;
     Houston, Winona, Jackson, and Chippewa counties. . . . .
    . . S. h. var. pulverulenta (Michx.) Gray (S. pulverulenta Michx.).
  B-Leaves paler beneath than the above, rounded, blunt, or short-
     cuspidate at the tip; peduncles seldom over twice as long as the
     petioles; fruit dark blue, the surface somewhat whitened or blued;
     our most common form, probably throughout the state, not
     recorded in Cook nor a few other counties . . . .
    . . . S. h. var. lasioneura (Hook.) A. DC. (S. lasioneura Hook.).

S. hispida Muhl. (S. tamnoides var. hispida (Muhl.) Fern.). Greenbrier, Catbrier. Stems often climbing high, with tan to blackish bristles; fruit black. Mesic to moist woods and thickets, Houston to Jackson Co., n. to Blue Earth, Carver, Benton, Kanabec, and Pine counties, and in Traverse Co.

STREPTOPUS ----- TWISTED STALK *

Perennial herbs from rhizomes; stems often branched, with alternate sessile leaves; flowers small, greenish white to purple, bisexual, single or paired in the axils, the peduncles fused to the stem for 1 internode above their point of origin, they or the pedicels often abruptly bent or twisted; perianth bell-shaped to spreading, its 6 segments similar, separate; stamens 6, attached to the base of the perianth; ovary superior, 3-locular with many ovules; style 1, 3-cleft to entire; fruit a red to orange berry. (Gr. streptos, twisted, pous, foot.)

A-Perianth pink to rose-purple; leaf margin fringed with fine hairs at least
 toward the leaf tip; nodes usually with scattered hairs . . . .
 . . . . S. roseus var. longipes
A-Perianth greenish-white; leaves entire or very minutely toothed, not
 fringed; nodes glabrous . . . . S. amplexifolius

S. amplexifolius (L.) DC. White Mandarin; Liverberry; Scootberry. Leaves sessile, cordate at base, strongly clasping the stem; pedicels usually abruptly bent or twisted near the joint; perianth segments wide-spreading or recurving from near the middle; stigma entire or barely 3-lobed. Rich soil in moist woods, Cook to St. Louis Co., mostly near Lake Superior.

S. roseus var. longipes (Fern.) Fassett. Rose Mandarin. Leaves sessile, half to fully clasping the stem; peduncles seldom bent or twisted; perianth segments mostly with only the tips recurved, or straight; stigma 3-cleft, the divisions 0.6-1.5 mm long. Mesic to moist woods, Cook to e. Roseau Co., s. to Mahnomen, Otter Tail, e. Stearns, and Chisago counties, and in Winona Co.

TRILLIUM ----- TRILLIUM, WAKE ROBIN *

Perennial herbs from rhizomes; stem erect with a single whorl of 3 net-veined leaves and a single large terminal bisexual flower; perianth segments separate, differentiated into 3 green sepals and 3 white or colored petals; stamens 6, hypogynous; ovary 3-locular with many ovules, style short or none, stigmas 3; fruit a berry. (Name of uncertain origin, but probably from Gr. tri-, three.)

A-Leaves 3-5 cm long, acute or obtuse; ovary roundly 3-lobed . . . T. nivale
A-Leaves 5-17 cm long, acuminate; ovary 6-angled.
 B-Stigmas straight to recurved, of uniform diameter; petals longer
 than sepals, white to rose, 4-7 cm long, 1.7-4.5 cm wide
 . . . . T. grandiflorum
 B-Stigmas strongly recurved, tapering to the apex; petals often
 no longer than sepals, normally white, 1.5-4 cm long, 1-2.3
 cm wide.
 C-Peduncles 0.5-5 cm long, recurved 120-180° from vertical; anthers
 1-2 times as long as the filaments. . . . T. cernuum var. macranthum
 C-Peduncles 4-12 cm long, straight, bent at base ca. 30-120°
 from vertical (rarely more); anthers 1.2-3.8 times as long
 as the filaments. . . . . T. flexipes

T. cernuum var. macranthum Eames & Wiegand. Nodding Trillium.
Petals 15-32 mm long, 10-20 mm wide; anthers 4-9 mm long. Blooming in May and June. Moist woods, throughout the state except for the lowest tier of counties w. of Mower Co.

68

T. flexipes Raf. (T. gleasoni Fern.). Declining Trillium. Petals 2-4 cm long, 1-2.3 cm wide; anthers 6-15 mm long. Blooming in May and June. Moist woods, Houston and Fillmore counties, n. and w. to Washington, Hennepin, and Blue Earth counties, and in Morrison and Clay counties.

T. grandiflorum (Michx.) Salisb. Large-flowered Trillium. Petals 4-7 cm long, 1.7-4.5 cm wide; anthers 10-16 mm long. Blooming in May and June. Rich soil in moist woods and thickets, Winona, Wabasha and Nicollet counties, and Chisago to Morrison, Becker, s. Beltrami, and s. St. Louis counties.

T. nivale Riddell. Snow Trillium. Petals 2-3.5 cm long, 0.7-1.3 cm wide; anthers 7-10 mm long. Blooming in April. Moist woods in se. part of state, uncommon, known only from Winona, s. Goodhue, Blue Earth, Nicollet, and ne. Dakota counties.

TULIPA ----- TULIP

Perennial herbs with bulbs; stem bearing a few oblong to linear alternate leaves, the lower ones usually larger; flowers terminal, usually single and erect, bell-shaped to saucer-shaped, bisexual; perianth segments 6, separate, similar; stamens 6, hypogynous; ovary 3-locular with many ovules, style short or none, stigma usually 3-lobed; fruit a loculicidal capsule. (From the oriental word for turban.)

A-Leaves sharply channelled along the midrib; flowers 1-4, bright brick-red, without basal blotches; filaments vermilion. . . . . T. praestans
A-Leaves flat, not channelled; flowers 1 per stem, of various colors, when red with basal blotches; filaments yellow, olive, purple, or black.
  B-Flowers red to white or yellow, with yellow basal blotches (red marks in yellow flowers) over 1/3 as long as the segments; backs of outer segments broadly streaked with red (not seen in red flowers); stamens yellow to orange; leaves often purple-streaked. . T. kaufmanniana
  B-Flowers of various colors, yellow blotches if present not over 1/3 the segment length; backs of outer segments not marked with red (when other than red); stamens of various colors; leaves not purple-streaked.
    C-Perianth segments mostly 5-8 cm long or if longer then often acuminate at apex, of various colors, sometimes scarlet with black yellow-edged blotches; stamens black, purple, olive, or yellow; inner surface of thin papery skin of bulb nearly glabrous, with a few appressed hairs, these often only at base or summit or both. . . . . T. gesneriana
    C-Perianth segments mostly 7-10 cm long, rounded with a small point, usually scarlet with black basal blotches edged with yellow; stamens black; sometimes blotch and stamens both yellow; inner surface of skin of bulb with numerous silky hairs . T. fosteriana

T. fosteriana Hoog. Emperor Tulip; cultivated. Largest leaves broadly ovate; stem glabrous. White and yellow cultivars exist. From Central Asia.

T. gesneriana L., in the broad sense. Common Garden Tulip; cultivated. A highly variable complex; leaves lanceolate to nearly ovate; stem glabrous or slightly pubescent; flowers in reds, purples, yellows, white, or combinations, the perianth segments with or without basal blotches, blunt to long-pointed, entire to deeply cut. Probably from sw. Asia.

T. kaufmanniana Regel. Water-lily Tulip; cultivated. Leaves ovate-elliptic or narrower; stem slightly pubescent. From Turkestan.

T. praestans Hoog. Cultivated. Leaves ovate-elliptic or narrower, not purple-streaked; stems slightly pubescent. From Central Asia.

UVULARIA ----- BELLWORT*

Perennial herbs from rhizomes; stem erect, leafy above, branched above the middle; leaves alternate, sessile or perfoliate, expanding during flowering; flowers yellow to cream, nodding, bisexual, terminal but later appearing axillary due to continued elongation of the branches; perianth narrowly bell-shaped, its 6 segments separate; stamens 6, lightly adherent to base of perianth; ovary superior, 3-locular with several ovules per locule, style deeply 3-cleft; fruit a loculicidal capsule. (The flowers hanging like the uvula, the soft palate, diminutive of L. uva, grape.)

A-Leaf base fused around the stem, enclosing it . . . . U. grandiflora
A-Leaves sessile, not enclosing the stem . . . . U. sessilifolia

U. grandiflora Sm. Large-flowered Bellwort. Leaves to 12 cm long, minutely pubescent beneath; perianth yellow, 25-45 mm long. Rich often calcareous soil in mesic to moist woods, Houston to Mower Co., n. to Blue Earth, Redwood, Douglas, Clay, Polk, Lake of the Woods, and Lake counties.

U. sessilifolia L. (Oakesia sessilifolia (L.) Wats.). Pale or sessile-leaved Bellwort. Leaves to 8 cm long; perianth pale straw to cream, 13-28 mm long. Dry to moist woods, Lake to Clearwater Co., s. to Morrison, Mower, and Fillmore counties, and in Roseau, Clay, and Yellow Medicine counties.

ZYGADENUS*

Poisonous perennial herbs with bulbs or thick rhizomes; leaves alternate, linear, elongate, often mostly near the base of the stem, progressively reduced upward; flowers in racemes or panicles, bisexual or polygamous, white to greenish-white or tinted with yellow, purple or brown; perianth widespreading, its 6 segments similar, separate to the attachment on receptacle or ovary, each with 1 or 2 small glands on the lower half; stamens 6, hypogynous when perianth is; ovary superior to partly inferior, 3-locular; ovules several per locule; styles 3; fruit a septicidal capsule. (Gr. zygon, yoke, and aden, gland.)

Z. elegans Pursh (including Z. glaucus Nutt.). White Camass, Alkali Grass. Leaves mostly near the base; ovary 1/2 inferior in flower, 1/4-1/3 in fruit. Mesic to wet prairies and meadows, occasionally in open woods, Houston to Rock Co., n. to Hennepin, Stearns, Mahnomen, Roseau, and Kittson counties, and in se. St. Louis Co. This species is customarily divided into two, the western Z. elegans and the eastern Z. glaucus. However, our plants appear to combine the characters of the two in various ways, and are not readily divisible into 2 groups. According to Dr. Sherman J. Preece Jr. there is a broad zone of intergradation between the 2 forms in which no clear separation is possible, and Minnesota is in that zone. The western form characteristically has racemes or seldom panicles, bracts with scarious margins and summits, perianth segments tinged with yellow, and capsules nearly twice as long as the perianth; the eastern form has only panicles, bracts not scarious, perianth segments tinged with green, bronze or purple, and capsules only slightly exceeding the perianth.

AMARYLLIDACEAE ----- AMARYLLIS FAMILY

Perennial herbs from bulbs, corms, rhizomes, or fibrous roots; stems leafy or leafless, the leaves alternate; flowers single or the inflorescence usually an umbel subtended by bracts; flowers usually bisexual, regular or somewhat zygomorphic; perianth segments 6, usually similar, separate or united at base, the perianth tube sometimes bearing a conspicuous crown-like or tubular appendage within; stamens 6; ovary usually inferior and 3-locular with few to many ovules on usually axile placentas; style 1; fruit a capsule or rarely a berry. Technically and perhaps artificially separated from the Liliaceae by the mostly inferior ovary and the bracted umbel.

A-Flowers with a crown-like or tubular appendage within the perianth;
    cultivated . . . . NARCISSUS
A-Flowers without such an appendage; native or cultivated.
  B-Perianth yellow, its segments alike; native . . . . HYPOXIS
  B-Perianth white and green, the inner segments shorter than the
    outer; cultivated . . . . GALANTHUS

GALANTHUS ----- SNOWDROP

Herbs with bulbs and 2 or 3 linear basal leaves; flower 1; perianth segments 6, separate, the inner 3 erect, shorter than the spreading outer 3; ovary inferior, ovules many, stigma capitate, fruit a loculicidal capsule. (Gr. gala, milk, and anthos, flower.)

G. nivalis L. Cultivated. Leaves 5-15 cm long, 3-15 mm wide at flowering, becoming much larger; flower nodding or declined; outer perianth segments white, the inner obcordate, white below, green at the notch, or the green more extensive, or sometimes marked with yellow. Central and s. Europe to the Caucasus.

HYPOXIS ----- STAR GRASS *

Small grass-like herbs from corms or rhizomes; leaves basal, narrow, usually hairy; flowers single or in an irregular umbel, usually yellow; perianth segments similar, separate nearly to the top of the ovary, the outer 3 of the 6 usually pubescent on the back; ovary inferior, ovules many; stigma entire; fruit indehiscent or a loculicidal capsule, usually crowned with the persistent perianth. (Gr. hypoxys, sour.)

H. hirsuta (L.) Cov. Yellow Star Grass. Leaves linear, more or less hairy, 2-10 mm wide, to 60 cm long at maturity, the main ones 5-9-nerved; flowers yellow, 1-6 in a cluster, the perianth segments 5-12 mm long; fruit indehiscent; seeds black, sharply roughened. Damp meadows, Houston to Rock Co., n. to Washington, Hennepin, Stearns, Mahnomen, Roseau, and Kittson counties, and in Morrison Co.

NARCISSUS ----- NARCISSUS, DAFFODIL

Herbs from bulbs, leaves basal, linear and flat or narrow and rush-like; flowers yellow or white, 1 to several in an umbel, arising from within an enclosing bract, on leafless stems; perianth segments similar, united below into a cylindrical or funnel-shaped tube which bears a tubular crown-like appendage of varying length; stamens borne on the perianth tube; ovary inferior, ovules many; stigma 3-lobed; fruit a loculicidal capsule. (L., from the Gr., perhaps in allusion to narcotic properties, perhaps from Gr. Narkissos, a mythological character.)

A-Flowers (2-) 4-8 in a cluster. . . . . N. tazetta

A-Flowers 1 (rarely 2).
  B-Crown nearly as long as to longer than the perianth segments. .
  . . . . N. pseudo-narcissus
  B-Crown 1/8-3/4 as long as the perianth segments.
    C-Flowers with pure white perianth segments, the crown
      1/8-1/5 their length. . . . . N. poeticus
    C-Flowers yellow or whitish; crown 1/2-3/4 the length
      of the perianth segments . . . . N. incomparabilis

N. incomparabilis Mill. Cultivated. Flower 1, horizontal or ascending,
without odor; perianth tube 16-20 mm long; crown crisped on the edge.
Spain and s. France to the Tyrol. Most garden plants of this general
description are actually hybrids between N. poeticus and N. pseudo-
narcissus.

N. poeticus L. Poet's Narcissus, Pheasant's Eye; cultivated. Flower
1 (rarely 2), horizontal or ascending, very fragrant; perianth tube 2-3 cm
long; crown a shallow cup with a crisped red or orange edge. France to
Greece. Many garden plants of this general type are actually of hybrid
origin.

N. pseudo-narcissus L. Daffodil, Trumpet Narcissus; cultivated.
Flower 1, horizontal or ascending, yellow to white, when yellow the perianth segments and crown usually of different shades; perianth tube mostly
15-20 mm long; crown with a more or less frilled edge. Sweden to England, Spain, and Romania.

N. tazetta L. Polyanthus Narcissus; cultivated. Flowers horizontal
or declined, fragrant; perianth white, crown light yellow (all-yellow and
all-white forms exist); tube 13-18 mm long; crown cup-shaped, 1/3-1/2
as long as the perianth segments. Canary Islands to Japan. This, the
commonest greenhouse species, is not hardy here but some of its hybrids
such as those with N. poeticus are.

IRIDACEAE ----- IRIS FAMILY

Mostly perennial herbs, with rhizomes, corms, bulbs, or fibrous roots;
stems leafy or leafless; leaves linear, mostly basal, often equitant (folded double,
clasping), linear; flowers showy, bisexual, regular or somewhat zygomorphic,
borne from 1 or a group of 2 or more enclosing bracts; perianth petal-like,
of 6 parts in 2 similar or somewhat differentiated whorls, all usually fused
into a tube at base; stamens 3, opposite the outer perianth segments; ovary
inferior, mostly 3-locular with axile placentation; style 1, usually 3-parted,
the divisions sometimes expanded and petal-like or divided; fruit a loculicidal
capsule.

A-Style branches expanded and petal-like, concealing the stamens . . . . IRIS
A-Style branches not expanded and petal-like, not concealing the
  stamens.
  B-Perianth segments 8-12 mm long; plant with evident stem above
    ground; native . . . . SISYRINCHIUM
  B-Perianth segments 20-45 mm long; no stem above ground; cultivated
    . . . . CROCUS

CROCUS

Herbs from bulbs, with linear basal leaves; stem very short, below
ground, the flowers emerging directly from the ground, funnel-shaped; the

perianth tube very long, the ovary often buried below the surface; perianth segments similar; stamens attached in the upper end of the tube; ovary 3-locular, many-ovuled, style long, the style-branches wedge-shaped, fringed, or of linear forked branches. (Gr. name of the saffron, C. sativus.)

A-Flowers violet to white . . . . C. vernus
A-Flowers yellow at least on the inside.
    B-Anthers and style branches pale yellow . . . . C. flavus
    B-Anthers orange, style branches orange-red . . . . C. angustifolius

    C. angustifolius Weston (C. susianus Ker-Gaw.). Cloth-of-gold Crocus; cultivated. Perianth segments yellow within, usually tinged or striped brown without, ovate; style-branches exceeding the stamens, broadly wedge-shaped. Caucasus s. to the Crimea.

    C. flavus Weston (C. maesiacus Ker-Gaw.). Cultivated. Perianth segments bright clear yellow, roundish to ovate-triangular; style-branches shorter than the stamens, fringed with narrowly wedge-shaped tips. Greece and Serbia to w. Asia Minor.

    C. vernus (L.) Hill. Cultivated. Perianth often striped purple, the throat pubescent; anthers lemon-yellow; style branches shorter to longer than the stamens, broadly wedge-shaped, entire or fringed, orange-scarlet. S. and central Europe.

IRIS ----- IRIS, BLUE FLAG, FLEUR-DE-LIS *

    Herbs from rhizomes or bulbs; stem simple or branched; leaves mostly basal, flat, linear to sword-shaped, usually equitant; flowers 1 to several in various clusters; perianth tube generally extending above the ovary, its 3 outer segments (sepals; "falls") reflexed or hanging, its 3 inner (petals; "standards") somewhat different in shape, often much smaller, usually erect; the 3 style-branches expanded, colored and petal-like, arched outward, covering the 3 stamens; stigmas each a delicate narrow transverse flap on the under side of the style-branch; ovary many-ovuled. (Gr. iris, rainbow.)
    Hybridization and selection in Iris have produced great numbers of cultivars which cannot be referred to any one original species or which are not normal for that species.

A-Outer perianth segments beardless, with at most a very short
    pubescence (of 1-celled hairs) at base; native or cultivated.
    B-Flowers yellow to cream color. . . . . I. pseudacorus
    B-Flowers blue to violet, often variegated with white and green
        (rarely all white).
        C-Leaves (5-) 8-30 mm wide; native.
            D-Outer segments unspotted or with a greenish or greenish-
                yellow spot at base; ovary 11-22 mm long at anthesis;
                style-branches not auricled . . . . I. versicolor
            D-Outer segments with a yellow basal spot; ovary 18-38 mm
                long at anthesis; style-branches auriculate at base
                . . . . I. virginica var. shrevei
        C-Leaves 2-8 mm wide; cultivated . . . . I. sibirica
A-Outer perianth segments conspicuously bearded (with multicellular
    hairs) along the midrib; cultivated.
    E-Plants dwarf, the stems less than 30 cm high or sometimes
        none . . . . I. pumila
    E-Plants with stems mostly 30 cm high or higher.
        F-Flowering stems about equalling the leaves . . . . I. variegata
        F-Flowering stems exceeding and overtopping the leaves . I. germanica

I. germanica L. German Iris; cultivated. Leaves 25-40 mm wide; flowers violet to purple, varying to white; perianth tube ca. 25 mm long; beard yellow; capsule 38-50 mm long. Central and s. Europe. Most plants keying out here belong to a polyploid hybrid complex derived from several species and contain little I. germanica.

I. pseudacorus L. Yellow Flag, Water Flag; cultivated and naturalized. Robust; leaves 10-25 mm broad; bracts large and leaf-like; perianth tube ca. 13 mm long; capsule 5-8.5 cm long. Europe, n. Africa, Syria, escaped and widely established in our range in marshes and shallow water, recorded from Hennepin, Kandiyohi, s. St. Louis and Lake of the Woods counties.

I. pumila L. Cultivated. Leaves 7-13 mm wide, 5-13 cm long; perianth tube 2-6 cm long; flowers purple or blue to yellow. Central Europe to Asia Minor.

I. sibirica L. Cultivated. Stem surpassing the leaves, hollow; bracts mostly brown-scarious, the upper ones 20-37 mm long; flowers violet to sometimes white; perianth tube 2-10 mm long. Europe.

I. variegata L. Cultivated. Leaves 10-25 mm wide; bracts 25-45 mm long, green; outer perianth segments yellow veined brown, inner yellow veined brown at base; perianth tube 25 mm or less long; capsule ca. 26 mm long. Se. Europe.

I. versicolor L. Blue Flag; Wild Iris. Leaves 5-30 mm wide; bracts 3.5-6 cm long; inner perianth segments 1/2-2/3 as long as the outer; perianth tube to 20 mm long; capsule 3-6 cm long, slow to open, its inner surface and the seeds shiny. Marshes, swamps, meadows, and shores, Cook to Kittson Co., s. to Becker, Todd, Cottonwood, Martin, Rice, and Washington counties.

I. virginica var. shrevei (Small) E. Anderson. Blue Flag. Similar to the preceding. Bracts to 14 cm long; inner perianth segments 2/3-4/5 as long as the outer; capsule 4-10 cm long, its inner surface and the seeds rather dull. Marshes, swamps, meadows, and shores, Houston to Jackson Co., n. to Ramsey, Mille Lacs, Stearns, and Chippewa counties.

SISYRINCHIUM ----- BLUE-EYED GRASS, GRASS-IRIS*

Low perennial grass-like herbs with fibrous roots; leaves mostly basal; stem simple or branched, 2-edged to 2-winged; flowers in few-flowered umbel-like clusters that arise usually from a pair of enfolding bracts; perianth red, blue, violet, or yellow, in ours mostly blue or violet to white with a yellow or greenish-yellow center, quickly withering; perianth segments similar, spreading, free nearly to the base; filaments united in our species; style-branches thread-like, unbranched; capsule globose to obovoid. (Old Gr. name, first applied to some other plant.)

A-Edges of the outer and longer bract of the visible pair fused 0-0.5
    mm at base; perianth pale blue to white (rarely yellow) . . S. campestre
A-Edges of the outer and longer bract fused for 1-6 mm above the base;
    perianth violet (rarely white).
  B-Stems 0.5-1.2 mm wide; leaves 0.5-1.4 mm wide; shorter (inner)
      bract of the visible pair 12-20 mm long; fruit 2-4 mm long
      . . . . S. mucronatum
  B-Stems 1-3 mm wide; leaves 1-4 mm wide; shorter bract 16-30
      mm long; fruit 4-6 mm long. . . . . S. montanum

S. campestre Bickn. Stem and leaves 0.5-2 mm wide; bracts often purple-tinged, the longer (outer) one 25-50 mm long, the shorter (inner) one 15-25

74

mm long; capsule 2-4 mm long. Prairies and dry open soil, Houston to Pipestone Co., n. to Chisago, Morrison, s. Wadena, Clay, and Kittson counties, and in Itasca Co.

S. montanum Greene. Bracts green or tinged with light red-purple, the outer one fused for 1-6 mm above the base, 25-85 mm long. Dry to moist open soil, widely scattered across the state, unrecorded from Koochiching Co., the counties se. of a line from Martin to Goodhue counties, and several interspersed counties. Typically the flowering stems are all or nearly all leafless and unbranched to the single bract-pair. Plants with a third to all flowering stems bearing a leaf 2.5-11 cm below the bract-pair, often with branches at this point, are usually treated as a separate species, S. angustifolium   Mill. (S. graminoides Bickn.). However, it seems more likely that ours at least are only forms of S. montanum. Such plants have been found from Cook to St. Louis Co. and in Kittson and McLeod counties.

S. mucronatum Michx. Bracts usually dark purple (when dry), rarely green, the outer one fused for 1-3 mm above the base, 1.5-4.5 cm long. Meadows, fields, sandy places, and woods, Pipestone and Rock counties to Brown and Houston counties, Kittson and Roseau counties to Mahnomen and Clay counties, and in Stearns, St. Louis, and Lake counties.

ORCHIDACEAE ----- ORCHID FAMILY

Perennial herbs, terrestrial (ours) or epiphytic, the terrestrial ones often with rhizomes or tubers, the epiphytic often with thickened stems ("pseudobulbs"); plants usually green but sometimes without chlorophyll and saprophytic; stems leafy or not, or the leaves sometimes reduced to scales; leaf sheath usually fused around the stem; flowers (fig. 68) zygomorphic, mostly bisexual; outer perianth segments (sepals) 3, or 2 by the fusion of 2, the inner segments (petals) 3, one of them, the lip, conspicuously to slightly different from the other 2, the lip varying greatly in form, morphologically uppermost but usually brought lowermost through a twist in the ovary and pedicel; stamens 1 or 2, united with the style and stigmas to form a single complex knob-like structure, the column, which bears the stigmatic surfaces on the face toward the lip, and the anthers (when 2) on the sides or (when 1) on the summit or back; pollen usually coherent into compact masses; ovary inferior, 1-locular with 3 parietal placentas (rarely 3-locular with axile placentas), with very many minute seeds. In the following, "petals" refers only to the lateral two of the inner segments, the lip being described separately.

A-Lip shoe-shaped or bag-shaped, at least its free end hollow and appear-
    ing either inflated or as the front of a sharp-pointed shoe or as an open
    bag.
  B-Lip smooth, the margin around the opening more or less inrolled;
      anthers 2 . . . . CYPRIPEDIUM
  B-Lip bearded with yellow hairs on a delicate flap attached to the
      front rim of the opening; anther 1 . . . . CALYPSO
A-Lip not shoe-shaped, the free end not hollowed.
  C-Lip prolonged at the attached end downward or backward into a
    spur 2 mm or more long, the plants green.
    D-Leaves 3 or more, usually on the stem . . . . HABENARIA
    D-Leaves 1 or 2, basal or nearly basal.
      E-Flowers yellowish-green. HABENARIA
      E-Flowers tinged or spotted with pink or purple (rarely all
        white). . . . . ORCHIS

C-Lip not prolonged into a spur as above, if with a short swelling
  the plants non-green.
  F-Flower solitary; lip 25-50 mm long . . . . ARETHUSA
  F-Flowers several to many; lip 3-15 mm long.
    G-Leaves 5 cm or more long.
      H-Leaves 2 . . . . LIPARIS
      H-Leaves 1 . . . . APLECTRUM
    G-Leaves none or up to 3 cm long.
      I-Leaves 2 in an opposite pair on the stem . . . . LISTERA
      I-Leaves none.
        J-Sepals, petals, and lip 10-15 mm long, not striped;
          ovary about as long as perianth parts; floral bracts
          tapering to a point . . . . APLECTRUM
        J-Sepals, petals, and lip 4-8 mm long or in one species
          the sepals and petals 10-14 mm, the lip 8-12; if the
          latter then sepals and petals conspicuously purple-
          striped, the ovary about 1/2 the length of the perianth
          at anthesis, and the floral bracts mostly blunt and
          irregularly notched. . . . . CORALLORHIZA

APLECTRUM ----- PUTTY ROOT, ADAM-AND-EVE*

Corm-bearing rhizomatous herb with a single leaf produced in late
summer, the leaf persisting through winter, often but not always withering
before flowering time; flowers in a raceme; sepals and petals similar, arching over the column; lip free, with 3 low parallel ridges, 3-cleft, unspurred;
anther 1. (Gr. a-, without, plektron, spur.)

A. hyemale (Muhl.) Torr. Leaf 10-15 cm long; flowers 7-15; sepals and
petals 10-15 mm long, purplish toward the base, brown distally; lip 10-15 mm
long, white, marked with violet; floral bracts tapering to a point; ovary ca.
as long as perianth. Rich soil in woods, Houston to Blue Earth, Dakota, and
Washington counties.

ARETHUSA*

Corm-bearing herbs; leaf 1, grass-like, arising shortly after anthesis
from within the upper bract on the stem, the bracts sometimes green; flower
1; sepals and petals similar, united at base, arching over the column; lip
joined to column at base, oblong, with 3 (-5) fringed lengthwise parallel
crests; column petal-like; anther 1. (Classical name of a nymph.)

A. bulbosa L. Dragon's Mouth, Swamp Pink. Leaf 2-4 mm wide; perianth
25-50 mm long; sepals and petals magenta, lip pinkish white, spotted and
streaked with yellow and purple. Sphagnum bogs and swampy meadows,
usually uncommon, Cook to Beltrami and Aitkin counties, and in Chisago
and Hennepin counties.

CALYPSO*

Herbs with corms, producing a single basal leaf in autumn which
persists through the next flowering; flower 1, on a stem; sepals and petals
similar, free, spreading; lip shoe-shaped, the toe pointed and notched, the
front rim of the opening of the shoe drawn out and folded forward to cover
the front part of the shoe with a delicate translucent apron; anther 1. (Gr.
and L. name of a goddess.)

C. bulbosa (L.) Oakes. Leaf 3-5 cm long; sepals and petals 1-2 cm long, pale purple; lip 16-20 mm long, whitish, yellowish toward the tip, irregularly streaked with red-brown within, the apron white and spotted with maroon and bearing 3 rows of yellow hairs near the upper end. Shaded mesic to moist coniferous forests, Cook to Koochiching, Clearwater, n. Cass, and Carlton counties.

CORALLORHIZA ----- CORAL ROOT

Leafless purple, brown, or yellowish saprophytes from a cluster of coral-like roots; stem with a few scales toward the base, the flowers in a raceme; sepals and petals similar, spreading; lateral sepals united at base with the base of the column, forming there with the lip a very small spur or sac; lip with 1 or 2 lengthwise ridges, often with 2 lateral lobes; anther 1; fruit pendent. (Gr. korallion, coral, rhiza, root.)

A-Stem yellowish. . . . . C. trifida
A-Stem pinkish-purple to magenta.
  B-Lip 3-lobed, spotted with purple . . . . C. maculata
  B-Lip not lobed, striped with purple . . . . C. striata

C. maculata Raf. Spotted Coral Root. Flowers 10-40; sepals and petals spotted or tinged with purple, 6-8 mm long; lip white, purple-spotted, 6-8 mm long; ovary about as long as the perianth segments. Woods, Cook to St. Louis Co., and in Clearwater, Hubbard, Chisago, Rice, and Fillmore counties.

C. striata Lindl. Striped Coral Root. Flowers 10-20; sepals and petals 10-14 mm long, yellowish-white with 3 purple stripes, also purple-edged; lip 8-12 mm long, white with purple stripes or all purple; ovary at anthesis ca. 1/2 the length of the perianth. Woods, Cook to Roseau, Clearwater, and Kanabec counties.

C. trifida Chat. Early Coral Root. Flowers 5-15; sepals and petals yellowish-green, 3-5 mm long; spur none; lip white, sometimes purple-spotted, 3-5 mm long, with 2 short lateral lobes below the middle; ovary about as long as the perianth segments. Mesic to moist woods, and swamps, Cook to Lake of the Woods Co., s. to Becker, ne. Todd, Hennepin, and Chisago counties.

CYPRIPEDIUM ----- LADY-SLIPPER, MOCCASIN FLOWER*

Herb from fibrous roots; leaves 2-several, alternate or all basal; flowers 1-few; sepals 3 or apparently 2 from the union of the lateral ones behind the lip; petals mostly narrower than the sepals; lip slipper-like or bag-like, the conspicuous opening next to the column; anthers two, one on each side of the column, a petal-like staminode also present in the center above the stigma. (Gr. Cypris, Venus, and pedilon, slipper.)

A-Leaves basal only, 2; flower 1 on a leafless stem . . . . C. acaule
A-Leaves borne on the stem, usually 3 or more; flowers 1 or more.
  B-Sepals 3 and separate. . . . . C. arietinum
  B-Sepals seeming 2 (from the union of 2 of the 3).
    C-Sepals and petals white, shorter than the lip . . . . C. reginae
    C-Sepals and petals yellowish to greenish to purple-brown, longer
      than the lip.

D-Lip yellow . . . . C. calceolus
D-Lip white . . . . C. candidum

C. acaule Ait. Stemless Lady-slipper. Leaf blades 10-20 cm long;
sepals and petals yellowish-green to greenish-brown, 3-5 cm long, the 2 lower
sepals united; lip pink with red veins (rarely white), 3-6 cm long, hairy within, cleft above from the opening to the free end. Acid soil, from swamps
and bogs to dry woods, Cook to Lake of the Woods Co., s. to Becker, Pope,
Hennepin, and Chisago counties.

C. arietinum R. Br. Ram's Head Lady-slipper. Leaf blades 5-10 cm
long; flower 1; sepals and petals 1.5-2.5 cm long, greenish-brown; lip whitish,
red-veined, 1-1.6 cm long, prolonged at free end into a conical pouch, the
point of the cone down. Moist, usually acid soils in coniferous woods, Cook,
Aitkin, Clearwater, Becker, Isanti, Anoka, Wright, and Hennepin counties.

C. calceolus L. Yellow Lady-slipper. Leaf blades 6-20 cm long; sepals
and petals 3-8 cm long; lip 2-6 cm long, usually veined with purple.

A-Lip 1.3-3.5 cm long; upper sepal 2.5-5 cm long; petals 3.5-5 cm long;
    sepals purple-brown; bogs, swamps, or cool wet places, Cook to
    Kittson Co., s. to Norman, Pope, Blue Earth, and Houston counties
    . . . . C. c. var. parviflorum (Salisb.) Fern. Small Yellow Lady-slipper.
A-Lip 3-5 cm long; upper sepal 4-7 cm long; petals 5-9 cm long;
    sepals greenish to brownish-yellow; mesic to moist woods, from
    Houston and Fillmore counties to Brown, Stearns, Clay, and
    Kittson counties on the w., to Lake Co. on the e. . . . .
    . . . . . C. c. var. pubescens (Willd.) Correll. Large Yellow Lady-slipper

C. candidum Muhl. White Lady-slipper. Leaf blades 8-15 cm long;
sepals and petals 2-4 cm long, greenish or greenish-yellow, sometimes red-
striped; lip 15-25 mm long, veined with violet within. Damp to wet grassland and shallow marshes, on calcareous soil, uncommon except locally,
widely scattered from Houston to Pipestone Co., n. to Hennepin, Stearns,
Mahnomen, and Marshall counties.

C. reginae Walt. Showy Lady-slipper. To 1 m high; leaf blades 10-20
cm long; sepals and petals 2.5-4.5 cm long; lip 3-5 cm long, white or usually
tinged or broadly streaked with rose especially at the front. Swamps, bogs,
or moist woods, St. Louis to Kittson Co., s. to Becker, Kandiyohi, Nicollet,
Waseca, Fillmore, and Winona counties.

HABENARIA ----- REIN ORCHIS

      Herbs from tubers, rhizomes, or thickened roots; leaves alternate
or basal; flowers in a bracted spike or raceme, green, white, yellow, pink,
or purple; sepals and petals separate, alike or not; lip flat, entire or 3-lobed,
toothed, or fringed, prolonged backward into a spur at base; anther 1. (L.
habena, a rein, referring to the strap-like lip or spur.)

A-Leaves basal only, 2 . . . . H. hookeri
A-Leaves on the stem, several.
    B-Lip entire . . . . H. hyperborea
    B-Lip 2-3-toothed near the free end . . . . H. viridis var. bracteata

H. hookeri Torr. Hooker's Orchid. Leaves elliptic to round, 6-12 cm
long; flowers yellowish-green; lip lance-triangular, 8-12 mm long, the spur

13-24 mm long. Rather dry woods, Cook to Lake of the Woods Co.,
Clearwater to Cass Co., Chisago and Washington counties, and Goodhue
to Houston Co.

H. hyperborea (L.) R. Br. Northern or Leafy Northern Green Orchid.
Leaves lanceolate to oblanceolate, to 25 cm long; flowers green or greenish-
white; lip lance-ovate, 3-6 mm long, the spur as long as the lip. Bogs to
mesic woods, Cook to Kittson Co., s. to Wilkin, Pope, Hennepin, and
Chisago counties, and in Brown and Blue Earth counties near the Minnesota R.

H. viridis var. bracteata (Muhl.) Gray. Bracted Orchid. Leaves
obovate to oblanceolate, 5-12 cm long; flowers greenish, often tinged with
purple; lip oblong, 6-10 mm long, the spur 2-3 mm long. Shores, meadows,
thickets, and mesic woods, widely scattered, Cook to Roseau Co., s. to
Clearwater, Morrison, Wright, Dakota, ne. Fillmore, and Houston counties,
and in Clay, Blue Earth, and Waseca counties.

LIPARIS ----- TWAYBLADE

Low herbs from corms, with 2 basal leaves; flowers small, in a few-
flowered raceme; sepals spreading, lanceolate; petals linear; lip flat, entire,
spurless; anther 1. (Gr. liparos, fat or shining, referring to the smooth
and lustrous leaves.)

L. liliifolia (L.) Rich. Leaves ovate to elliptic, 5-15 cm long; sepals
greenish-white; petals greenish to pale purple; lip pale purple, rhomboid-
obovate. Mesic woods and clearings, Houston and Fillmore counties to
Hennepin Co.

LISTERA ----- TWAYBLADE

Delicate herbs with fibrous roots, the erect stem with a single pair
of opposite sessile leaves and a bracted raceme of small green to purple or
red flowers; sepals and petals similar, separate, spreading or reflexed;
lip (in ours) much longer than the petals, shallowly to deeply notched down
the center; anther 1. (Named for Martin Lister, English naturalist.)

L. cordata (L.) R. Br. Leaves 1.5-3 cm long; sepals and petals 2-2.5
mm long; lip purplish-green, 3-5 mm long, with 2 projecting lateral teeth
near the attached end. Moist woods and sphagnum bogs, Cook to Clearwater,
Otter Tail, and Isanti counties.

ORCHIS*

Herbs from short rhizomes and thickened roots; leaves 1 or 2 near
the base; flowers few in a raceme; sepals and petals similar in color but
differing in size, some or all of them converging to form a hood over the
column; lip large, prolonged near the attached end into a conspicuous spur;
anther 1. (The ancient Gr. name.)

A-Leaf 1; lip 3-lobed, notched at the tip . . . . O. rotundifolia
A-Leaves 2; lip not lobed or notched . . . . O. spectabilis

O. rotundifolia Banks. Leaf 4-11 cm long; sepals and petals 5-8 mm long,
pale purple to white; lip 6-9 mm long, white spotted with pale purple; spur

much shorter than the lip. Moist woods and swamps, St. Louis Co., and from
s. Beltrami and Clearwater to Becker and ne. Otter Tail counties, and in
Isanti Co.

O. spectabilis L. Showy Orchis. Leaves 8-15 cm long; sepals and petals
13-18 mm long, pink to pale purple; lip 12-20 mm long, white; spur about as
long as the lip. Rich, mostly calcareous soil, in woods, Houston and Fillmore
to Blue Earth, Meeker, and Chisago counties, and in Pope Co.

DICOTYLEDONS

SALICACEAE ----- WILLOW FAMILY

Dioecious trees and shrubs with simple, alternate, stipulate leaves;
flowers in catkins, without perianth; male flowers of 1-60 stamens; female of
a single 1-locular ovary with several to many ovules on 2-4 parietal placentas;
stigmas or lobes of the style as many as the placentas; fruit a capsule; seeds
with a tuft of long hairs. Catkins occasionally with a few flowers of the
opposite sex, especially in Populus where such flowers may be numerous.

A-Bracts subtending flowers cut or fringed; stamens 5-many; stigmas
    elongate; leaf buds with several scales ; leaves broad . . . . . POPULUS
A-Bracts entire; stamens 1-12; stigmas mostly short; leaf buds with
    1 scale; leaves narrow to broad. . . . . SALIX

POPULUS ----- POPLARS, COTTONWOODS, ASPENS *

Trees or tall shrubs with mostly ovate to deltoid deciduous leaves
with long petioles; leaf buds covered with several scales, often with a sticky
resinous coating; catkins pendulous; floral bracts cut or fringed; each flower
borne in a cup-shaped, more or less one-sided structure (the disk); stamens
5-many; stigmas and placentas 2-4. (The classical L. name.)

A-Leaves densely cottony-pubescent beneath at maturity, often lobed
    . . . . P. alba
A-Leaves at maturity not as above, pubescent only on the veins or glabrous,
    entire or toothed but not lobed.
  B-Petioles roundish in section, usually shallowly channeled above;
    leaves whitish beneath.
    C-Young twigs, petioles, and lower leaf surface glabrous; leaf
      blades ovate to ovate-lanceolate; native. . . . . P. balsamifera
    C-Young twigs, petioles, and veins of lower leaf surface pubescent;
      leaf blades broadly ovate or cordate; cultivated . . . . . P. candicans
  B-Petioles strongly flattened laterally, especially near the blade,
    not channeled at least near the blade; mature leaves greenish
    beneath.
    D-Leaf blades broadly ovate to round, rounded or subcordate at
      base, rounded to short-acuminate at apex, without a translucent
      border; buds not resinous.
     E-Normal leaves with 16-45 teeth per side; terminal bud glabrous
       or its lowest scales with a few hairs; young growth glabrous
       or nearly so . . . . P. tremuloides
     E-Normal leaves with 5-15 teeth per side; terminal bud and
       young growth gray-pubescent . . . . P. grandidentata
    D-Leaf blades triangular to ovate-triangular, truncate or broadly
      wedge-shaped at base, acuminate at apex, with a definite
      translucent border; buds more or less resinous.

F-Blades broadly triangular, truncate at base, all or many of
　　them with a few glands present along the edge at the base;
　　branches widely spreading, crown broad . . . . P. deltoides
F-Blades rhombic to rhombic-ovate, broadly wedge-shaped or
　　rounded at base, usually without distinct glands at base;
　　branches ascending to erect, crown pyramidal to very narrow.
　　G-Leaf bases mostly wedge-shaped, the fine teeth only slightly
　　　　if at all incurved; blades nearly as wide as or wider than
　　　　long, 3-7 cm long; crown very narrow . . . . P. nigra
　　G-Leaf bases mostly truncate, the prominent teeth with incurved
　　　　points, blades longer than wide, 7-14 cm long; crown
　　　　pyramidal . . . . P. X canadensis

P. alba L. White or Silver-leaf Poplar; cultivated. Bark whitish-gray;
terminal bud and young twigs densely pubescent; leaves palmately 3-7-lobed
to ovate and irregularly dentate; leaves toothed or lobed; stigmas 2. Eurasia.
In its original form the tree has spreading branches, a broad crown, and
variable leaves; in the Bolleana Poplar, P. alba cv. Pyramidalis, the branches
are erect, the crown narrow as in the Lombardy Poplar, and the leaves
strongly 3-5-lobed.

P. balsamifera L. Tacamahac, Balsam Poplar. Older bark dark gray
and furrowed; terminal bud resinous; leaf blades acute or short-acuminate,
finely serrate, silvery white beneath or often rust-colored owing to the
resinous secretion, fragrant; bracts deeply fringed; stamens 12-30; stigmas
2. Mesic to moist woods, swamps, river banks, and shores, Cook to
Kittson Co., s. to Wilkin, Douglas, Benton, and Carlton counties, and in
Rice and Winona counties.

P. X canadensis Moench, cv. Eugenei (hybrid between P. deltoides and P.
nigra). Eugene Poplar, Norway Poplar, Sudden Sawlog; cultivated. Trees
all staminate; stamens 15-25.

P. candicans Ait. Balm of Gilead; cultivated. Planted in the s. half of
the state. Origin uncertain, perhaps a cultigen derived from P. balsamifera
which it resembles.

P. deltoides Marsh. Cottonwood. Older bark nearly black, deeply
furrowed; leaf teeth with points incurved; bracts fringed; stamens ca. 60;
stigmas 3 or 4. Bottomlands, river banks, lake shores, and moist prairies,
Houston to Rock Co., n. to s. Pine, nw. Cass, Lake of the Woods, and
Kittson counties, and in s. St. Louis Co. Often planted.

P. grandidentata Michx. Big-or Large-toothed Aspen. Young bark
usually greenish-gray tinged with yellow-orange, becoming dark brown in
age; bracts cleft into 5-7 lance-triangular lobes; stamens 5-12; stigmas
4. Moist to dry woods, Lake to Lake of the Woods Co., s. to Otter Tail,
Kandiyohi, Le Sueur, Fillmore, and Houston counties.

P. nigra L., cv. Italica. Lombardy Poplar; cultivated. Young bark
yellowish, then gray, becoming dark brown and more or less ridged in age;
branches strongly ascending, the crown straight and narrow; bracts fringed;
trees all staminate; stamens up to 30. A horticultural form of the parent
species which is native to Eurasia.

P. tremuloides Michx. Quaking Aspen, American Aspen, Trembling
Poplar. Young bark whitish, greenish or gray, becoming dark and furrowed
in age; bracts cleft to below the middle into 3-5 lance-triangular lobes;
stamens 5-12; stigmas 4. Moist to dry woods, especially in logged or
burned areas, occasionally in prairie, throughout the state except for
counties sw. of a line through Lincoln and Martin counties and a few other
counties in that area.

Trees or shrubs with entire or serrate, mostly long and narrow, deciduous leaves; leaf buds covered by a single non-resinous scale; catkins appearing with or before the leaves, seldom later, mostly ascending to spreading, their bracts mostly entire, sometimes irregularly notched at the tip; stamens usually 2 (1-12), with 1 or 2 (-4) nectar glands at the base; stigmas and placentas 2, the female flower with 1-4 nectar glands at base opposite the bract. The species are often difficult to distinguish, and often hybridize. (The classical Latin name.)

Separate keys are provided for staminate and pistillate material. A key to willows can be written based on mature foliage alone, but since many of our species do not develop mature leaves until mid June, such a key is not included here.

KEY TO STAMINATE MATERIAL

A-Stamens 3 or more per flower.
  B-Blades of reduced leaves (those 3 cm or less long) on peduncles of catkins or at bases of leafy twigs less than 2 times as long as wide; mature normal blades 1.7-3 times as long as wide; cultivated shrub to small tree . . . . S. pentandra
  B-Blades of such reduced leaves more than 2 times as long as wide; mature normal blades 2.5-9.5 times as long as wide; native trees or shrubs
    C-Blades of reduced leaves on peduncles entire on sizes up to 15 mm long or often longer, or if unusually with teeth, the teeth only up to 3 per mm, their glandular tips mostly appressed to the margin and not over 0.1 mm wide, usually not markedly enlarged at junction of blade and petiole; mature normal blades 3-9.5 times as long as wide.
      D-Leaves slightly whitened or a pale blue-green beneath; petiole and midrib glabrous by the time the leaf has reached 1/2 size; blade 4.5-9 times as long as the petiole, 3-5.5 times as long as wide . . . . S. amygdaloides
      D-Leaves green on both sides; petiole and lower midrib usually hairy at maturity; blade 8-16 (-37) times as long as the petiole, 4.5-9.5 times as long as wide . . . . S. nigra
    C-Blades of reduced leaves on peduncles all regularly toothed, the teeth up to 5 per mm on sizes up to 15 mm long, the glandular tips on the teeth prominent, out-turned, blunt, up to 0.3 mm wide, especially well developed at base of blade and on upper surface of petiole at junction with blade; mature normal blades 2.5-4.1 times as long as wide.
      E-Very immature leaves pubescent with reddish or brownish to light tan hairs, these sometimes falling before the leaves unfold; stipules of leaves on the catkin stalk 0.5-1.5 mm wide; teeth of mature leaves 5-9 per cm of margin . . . S. lucida
      E-Immature leaves glabrous or with a few scattered silky hairs; stipules none or to 0.4 mm wide; teeth of mature leaves 9-20 per cm of margin . . . . S. serissima
A-Stamens all or mostly 2 per flower.
  F-Filaments of the 2 stamens wholly united; leaves (or leaf scars) of vigorous shoots chiefly opposite or nearly so . . . . S. purpurea
  F-Filaments nearly or totally free; leaves alternate.

G-Flowers with 2 or more nectar glands at base, before and behind
the stamens; filaments hairy at least at base; cultivated trees
except for the native shrub S. interior, sometimes escaped.
H-Native stoloniferous shrub, forming colonies; filaments densely
long-hairy below the middle; leaf blades 8-23 times as long as
wide, 16-36 times as long as the petiole; branchlets not pendulous
. . . . S. interior
H-Cultivated trees, sometimes escaped; filaments sparsely hairy
at base; leaf blades 3.7-12 times as long as wide, 5-18 times
as long as the petiole, if more than 8 times as long as wide
the branchlets pendulous.
I-Branchlets erect to spreading.
J-New twigs and both sides of leaf blades silvery pubescent
when young (excluding first leaves of season), the blades
remaining pubescent at least on one side at maturity;
blades 10-17 times the petiole length; glandular teeth at
base of blade not usually markedly enlarged (see chart on
page 88) . . . . S. alba
J-New twigs and leaf blades glabrous to pubescent when
young, not silvery, the blades glabrous or nearly so
at full size, completely so in age; blades 5-10 (-15)
times the petiole length; glandular displaced leaf teeth
on upper surface of petiole at its junction with blade enlarged and prominent at least on later leaves . . . S. fragilis
I-Branchlets conspicuously pendulous: "weeping" willows.
K-New twigs and both sides of leaf blades silvery pubescent
when young (excluding first leaves of season), the
blades somewhat pubescent at least on one side at
maturity; mature twigs yellow; catkins 3-7 cm long
. . . . S. alba cv. Tristis (and see under S. babylonica)
K-New twigs and leaf blades glabrous to pubescent when young,
not silvery, the blades glabrous on both sides on reaching
3/4 their full size; mature twigs greenish to brown; catkins 1.5-4.5 cm long . . . . S. babylonica
G-Flowers each with 1 basal nectar gland, next the axis; filaments
glabrous except in S. bebbiana and sometimes S. discolor, S. gracilis,
and S. humilis; native shrubs or small trees to 6 m high.
L-Catkins expanding and blooming well before the leaves, with
only yellowish bracts or none at their bases, unfolding leaves
absent.
M-Last year's twigs with a close gray pubescence or its remnants.
N-Catkins 15-40 mm long; floral bracts 1.6-2.6 mm long;
filaments often hairy at base; moist to wet places . S. discolor
N-Catkins 7-20 mm long; floral bracts 0.8-1.8 mm long;
filaments rarely hairy at base; dry to moist places. S. humilis
M-Last year's twigs glabrous.
O-Anthers yellow; terminal buds (morphologically subterminal)
often bent over at an angle; widespread . . . . S. discolor
O-Anthers reddish; terminal buds straight or nearly so;
Cook to St. Louis counties. . . . . S. pellita
L-Catkins accompanied either by 1 or more green bracts at their
bases, or by young or unfolding leaves there or elsewhere, or
both.
P-Filaments hairy to puberulent at least at very base.
Q-Floral bracts greenish-yellow to light brown, usually with
reddish tips; leaf blades 2-3.5 times as long as wide. S. bebbiana

Q-Floral bracts a light to dark brown, the tips often blackish;
leaf blades 4.5-7.5 times as long as wide . . . . . S. gracilis
P-Filaments glabrous.
   R-Leaves entire, the edges often wavy or revolute.
      S-Stalks of catkins bearing 3-6 distinctly petioled leaves
nearly as long to longer than the catkins; floral bracts
yellow-brown, sometimes red-tipped . . . . . S. pedicellaris
      S-Stalks of catkins with 0-5 bracts, these sessile or in-
distinctly petioled, much shorter than the catkins;
floral bracts light to dark brown or blackish.
         T-Leaves usually densely white woolly at least beneath,
4-16 times as long as wide . . . . S. candida
         T-Leaves gray-pubescent to glabrous beneath, 2-3.5
(-4) times as long as wide . . . . S. planifolia
   R-Leaves toothed, the teeth visible on young leaves with a lens.
      U-Stalks of catkins bearing distinctly petioled young leaves,
their blades truncate to cordate at base; young growth
with a resinous balsam-like odor . . . . S. pyrifolia
      U-Stalks of catkins bearing 1-5 bracts, these sessile or in-
distinctly petioled or the blade base acute to seldom
rounded; plants without such odor.
         V-Leaves elliptic to obovate, typically 2-3.5 times as
long as wide .S. planifolia
         V-Leaves lanceolate to oblanceolate or linear, typically
3.5-7 times as long as wide.
            W-Bud scale often persistent at base of catkins and
vegetative shoots; stipules regularly present,
very small on early leaves, increasing in size
on later ones . . . . S. rigida complex
            W-Bud scales not persistent; stipules rare and
minute on early leaves, none on later ones . S. gracilis

KEY TO PISTILLATE MATERIAL

For the identification of most species it is necessary to have well-
developed capsules and at least partially expanded leaves.

A-Capsule (and ovary) pubescent at least at base.
   B-Leaves (or leaf scars) of vigorous shoots chiefly opposite or subopposite; catkins often paired at the nodes, expanding before the
leaves, sessile; capsules 2-3 mm long, sessile; cultivated .. S. purpurea
   B-Leaves alternate; catkins borne singly; other characters various;
native.
      C-Catkins expanding and blooming well before the leaves appear,
sessile or on stalks up to 10 mm long, the stalks usually bearing
none to a few yellowish to green bracts up to 10 mm long.
         D-Catkins 3.5-10 cm long; floral bracts 1.6-2.6 mm long; styles
0.4-1 mm long (not including stigmas); catkin-bearing
twigs pubescent to usually glabrous. . . . . S. discolor
         D-Catkins 1.2-4 cm long; floral bracts 1-1.8 mm long; styles
0.2-0.5 mm long; catkin-bearing twigs with a close gray
pubescence or its remnants . . . . S. humilis
      C-Catkins coming into bloom as the leaves appear or afterward,
sometimes beginning to expand earlier, sessile to long-
stalked, the stalks with or without bracts, sometimes with
bracts or leaves longer than 10 mm.

E-Catkins terminating lateral leafy twigs 3-10 cm long; floral
    bracts light yellow-brown, dropping before capsules are ripe
    . . . . **S.** interior
E-Catkins sessile or on lateral bracted or leafy stalks up to
    2 cm long; floral bracts yellowish or reddish to brown to
    black, persistent until after opening of capsules.
    F-Styles 0.1-0.4 mm long (not including stigmas); pedicels
        1.5-4 mm long.
        G-Floral bracts greenish-yellow to light brown, usually
            with reddish tips; catkins 2.5-6 cm long in fruit; leaf
            blades 2-3.5 times as long as wide . . . . **S.** bebbiana
        G-Floral bracts pale to dark brown, the tips often blackish;
            catkins 1.5-3.5 cm long; leaf blades 4-7 times as long
            as wide . . . . **S.** gracilis
    F-Styles (0.6-) 0.8-1.5 mm long; pedicels 0.2-1.2 (-1.6)
        mm long.
        H-Leaf blades 2-4 times as long as wide, gray-pubescent
            to glabrous beneath; floral bracts blackish at least
            above . . . . **S.** planifolia
        H-Leaf blades 4-12 times as long as wide, usually densely
            white-woolly or -silky below, rarely glabrous; floral
            bracts brown to blackish.
            I-Floral bracts a light to medium brown; widespread
            . . . . **S.** candida
            I-Floral bracts blackish at least on the upper half;
                Cook to St. Louis counties . . . . **S.** pellita
A-Capsule (and ovary) glabrous.
    J-Floral bracts light to dark brown or yellowish- to reddish-brown,
      persistent on the catkin; leaf blades 1.3-8 times as long as wide.
    K-Leaves all entire; catkins in fruit 1-3 cm long . . . . . **S.** pedicellaris
    K-Leaves toothed, the teeth visible on young leaves with a lens;
      catkins in fruit 2.5-8 cm long.
        L-Bracts or leaves at base of catkin sessile to petioled, the base
          of the blade acute to rounded; pedicels 0.5-2 (-2.5) mm long;
          mature leaf blades 3-8 times as long as wide; young growth
          without balsamic odor . . . . **S.** rigida complex
        L-Bracts or leaves at base of catkin distinctly petioled, their
          blades truncate to cordate at base; pedicels 2.5-3.5 mm
          long; mature leaf blades 1.3-3 times as long as wide;
          young growth with resinous balsam-like odor . . . **S.** pyrifolia
    J-Floral bracts greenish-yellow to yellow or yellow-brown (before
      withering), falling before the capsules ripen, if yellow-brown
      the blades 8-23 times as long as wide.
      M-Branchlets conspicuously pendulous; cultivated "weeping"
        willows.
        N-New twigs and both sides of leaf blades silvery pubescent
          when young (excluding first leaves of season), the blades
          somewhat pubescent at least on one side at maturity;
          mature twigs yellow; catkins in fruit 3-6 cm long
          . . . . **S.** alba cv. Tristis (and see under **S.** babylonica)
        N-New twigs and leaf blades glabrous to pubescent when young,
          not silvery, the blades glabrous on both sides on reaching
          3/4 their full size; mature twigs greenish to brown; catkins
          in fruit 1.5-2.8 cm long . . . . **S.** babylonica
      M-Branchlets erect to spreading; trees or shrubs, native or cultivated.

O-Petioles 1-5 mm long, the blades 16-36 times as long as the
petiole, 8-23 times as long as wide; leaf teeth 1-5 per cm;
stalks of catkins 3-10 cm long, leafy; native stoloniferous
shrubs . . . . S. interior
O-Characters not present in above combination, the petioles
3-20 mm long, the blades 4-17 times as long as the
petioles, 3-9.5 times as long as wide; leaf teeth 5-20 per
cm; stalks of catkins 1-3 (-5) cm long; native or cultivated,
trees or shrubs.

   P-Blades of reduced leaves on stalks of catkins all regularly
toothed, the teeth up to 5 per mm on sizes up to 15 mm
long, the glandular tips on the teeth prominent, out-
turned, blunt, up to 0.3 mm wide, especially well developed
at base of blade and on upper surface of petiole at junction
with blade.

      Q-Very immature leaves pubescent with reddish or brownish
to light tan hairs, these sometimes falling before the
leaves unfold; stipules of leaves on the catkin stalk 0.5-
1.5 mm wide; teeth of mature leaves 5-9 per cm of
margin . . . . S. lucida
      Q-Immature leaves glabrous or with a few scattered silky
hairs; stipules none or to 0.4 mm wide; teeth of mature
leaves 9-20 per cm of margin. . . . . S. serissima

   P-Blades of reduced leaves on stalks of catkins entire on
sizes up to 15 mm long or often longer, or if unusually
with teeth, the teeth only up to 3 per mm, their glandular
tips mostly appressed to the margin and not over 0.1
mm wide, usually not markedly enlarged at junction of
blade and petiole.

      R-Mature normal blades 1.7-3 times as long as wide;
blades of reduced leaves (those 3 cm or less long)
on peduncles or at bases of leafy twigs less than 2
times as long as wide; cultivated shrub to small tree
. . . . S. pentandra
      R-Mature normal blades 3-9.5 times as long as wide, if
3 times then the blades of the reduced leaves more
than 2 times as long as wide; native or cultivated,
trees or shrubs.

         S-Leaf blades silvery-pubescent on both sides when
young (excluding first leaves of season), remaining pubescent at least on one side at maturity . . . . S. alba
         S-Leaf blades glabrous or pubescent when young, not sil-
very, glabrous or nearly so at full size, completely so
in age except sometimes for the lower midrib.

            T-Principal leaf blades green on both sides, lanceo-
late to lance-linear, 4.5-9.5 times as long as
wide, 8-16 (-37) times as long as the petiole;
petiole and lower midrib usually pubescent at
maturity. . . . . S. nigra
            T-Principal leaf blades usually whitish to pale blue-
green beneath, ovate-lanceolate to narrowly lanceolate but not lance-linear, 3-6.7 times as long as
wide, 4.5-10 (-15) times as long as the petiole;
petiole and midrib glabrous or the petiole puberulent
above at maturity.

U-Capsule 2-4 times as long as the pedicel, pedicels
1-2.6 mm long; capsule occasionally grooved down
the side near the base but only rarely sub-cordate;
twigs often flexible, not snapping off easily at base;
glandular teeth at base of blade not usually markedly
enlarged; leaf teeth 0.1-0.4 mm deep. . S. amygdaloides
U-Capsule 4-6.5 times as long as the pedicel, pedicels
0.5-1.2 mm long; capsules usually cordate at
base, often strongly so, between the dehiscence
lines; twigs snapping off easily at base; glandular
displaced leaf teeth on upper surface of petiole
at its junction with blade enlarged and prominent at
least on later leaves; leaf teeth 0.3-0.8 mm deep. S. fragilis

S. alba L. White Willow; cultivated. Tree to 20 m high; stipules minute
or none; earlier leaves glabrous to variously pubescent, later ones pubescent at least below at maturity; leaf blades narrowly lanceolate to lanceolate, 4-8 (-10) cm long, 1-2.5 cm wide, with 4-10 teeth per cm of margin.
From Europe and N. Africa to central Asia. A form with yellow branchlets
that soon become glabrous and leaves that may be nearly glabrous when
mature is known as S. alba cv. Vitellina. A similar plant but with pendu-
ous branchlets and thus a "weeping" form is termed S. alba cv. Tristis,
apparently our most common weeping willow; this plant appears to be regarded by some European authors as a hybrid between S. alba cv. Vitellina
and S. babylonica, with the name S. X chrysocoma Dode. Apparent hybrids
of S. alba with S. fragilis are not uncommon in the state. See chart on
following page.

S. amygdaloides Anderss. Peach-leaved Willow. Shrub or tree 3-12 m
high; stipules usually none but sometimes to 12 mm long; leaf blades lanceolate to lance-ovate, 5-10 (-12) cm long, 1.2-3 cm wide, long acuminate,
glabrous on both sides at maturity or sooner, with 5-10 teeth per cm of
margin. Shores, low woods, and swamps, throughout the state except for
Cook, Lake, Pipestone, and Rock to Jackson counties, not recorded from
several others.

S. babylonica L. Weeping Willow; cultivated. Tree to 12 m high; stipules none or to 7 mm long; leaf blades narrowly lanceolate, long acuminate,
5-12 cm long, 5-15 mm wide, glabrous, more or less whitened beneath,
with 5-9 teeth per cm of margin. Probably from China. There is some
doubt if this species exists in its pure form in Minnesota, since it is not
very hardy. It has been hybridized to produce other more hardy weeping
willows, of which probably the most common here is one of the hybrids
with S. fragilis, S. X blanda Anderss., the Niobe or Wisconsin Weeping
Willow, which has both green- and yellow-twigged forms. Others may occur,
including the hybrid with S. alba, S. X sepulcralis Simonk. (and S. X
chrysocoma Dode if this is truly a hybrid and not a form of S. alba; see
under S. alba). The chart on the following page is provided to enable the
reader to judge better the nature of any apparent hybrid plants he may encounter.

S. bebbiana Sarg. Long-beaked Willow. Shrub to small tree 2-5 m high;
stipules small or none; leaf blades elliptic to broadly rhombic-oblanceolate
or obovate-oval, acute or abruptly short-acuminate, 4-7 (-10) cm long, 1.5-
(-4) cm wide, nearly entire to undulate-crenate, whitened beneath, more
or less gray-hairy on both sides, the veins impressed above, raised below,
the teeth when present 2-5 per cm of margin. Damp to wet places, throughout the state, infrequent in the sw.

Character	S. babylonica	S. alba	S. fragilis
Branchlets	pendulous	ascending to pendulous	ascending to spreading
Twig bases	normal to somewhat brittle	normal to brittle	brittle
Leaf pubescence	glabrous at maturity	pub. at maturity 1 or both sides	glabrous at maturity
Petiole length	2-7 (-10) mm	3-12 mm	(5-) 8-20 mm
Ratio blade 1. over petiole 1.	10-22	10-17	5-10 (-15)
Tooth depth	0.1-0.3 mm	0.1-0.3 mm	0.3-0.8 mm
Glandular teeth at blade base	None or small	Usually none or small	Enlarged on later leaves
Nectar glands in female fl.	1	1	1 or 2
Male catkin length	1.5-4.5 cm	3-7 cm	2-6.5 cm
Fruiting catkin length	1.5-2.8 cm	3-6 cm	3-8 cm
Capsule length	1.5-2.5 mm	3-4.5 mm	3.5-7 mm
Capsule stalk	0.1-0.4 mm	0.3-0.5 mm	0.5-1.2 mm

S. candida Fluegge. Sage-leaved Willow. Shrub 2-10 dm high; stipules lanceolate, glandular; leaf blades linear-oblong to oblong to narrowly or rarely broadly oblanceolate, 4-8 (-12) cm long, 0.7-2 (-2.4) cm wide, mostly acute at both ends, revolute, entire to glandular-crenulate, densely white-hairy beneath, less so above, occasionally becoming glabrous in age. Bogs and swamps, St. Louis to Roseau Co., s. to Wilkin, Kandiyohi, Hennepin, and ne. Goodhue counties.

S. discolor Muhl. Pussy Willow. Shrub to small tree 2-6 m high; stipules roundish to semi-ovate; leaf blades mostly elliptic to elliptic-oblanceolate, 5-8 (-10) cm long, 2-3.5 cm wide, acute to short-acuminate, glabrous, whitened with raised veins beneath, subentire to irregularly crenate-serrate, the irregularity of the teeth being a characteristic of the species. Swamps and wet ground, Cook to Kittson Co., s. to Wilkin, Renville, Le Sueur, Fillmore, and Houston counties.

S. fragilis L. Brittle or Crack Willow; cultivated. Tree to 20 m high, the trunk to 1 m thick; stipules none or small and dropping early; leaf blades narrowly lanceolate to lanceolate, 7-12 (-15) cm long, 2-3.5 cm wide, with 4-8 teeth per cm of margin; blades sometimes pubescent on lower midrib or teeth or both even in age. A yellow-twigged form exists but is suggested by some to be a hybrid. From Europe, often escaping from cultivation. See S. alba and the chart above.

S. gracilis Anderss. (S. petiolaris Sm.) Slender Willow. Shrub to tree 2-7 m high; stipules none; leaf blades narrowly lanceolate to oblanceolate, 5-10 (-15) cm long, 0.8-2 (-3) cm wide, acute to acuminate, glabrous above, glabrous and somewhat whitened beneath (thinly hairy when young), with 3-8 teeth per cm of margin. Moist and poorly drained areas, Cook to Kittson Co., s. to Clay, Chippewa, Blue Earth, Mower, and Houston counties.

S. humilis Marsh. Upland Willow, Prairie Willow. Shrub 0.5-3 m high;
stipules lanceolate or none; leaf blades narrowly to broadly oblanceolate to
narrowly obovate to subelliptic, acute to abruptly short-acuminate, somewhat revolute, entire to undulate-dentate, often hairy above, somewhat
whitened and gray-hairy beneath, often becoming glabrous in age, 2-10
(-15) cm long, 0.7-2 (-3) cm wide. Mesic to dry woods and prairies.

A-Shrub 0.25-1 m high; staminate catkins 5-12 mm long; fruiting
    catkins 10-25 mm long; leaves mostly 1.5-7 cm long; Olmsted to
    Washington, Anoka, and Hennepin counties, and in Crow Wing and Kittson
    counties . . S. h. var. microphylla (Anderss.) Fern. (S. tristis Ait.)
A-Shrub 1-3 m high; staminate catkins 10-30 mm long; fruiting catkins
    20-50 (-80) mm long; leaves mostly 4-10 cm long.
    B-Mature leaves narrowly elliptic to oblanceolate, 3-4 times as
        long as wide, mostly 1-2 (-3) cm wide; pubescence often ob-
        scuring the veinlets but not the lateral veins; Cook to Kittson
        Co., s. to Clay, Otter Tail, Ramsey, Freeborn, and
        Houston counties . . . . S. h. var. humilis
    B-Mature leaves broadly oblanceolate to elliptic to obovate,
        as little as 2 times as long as wide, mostly 1.5-5 cm wide;
        pubescence obscuring the lateral veins; Lake and St. Louis
        counties . . . . S. h. var. keweenawensis Farw.

S. interior Rowlee. Sandbar Willow. Many-stemmed shrub 2-5 m high;
stipules none; leaf blades linear to broadly linear to linear-oblanceolate,
5-14 cm long, 5-12 (-18) mm wide, acute or acuminate at both ends, green
on both sides but paler beneath, often pubescent when young, with 1-5 teeth
per cm of leaf margin. Mostly on sand bars, sandy shores, and alluvial
soil, throughout the state except in Cook Co.

S. lucida Muhl. Shining Willow. Shrub or small tree to 6 m high;
stipules 2-5 mm long; leaf blades lanceolate to lance-ovate, 5-15 (-20)
cm long, 2-5 (-8) cm wide, the principal ones long-acuminate, glabrous,
or somewhat pubescent when very young, shining green on both sides but
darker above, with 5-9 teeth per cm of leaf margin. Stream banks, ditches,
and other moist low ground, Lake to Kittson Co., s. to Becker, Todd,
Wright, Scott, and Goodhue counties, and in Houston Co.

S. nigra L. Black Willow. Tree to 20 m high or sometimes a shrub;
stipules minute or up to 10 mm long, persistent or deciduous; leaf blades
linear-lanceolate to linear, 5-10.5 cm long, 0.9-1.5 (-2.3) cm wide,
glabrous to pubescent when young, glabrous on both sides except usually
on petiole and lower midrib at maturity, with 5-11 teeth per cm of leaf
margin. Stream banks, shores, and low woods, Houston to Pipestone Co.,
n. to Lincoln and Rice counties, then from Washington and Anoka counties
n. to Todd, s. Itasca, and sw. St. Louis counties.

S. pedicellaris Pursh. Bog Willow. Shrub 3-10 (-15) dm high, glabrous
throughout; stipules early deciduous; leaf blades obovate-oblong to oblanceolate, 2-4 (-6) cm long, 6-19 mm wide, green above, somewhat whitened
beneath, obtuse or subacute at apex, the margin entire and often revolute.
Bogs and wet meadows, Cook to Koochiching Co., s. to Clearwater,
Stearns, Hennepin, Blue Earth, and Goodhue counties.

S. pellita Anderss. Shrub to small tree 3-5 m high; stipules none or
minute and early deciduous; leaf blades lance-linear to lanceolate to linear-
oblanceolate, 4-10 (-13) cm long, 8-15 (-22) mm wide, 4-12 times as long
as wide, somewhat revolute, entire or slightly undulate-crenate, densely
white-silky beneath but sometimes becoming glabrous in age. Stream banks,
shores, and swamps, Cook to St. Louis counties.

S. pentandra L. Bay Willow, Laurel-leaved Willow; cultivated. Shrub or small tree 1.5-13 m high; stipules small, early deciduous, or reduced to a pair of glands; leaf blades lanceolate to ovate to ovate-oblong, 5-15 cm long, 2-4 cm wide, acute to acuminate, glabrous, shining and bright green above, slightly paler and duller below, with 5-12 teeth per cm of leaf margin. From Europe and n. Asia.

S. planifolia Pursh. Shrub 1-3 m high; stipules small or none; leaf blades narrowly elliptic to elliptic-oblanceolate to narrowly obovate, 2.5-6 (-8) cm long, 1-2.5 (-3.5) cm wide, 2-3.5 (-4) times as long as wide, acute, glabrous above, sparsely pubescent to glabrous and somewhat whitened beneath, entire to sparingly toothed. Stream banks, shores, damp places, and woods, Cook to Kittson Co.

S. purpurea L. Purple Osier, Basket Willow; cultivated. Many-stemmed shrub 1-2.5 m high; stipules none; leaf blades spatulate to linear-oblanceolate to linear, 4-7 (-10) cm long, 7-14 (-18) mm wide, glabrous, somewhat whitened beneath, entire toward the petiole, irregularly toothed toward the tip. North Africa and Europe to central Asia and Japan. Mostly planted here is the small-leaved dwarf form S. p. cv. Gracilis (S. p. cv Nana).

S. pyrifolia Anderss. Balsam Willow. Shrub to 5 m high or occasionally a small tree to 7 m high; stipules none or small and early deciduous; leaf blades ovate to oblong-lanceolate to lanceolate, 3-10 cm long, 1.5-4 cm wide, rounded to cordate at base, acute to abruptly acuminate at apex, pubescent beneath when young, glabrous at maturity, with 1-8 teeth per cm of leaf margin. Mostly in bogs throughout the coniferous forest area, Cook to Kittson Co., s. to Clearwater, Crow Wing, and Ramsey counties.

S. rigida Muhl. Heart-leaved Willow. Shrub 2-4 (-6) m high; stipules 5-10 (-15) mm long; leaf blades lanceolate to oblanceolate, 7-12 (-15) cm long, 1.5-3 (-4) cm wide, acute to rounded to cordate at base, glabrous except when young, more or less whitened beneath, with 5-8 teeth per cm of leaf margin. Stream banks, shores, and other damp places, widely scattered over most of the state, not recorded from Cook or Lake counties and many others. A second species, S. eriocephala Michx., the Missouri Willow, is often recognized in this complex, on the following basis:

A-Young twigs and bud scales puberulent to pubescent; leaf blades pale or whitish beneath; stipules of vigorous shoots large and conspicuous; fruiting catkins 2.5-6 cm long; capsules 4-7 mm long .... S. rigida
A-Young twigs and bud scales usually pubescent to long-hairy; blades strongly whitened beneath; stipules of vigorous shoots small and inconspicuous; fruiting catkins 6-10 cm long; capsules 7-10 mm long .... S. eriocephala

Our Minnesota material of this complex, some of which has been identified as S. eriocephala, does not appear to this author to be readily separable into two groups, and as the dimensions of the fruiting specimens all fall within those given for S. rigida, it seems best to him to treat all our plants as of that species until the presence of a second entity can be clearly demonstrated.

S. serissima (Bailey) Fern. Autumn Willow. Shrub 1-4 m high; stipules early deciduous; leaf blades lanceolate to lance-elliptic to lance-oblong, 5-8 (-10) cm long, 1-2.5 (-3.5) cm wide, glabrous, green and shining above, usually whitened beneath, with 9-20 teeth per cm of leaf margin. Swamps and bogs, St. Louis to Roseau and Wilkin counties, and in Anoka, Hennepin, and Le Sueur counties.

MYRICACEAE ----- SWEET GALE FAMILY

Monoecious or dioecious shrubs or small trees with alternate, simple, fragrant leaves, at least the upper leaf surface and the floral bracts dotted with tiny golden resin granules; flowers without perianth, in globose to cylindric bracted catkins; stamens 2-20 (usually 4-8); pistillate flower subtended by 2-8 minute bractlets in addition to the primary bract, the ovary 1-locular; stigmas 2; ovule 1, basal; fruit a small drupe.

A-Leaves entire to slightly serrate; plants of moist habitats . . . . . MYRICA
A-Leaves deeply cut; plants of dry sandy areas . . . . COMPTONIA

COMPTONIA ----- SWEET FERN*

Monoecious or dioecious plants; stipules present; pistillate flower subtended by 8 linear bractlets that overtop the ovary and form a bur in fruit; fruit not waxy. (Named for H. Compton, English patron of botany.)

C. peregrina (L.) Coult. (Myrica asplenifolia L.). Shrub to 6 dm high; leaves linear-oblong, 4-12 cm long, 5-15 mm wide, pinnately cleft, hairy on one or both surfaces; catkins preceding the leaves, the male 1-4 cm long, the female subglobose, 1.5-2.5 cm thick in fruit. Dry open woods and clearings on sandy acid soil, often in Jack Pine woods, Cook to Hubbard, Cass, and Pine counties.

MYRICA*

Mostly dioecious; stipules none; pistillate flower subtended by 2-4 bractlets (2 in ours); fruit in ours with a waxy coat or resinous specks. (Gr. myrike, tamarisk or some other fragrant shrub.)

M. gale L. Sweet Gale. Dioecious shrub to 1.5 m high; leaves oblanceolate, 3-6 cm long, glabrous to finely hairy on both sides; catkins preceding the leaves, the male 10-20 mm long, the female ovoid, 8-12 mm long in fruit. Swamps and shallow water along lakes and streams, Cook to St. Louis and ne. Koochiching counties and near the St. Croix R. in Pine Co.

JUGLANDACEAE ----- WALNUT FAMILY

Mostly monoecious trees or shrubs with odd-pinnate exstipulate mostly alternate leaves; staminate flowers in long usually lateral catkins; pistillate flowers terminal, single or in short spikes or catkins; flowers each with a perianth-like series of bracts and tepals, the flower adnate to the 1 or 3 bracts, the tepals 0-4; stamens 3 to many; ovary inferior, 1-locular above, 2-4-locular below, with 1 erect ovule; styles 2 or the style 2-branched, stigmas usually feathery; fruit a drupe-like nut or a winged nutlet.

A-Pith of twigs with transverse separations; staminate catkins borne singly, sessile; median lateral leaflets larger than the basal or terminal ones. . . . . JUGLANS
A-Pith of twigs continuous, not partitioned; staminate catkins in groups of 3, each group with a common stalk; terminal leaflets largest . . . . CARYA

CARYA ----- HICKORY*

Trees with continuous pith; the 3 terminal leaflets larger than the others; staminate catkins in peduncled groups of 3; bract-group of staminate flower 2-3-lobed, the tepals none; stamens 3-10; pistillate flowers 1 or in spikes of 2-10, the subtending perianth-like involucre 4-lobed, the true pistillate perianth none or 1-lobed; fruit a hard-shelled nut enclosed in a husk that is more or less dehiscent in 4 segments. In some species the winter bud-scales become greatly enlarged and petal-like in spring. (Ancient Gr. name for the walnut.)

A-Bark smooth to somewhat scaly; outer bud scales sulfur-yellow, the scales of the terminal bud 4-6, valvate; margins of mature leaflets almost smooth . . . . C. cordiformis
A-Bark peeling off in long wide strips; outer bud scales dark, the scales of the terminal bud 10-12, imbricate; some or all teeth of the leaflets with a persistent tuft of hairs on one or both sides. . . . . C. ovata

C. cordiformis (Wang.) K. Koch. Bitternut, Smoothbarked, or Pignut Hickory. Leaflets 7-9 (5-11); fruit with narrowly winged separation lines, the husk splitting to about the middle; kernel bitter. Moist to dry woods, Houston to Faribault Co., w. and n. to Redwood, Meeker, Aitkin, and Pine counties, and in Itasca Co.

C. ovata (Mill.) K. Koch. Shagbark or Shellbark Hickory. Leaflets 5 (-7); fruit wingless, the husk splitting to the base; kernel edible. Mesic to moist rich soil, Houston to Freeborn and Wabasha counties.

JUGLANS ----- WALNUT, BUTTERNUT*

Trees; pith with transverse separations; median lateral leaflets largest; staminate catkins borne singly, sessile; bracts of staminate flower 3, the tepals 1-4; stamens 8-40; pistillate flowers 1 or in short spikes, each flower with a 3-lobed cup-shaped involucre and 4-parted perianth, all adherent to the ovary; fruit a rough hard-shelled nut in an indehiscent husk. (Ancient Latin name from Jovis glans, nut of Jupiter.)

A-Pith dark brown; bark grayish-brown with smooth ridges; terminal leaflet well-developed; fruit ovoid to short-cylindric . . . . . . J. cinerea
A-Pith light brown; bark blackish-brown with very rough ridges; terminal leaflet often poorly developed; fruit mostly subglobose . J. nigra

J. cinerea L. Butternut, White Walnut. Tree to 30 m high; twigs and petioles downy with sticky hairs, the leaflets downy with clustered hairs especially beneath. Rich moist soil, from Houston and Fillmore counties w. and n. to Brown, McLeod, and Chisago counties, and in Morrison, Crow Wing, Aitkin, and s. St. Louis counties (the last probably an escape from cultivation).

J. nigra L. Black Walnut. Tree to 40 m high; twigs and petioles downy with sticky hairs, the leaflets minutely downy, nearly smooth, the hairs single or in pairs. Often planted. Rich moist soil, Houston to Nobles Co., n. to Brown, Scott, and s. Washington counties.

92

BETULACEAE ----- BIRCH FAMILY

Monoecious (rarely dioecious) trees or shrubs with alternate, simple, serrate leaves; flowers in unisexual usually many-flowered catkins, the pistillate catkins sometimes few-flowered; each primary bract of the catkins subtending 1-3 flowers and 0-6 bractlets, sometimes fused to the bractlets; perianth none or minute, undifferentiated when present, the tepals 1-4 (-6); stamens 1-4 (-6) per individual flower, opposite the tepals when tepals present, sometimes deeply cleft with separated anther-halves and appearing double the true number; ovary inferior, 2-locular below, the partition not reaching the apex, the 2-4 ovules attached at the top of the partition; style 2-cleft; fruit a small nut or samara, 1-seeded.

A-Anthers or anther-halves glabrous; pistillate flowers many in the catkin, the bracts subtending each flower-group all grown together to form a single scale, the scales not leafy in texture, deciduous or persistent, when persistent the catkin in fruit resembling a small cone.
  B-Stamens 1-2 per flower, 3-6 per primary bract, deeply cleft, the anther-halves separate; pistillate scales mostly 3-lobed, eventually deciduous . . . . BETULA
  B-Stamens 4 (-6) per flower, 12 (-18) per primary bract, the anther-halves only slightly separated; pistillate scales entire in flower, obscurely 5-lobed in fruit, persistent, the fruiting catkin resembling a small cone . . . . ALNUS
A-Anthers or anther-halves hairy at tip; pistillate flowers few to many in the catkin, the persistent bracts becoming green and greatly enlarged and leafy in texture in fruit (the primary bract subtending each flower-group separate from the others and often deciduous), the pistillate catkin not cone-like.
  C-Shrub; pistillate flowers few in very short head-like catkins, the stigmas red to rose-colored; fruits 10-15 mm long, born in ones and twos . . . . CORYLUS
  C-Small trees; pistillate flowers numerous in normally elongate catkins, the stigmas not red; fruits about 5 mm long, several to many along the elongated catkin.
    D-Trunk regularly shaped, the bark checked; staminate catkins usually in groups of 3; pistillate bracts forming a closed sac around the fruit . . . . .OSTRYA
    D-Trunk with irregular smooth ridges, as if with muscles; staminate catkins single; pistillate bracts forming an open 2-3-lobed structure subtending the fruit . . . . CARPINUS

ALNUS ----- ALDER*

Trees or shrubs; staminate flowers 3 to each primary bract, each with a minute 4- (-6-) parted perianth and 4 (-6) stamens (rarely tepals 0 and stamens 1 or 2), the anther-halves only slightly separated; pistillate catkins short, ovoid to ellipsoid, the primary bracts each fused to 4 bractlets to form a single scale, each scale subtending 2 flowers, the flowers without perianth; fruit a nutlet with or without a marginal wing; scales of the catkin persistent in fruit, becoming woody, obscurely 5-lobed at apex, the catkin then resembling a small cone. (The ancient Latin name.)

A-Leaf buds sessile; leaves finely and mostly singly serrate, resinous beneath when young . . . . A. crispa

A-Leaf buds short-stalked; leaves mostly doubly serrate, not resinous
. . . . A. rugosa

A. crispa (Ait.) Pursh. Green or Mountain Alder. Shrub; sub-terminal "cones" of the cluster on stalks 4-25 mm long. Bogs, shores, and cool woods, Cook to Koochiching, Clearwater, Cass, and Carlton counties.

A. rugosa (DuRoi) Spreng. Speckled Alder. Shrub; sub-terminal "cones" of the cluster sessile or on stalks up to 3 mm long. Swamps, lake shores, and other wet soil, Cook to Kittson Co., s. to Clearwater, ne. Todd, Sherburne, and Washington counties.

BETULA ----- BIRCH*

Trees or shrubs, often with bark separating into thin papery layers; staminate flowers 3 to each primary bract, each with a 2- (1-4-) parted perianth and 2 (1-4) stamens, one tepal larger than the other; stamens deeply cleft, the anther-halves separate; pistillate catkins ovoid to cylindric, the primary bract and bractlets grown together to form a single scale, each scale subtending 3 (rarely 1) flowers without perianth; fruit a lens-shaped nutlet with a marginal wing; scales of catkin usually 3-lobed at least in fruit, deciduous with the nutlets. (The ancient Latin name.)

A-Trees with silvery- to creamy-white bark at least on upper trunk and
    main branches; native or cultivated.
  B-Leaves ovate to cordate, serrate to doubly serrate, pubescent at
    least in the vein- axils beneath; twigs not pendulous; bark not
    dark-furrowed toward the base; native.
    C-Leaves broadly wedge-shaped to rounded at base, simply serrate
    . . . . B. papyrifera
    C-Leaves truncate to subcordate at base, doubly serrate . B. cordifolia
  B-Leaves rhombic-ovate to triangular, doubly serrate to deeply cut,
    glabrous; branchlets usually drooping; bark becoming dark-
    furrowed toward base of trunk; cultivated . . . . B. pendula
A-Trees or shrubs with gray, yellowish, or reddish-brown bark;
    native.
  D-Shrubs of bogs with close non-peeling bark; young stems and leaves
    usually dotted with sticky "glands"; leaves 2-3 cm long, with 3-6
    pairs of lateral veins . . . . B. pumila var. glandulifera
  D-Trees with peeling bark on upper trunk and branches; stems
    and leaves glandless; leaves 4-10 cm long, with 6-12 pairs
    of lateral veins.
    E-Bark where peeling yellowish-gray, somewhat lustrous; crushed twigs
      with flavor of wintergreen; leaves rounded to subcordate at base . B. lut
    E-Bark where peeling tan-orange to pinkish or greenish-brown,
      dull; crushed twigs without wintergreen odor; leaves broadly
      wedge-shaped to truncate at base . . . . B. nigra

B. cordifolia Regel. Heart-leaved Paper Birch. Tree to 25 m high; bark smooth, peeling in papery layers, creamy to pinkish-white; fruiting catkins 3-5 cm long, the scales 5.6-9.7 mm long, the fruits 4.1-6.7 mm wide. Cook to St. Louis Co. Perhaps a hybrid between B. lutea and B. papyrifera.

B. lutea Michx. f. Yellow Birch. Tree to 30 m high; bark smooth, peeling in papery layers; leaves ovate to oblong-ovate or somewhat obovate, 6-10 cm long; fruiting catkins 2-3 cm long, the scales 6-13 mm long, the fruits 2.5-4.5 mm wide. Moist woods, often in bogs, Cook to Clearwater Co., s. to

Morrison, Carver, and Washington counties, and in Blue Earth, Winona, Fillmore, and Houston counties. See B. X purpusii.

B. nigra L. River Birch; Red Birch. Tree to 30 m high; bark deeply furrowed at base on old trunks, smooth and peeling higher up; leaves triangular-ovate to ovate-oblong, 4-8 cm long; fruiting catkins 1.5-3 cm long, the scales 6-8 mm long, the fruits 4-7 mm wide. Bottomlands of the Mississippi R., n. to the St. Croix R. with a stand ca. 3 miles n. on the St. Croix in Washington Co.

B. papyrifera Marsh. Paper or Canoe Birch. Tree to 25 m high; bark smooth, peeling in papery layers, white except on young trees where it is reddish-brown; leaves ovate, 5-10 cm long; fruiting catkins 3-5 cm long, the scales 3.9-6.2 mm long, the fruits 2.7-5 mm wide. Moist to dry soil, Cook to Kittson Co., s. to Clay, Kandiyohi, Le Sueur, Fillmore, and Houston counties, and in Blue Earth Co. See B. cordifolia and B. X sandbergii.

B. pendula Roth (B. verrucosa Ehrh.). European White Birch; cultivated. Tree to 20 m high; leaves 4-8 cm long, more or less dotted with glands on both surfaces; fruiting catkins 2-3.5 cm long, the scales 5-7 mm long, the fruits 5-6 mm wide. Europe to Asia Minor. In B. p. f. dalecarlica (L. f.) Schneid., the branches are more pendulous and the leaves are deeply lobed.

B. pumila var. glandulifera Regel. Bog or Swamp Birch, Low or Dwarf Birch. Shrub to 3 m high; bark dark gray to reddish-brown; leaves broadly ovate to obovate; fruiting catkins 8-20 mm long, the scales 3-4.5 mm long, the fruits 1.7-3 mm wide. Bogs, swamps, and acid meadows, Cook to Kittson Co., s. to Clay, Kandiyohi, Scott, Fillmore, and Houston counties, infrequent s. of Hennepin Co. See B. X purpusii and B. X sandbergii.

B. X purpusii Schneid. Hybrid between B. lutea and B. pumila var. glandulifera. Shrub or small tree to 6 m high; bark grayish-brown, not peeling in layers; crushed twigs with wintergreen odor; young stems and leaves often gland-dotted; leaves ovate to oblong-ovate, 2.5-6 cm long; fruiting catkins 1.5-2.8 cm long, the scales 5.4-7 mm long, the fruits 2.5-3 mm wide. Swamps; uncommon.

B. X sandbergii Britton. Hybrid between B. papyrifera and B. pumila var. glandulifera. Shrub to small tree to 10 m high; bark dark brown, not peeling in layers; crushed twigs without wintergreen odor; young stems and leaves gland-dotted; leaves ovate to rarely obovate, 2.5-5.5 cm long; fruiting catkins 2-2.5 cm long, the scales ca. 4 mm long, the fruits 3.2-3.5 mm wide. Infrequent, widely scattered in moist habitats.

CARPINUS ----- HORNBEAM, BLUE BEECH*

Shrubs to trees with smooth bark; perianth of male flower none; stamens several to each primary bract, appearing as 1 flower but actually representing 3; stamens cleft, the anther-halves separate and hairy at the apex; pistillate catkins cylindric, the flowers 2 to each primary bract, each flower also subtended by 3 fused bractlets which enlarge to form a 3-lobed wing at maturity; ovary 2-locular, crowned with a minute perianth; fruit a small ribbed nutlet. (The early Latin name.)

C. caroliniana Walt. Shrub or small tree to 10 m high; trunk irregularly ridged, as if with muscles, the bark smooth and gray; leaves oblong-ovate to oblong-obovate, 5-12 cm long; fruiting catkin 2-9 cm long, the bracts 2-3 cm long. Moist woods, Houston and Fillmore counties w. and n. to Le Sueur, Morrison, Becker, s. Clearwater, and s. St. Louis counties.

CORYLUS ----- HAZELNUT*

Shrubs or small trees with doubly serrate leaves; perianth of male flower none; stamens 4 to each primary bract, appearing as 1 flower but actually representing 3, the stamens cleft, the anther-halves separate and with a few apical hairs; pistillate flowers few in very short nearly head-like catkins, 2 flowers to a primary bract, each flower in addition subtended by 2 bractlets that enlarge in fruit to form a leafy involucre or husk enclosing the fruit; ovary 2-locular, crowned with a small perianth; fruit an ovoid or subglobose nut. (Corylus, the classical name of the hazel.)

A-Young twigs and petioles densely hairy, the hairs mostly glandular (globular-tipped and sticky); involucre consisting of 2 broad fringed bracts . . . . C. american
A-Young twigs and petioles sparsely to densely pubescent with glandless hairs, becoming glabrous (rarely a few glands near the nodes); involucral bracts united to form an elongate tube sharply narrowed beyond the fruit . . . . C. cornuta

C. americana Walt. American Hazelnut. Shrub 1-2.5 m high; leaves ovate to elliptic, 6-16 cm long; involucre 1.5-3 cm long in fruit. Dry to moist woods and thickets, St. Louis to Kittson Co., s. to Clay, Pope, Blue Earth, Freeborn, and Houston counties.

C. cornuta Marsh. Beaked Hazelnut. Shrub 1.5-5 m high; leaves ovate to elliptic, 5-13 cm long; involucre 4-7 cm long in fruit. Mesic to moist woods and thickets, common in the north, Cook to Roseau Co., s. to Polk, Morrison, Hennepin, Olmsted, and Houston counties.

OSTRYA ----- IRONWOOD, HOP HORNBEAM*

Tall shrubs or trees with brown checked and somewhat flaky bark; perianth of male flower none; stamens several to each primary bract, appearing as 1 flower but actually representing 3; stamens cleft, the anther-halves separate and hairy at the apex; pistillate catkins cylindric, the flowers 2 to each primary bract, each flower enclosed by 3 fused bractlets which enlarge to form a loose pouch enclosing the fruit; ovary 2-locular, crowned with a minute perianth; fruit an ovoid to oblong nutlet. (The classical name for the tree.)

O. virginiana (Mill.) Koch. Tree to 20 m high; leaves ovate to oblong-ovate, slightly pubescent, finely toothed, 5-11 cm long; fruiting catkins 3-5 cm long. Moist to dry woods, Houston to Jackson Co., n. to Lyon, Pope, Otter Tail, Norman, Clearwater, Koochiching, and Lake counties.

FAGACEAE ----- BEECH FAMILY

Trees or shrubs, ours monoecious; leaves alternate, simple, entire to lobed; staminate flowers single or in catkins or heads, with a small, deeply 4-8-parted undifferentiated perianth and 3-40 stamens; pistillate flowers solitary or in small clusters or short spikes, more or less enclosed by an involucre of many bracts; ovary inferior, bearing a minute mostly 6-parted undifferentiated perianth, the locules commonly 3 or 6, with 2 axile ovules per locule, the styles as many as the locules; fruit a 1-seeded nut, wholly or partly surrounded by the enlarged involucre.

QUERCUS ----- OAK*

Trees or shrubs, ours with tardily deciduous, toothed to lobed leaves; staminate flowers in catkins, the bracts none or dropping early, tepals 3-7, stamens 3-12; pistillate flowers solitary or in small spikes in the axils of the developing leaves, each flower surrounded at base with a cup-like involucre of many cohering bractlets; ovary 3-locular; fruit an "acorn", partly enclosed at the base by the enlarged involucre. (The classical Latin name.)

A- Lobes of leaves drawn into bristle-tips: the Black or Red Oaks (also the fruit maturing in the second autumn, the stigmas elongate, and the abortive ovules near the top of the seed).
  B-Leaves cut 1/2-2/3 (-3/4) of the way to the midrib, the sinuses narrowing to the base; acorn cup covering 1/6-1/3 of the acorn . . . . Q. borealis
  B-Leaves cut 6/10-9/10 of the way to the midrib, the sinuses narrowing to the base or sometimes as wide below as above or wider; acorn cup covering 1/3-1/2 of the acorn.
    C-Terminal buds not strongly angled, 3-5 mm long, their bracts glabrous to hairy-edged; upper scales of acorn cup tightly appressed, not forming a definite fringe . . . . Q. ellipsoidalis
    C-Terminal buds strongly 4-angled or -grooved, 5-10 mm long, slightly to densely hairy; free tips of the upper cup scales forming a loose fringe . . . . Q. velutina
A-Lobes or teeth of leaves rounded to acute, not bristle-tipped: the White Oaks (also the fruit maturing in the first autumn, the stigmas sessile or nearly so, and the abortive ovules at the base of the seed).
  D-Leaves cut more than halfway to the midrib, the lobes 3-7 on each side.
    E-Leaves pubescent beneath at maturity, the veinlets usually obscured; blades usually tending to be most deeply lobed near the middle or base; scales near the rim of the acorn cup drawn into tail-like tips forming a matted fringe-like border . . . . Q. macrocarpa
    E-Leaves glabrous to sparsely pubescent beneath at maturity, the veinlets plainly visible; blades cut to a rather uniform depth; cup not fringed. Q. alba
  D-Leaves coarsely toothed, cut less than 1/3 of the way to the midrib, with 6-12 teeth on each side.
    F-Acorns on peduncles 20-70 mm long; lower leaf surface with both short appressed hairs (0.1-0.2 mm long) and longer more erect ones (0.4-0.6 mm long) . . . . Q. bicolor
    F-Acorns sessile or on peduncles up to 12 mm long; lower leaf surface with short appressed hairs only (0.1-0.2 mm long) . . . . Q. muhlenbergii

Q. alba L. White Oak. Bark light gray, scaly but not deeply furrowed. Upland woods, of the se. 1/4 of the state, avoiding high lime soils, in an area bounded by Houston, Fillmore, Steele, Morrison, and Pine counties.

Q. bicolor Willd. Swamp White Oak. Bark gray-brown, thick and furrowed; scales near rim of acorn often with tail-like tips forming a fringe but not so prominently as in Bur Oak. Moist soil; from Houston Co. infrequent nw. to Ramsey and Yellow Medicine counties.

Q. borealis Michx. f. (Q. rubra L.). Northern Red Oak. Bark of older trunks gray-brown, deeply furrowed; scales of acorn cup closely appressed, the cup not striped. Uplands, Houston to Freeborn Co., w. and n. to Blue Earth, Stearns, se. Clay, Polk, Itasca, St. Louis, and n. Lake counties.

A-Acorn cup 1.5-2 cm wide, covering about 1/3 of the acorn, the
    latter 1.5-2.5 cm long; less common southward than the following
  . . . . Q. b. var. borealis.
A-Acorn cup 2-3 cm wide, covering about 1/4 of the acorn, the
    acorn 2-3 cm long; absent from the extreme north . . . . . .
  . . . . Q. b. var. maxima (Marsh.) Ashe.

Q. ellipsoidalis E. J. Hill. Northern Pin, Jack, or Hill's Oak. Bark of older trunks dark brown to blackish, furrowed; acorn usually striped with darker lines. Dry often sandy upland, Houston to Mower Co., w. and n. to Blue Earth, Stearns, Otter Tail, Polk, s. Beltrami, Aitkin, and Carlton counties, and in ne. Koochiching and n. Lake counties, and in Murray Co.

Q. macrocarpa Michx. Bur Oak. Small to large tree, the older bark dark gray-brown, deeply furrowed; leaves somewhat obovate, tending to be most deeply lobed near the middle or base, leaving a broad terminal part toothed or shallowly lobed. Moist to dry soil, throughout the state except for Cook Co. and immediately n. of Lake Superior in Lake and St. Louis counties. Very variable in form and habitat.

Q. muhlenbergii Engelm. (Q. prinoides var. acuminata (Michx.) Gl.). Yellow or Chestnut Oak. Bark light brown, scaly; acorn cup with many small scales free at the tip but without tail-like tips. Dry calcareous slopes in Houston Co., perhaps now extinct in the state.

Q. velutina Lam. Black Oak. Bark dark brown to nearly black, deeply furrowed; acorn usually not striped. Mesic to dry upland woods mostly on noncalcareous often poor soil or sand dunes; from Houston and Fillmore counties n. along the Mississippi River to se. Goodhue Co.

ULMACEAE ----- ELM FAMILY

Trees or shrubs with alternate simple leaves, the blades often asymmetrical at base; flowers bisexual or unisexual, single or in cymes or clusters; tepals 3-9, often united; stamens usually as many as the tepals and opposite them; ovary superior, of 2 fused carpels, mostly 1-locular; ovule 1, suspended; styles 2 or stigmas 2; fruit a samara, drupe, or nut.

A-Leaves regularly pinnate-veined; flowers appearing before the leaves
    on last year's twigs; fruit dry, flattish, with a circular wing . . . ULMUS
A-Leaves usually 3-veined from the base; flowers borne on the new
    growth with the leaves; fruit a globose drupe . . . . CELTIS

CELTIS ----- HACKBERRY, SUGARBERRY*

Monoecious or polygamous trees or shrubs; leaves entire or serrate, usually 3-5-nerved from near the base; the base usually asymmetrical; staminate flowers in small clusters near the base of the new twigs; pistillate or bisexual flowers solitary or sometimes 2 from the upper axils of the same twigs; tepals 4-6; ovary 1-locular; fruit a globose drupe. (Latin name for the sweet-berried Lotus of Gr. authors.)

C. occidentalis L. Hackberry. Tree to 16 m high; bark of trunk rough with short prominent corky ridges; leaves lance-ovate to deltoid, 6-12 cm long; drupe 7-11 mm long, dark purple to nearly black. Usually on rich moist soil, Houston to Rock Co., n. to Chisago, Mille Lacs, Otter Tail, and Clay counties, and in Cass and Beltrami counties.

ULMUS ----- ELM*

Trees; leaves mostly doubly serrate, usually asymmetrical at base; flowers bisexual, in short racemes or fascicles; tepals 4-9, united below; ovary 1- or 2-locular; fruit flattened, the central body surrounded by a wing. (The classical Latin name.)

A-Pedicels mostly 4-10 mm long; fruit hairy along the edge.
  B-Flowers in umbel-like clusters; sides of fruit glabrous. . U. americana
  B-Flowers in racemes; sides of fruit pubescent. . . . . . . U. thomasi
A-Pedicels mostly 1-2.5 mm long; fruit smooth along the edge.
  C-Bud scales (at least the inner ones) conspicuously woolly with
    red-brown hairs; fruit pubescent over the seed, often also
    with minute globules ("glands"); upper leaf surfaces and new
    twigs scabrous, more so when dry; bark layers tan and brown;
    native. . . . . U. rubra
  C-Bud scales nearly glabrous except for the edges or with straight
    appressed pale to reddish hairs; fruit wholly glabrous or with
    scattered minute glands; upper leaf surfaces and new twigs
    smooth or slightly scabrous; bark layers all brown or usually
    with alternating whitish layers; cultivated.
    D-Fruits 9-15 mm long, mostly as wide as long or wider; leaves
      2-7 (-9) cm long, usually almost symmetrical at base, the
      teeth singly or doubly serrate or both . . . . U. pumila
    D-Fruits 16-24 mm long, longer than wide; leaves 6-16 cm
      long, very asymmetric at base, doubly serrate . . . . . . U. glabra

U. americana L. American or White Elm. Bark of alternating brown and whitish layers; inner bark astringent; leaves mostly 8-14 cm long, not strongly folded along the midrib, smooth to rough above; stamens 7 or 8; fruit 9-12 mm long. In various habitats, most common on moist soil; throughout the state except for Cook Co.; widely cultivated.

U. glabra Huds. Wych or Scotch Elm; cultivated. Bark remaining smooth for many years, that of the trunk with alternating brown and whitish layers, neither trunk nor branchlets corky; inner bud scales with appressed hairs; leaves not characteristically folded lengthwise; stamens 5 or 6; stigmas red. Europe to w. Asia. Cv. Camperdownii, the Camperdown Elm, has pendulous branches; many other cultivars exist.

U. pumila L. Siberian Elm; cultivated. Bark of trunk somewhat corky, more so when damp, all brown or with alternating whitish layers, bark of branchlets not corky; inner bud scales with fringed edges, otherwise glandular or nearly glabrous; leaves flat to folded lengthwise; stamens 4 or 5; stigmas white. E. Siberia to Turkestan.

U. rubra Muhl. Slippery or Red Elm. Neither trunk nor branches corky; inner bark mucilaginous; leaves mostly 6-15 cm long, usually strongly folded upward along the midrib; stamens 5-9; stigmas pink; fruits 12-18 mm long. Moist rich soil, Houston to Jackson Co., n. to Clay, Clearwater, and Lake counties.

U. thomasi Sarg. Cork or Rock Elm. Bark of alternating brown and dull
whitish layers; branchlets sometimes with prominent corky ridges after their
second year; leaves 5-14 cm long, not strongly folded along the midrib,
smooth above; stamens 5-8; fruits 15-22 mm long. Usually moist soil,
Houston to Jackson Co., n. to Chippewa, Wilkin, s. Clearwater, Itasca,
and Pine counties.

MORACEAE ----- MULBERRY FAMILY

Trees to herbs with alternate or rarely opposite simple or compound
leaves; milky juice usually present; flowers unisexual, regular, crowded in
a convex to concave inflorescence; tepals 4 (2-6); stamens usually as many
as the tepals and opposite them (rarely to 1); ovary superior to inferior, 2-
carpellate, 1- (-2-) locular; ovules 1 (or 2), mostly pendulous; fruit a drupe
or achene.

MORUS ----- MULBERRY *

Monoecious or dioecious trees or shrubs with milky juice; leaves
alternate, serrate, often lobed, pinnately to palmately veined; flowers in
catkins, the male catkin more elongate than the female, the female sometimes with some male flowers present at its base; tepals and stamens 4;
tepals becoming lightly adherent to the ovary, becoming fleshy in fruit;
ovary superior, 1-locular; style branches 2; fruit an achene surrounded
by the fleshy perianth, the whole catkin becoming an ellipsoid fleshy multiple fruit resembling a blackberry. (The classical Latin name.)

A-Leaves pubescent below, scabrous or glabrous above; fruit dark
 purple; native . . . . M. rubra
A-Leaves glabrous, or sparsely pubescent along the larger veins
 beneath; fruit white to pink to light or dark purple; cultivated. M. alba

M. alba L. White Mulberry; cultivated. Tree; leaves 5-12 cm long,
serrate to irregularly 2-5-lobed; fruit 15-50 mm long. China. M. alba
var. tatarica (L.) Ser., Russian Mulberry, is a small bushy tree with
small leaves commonly much lobed, the fruits ca. 15 mm long.

M. rubra L. Red Mulberry. Small tree or shrub; leaves 7-19 cm long,
serrate to irregularly 2-5-lobed; fruit 25-40 mm long. Sandy soil in
Houston Co., perhaps no longer occurring naturally, sometimes cultivated.

URTICACEAE ----- NETTLE FAMILY

Herbs to trees with alternate to opposite leaves, often with stinging
hairs; flowers unisexual or rarely bisexual, regular; tepals 3-5, more or less
united below (rarely absent); stamens as many as the tepals and opposite them
ovary superior, 1-locular; style 1; ovule 1, basal; fruit an achene or drupe.

PARIETARIA ----- PELLITORY *

Monoecious or polygamous herbs with alternate entire leaves; stinging hairs none; flowers in short axillary clusters subtended and exceeded by
green bracts; tepals 4, united below; ovary compressed; stigma subsessile;
fruit an achene, loosely enclosed by the enlarged calyx. (The L. name.)

P. pensylvanica Muhl. Annual, to 4 dm high; leaves lanceolate, 3-8 cm
ong, 3-nerved from near the base. Dry woods and banks, Houston to
ipestone Co., n. to Washington, Morrison, Wilkin, and Kittson counties.

SANTALACEAE ----- SANDALWOOD FAMILY

Herbs to trees, often parasitic on roots or on tree branches, with simple
lternate or opposite leaves; flowers unisexual or bisexual, regular, single or
a clusters; tepals 3-6; stamens as many as the tepals and opposite them; ovary
i ours inferior, 1-locular; ovules 1-few from top of a free-central placenta;
tyle 1; fruit a 1-seeded nut or drupe.

COMANDRA ----- FALSE or BASTARD TOADFLAX*

Herbs, green but parasitic on roots of herbs or shrubs; leaves alter-
ate, entire; flowers bisexual or staminate, in terminal or axillary cymose
lusters; inferior ovary and hypanthium together bell- or urn-shaped, the
ypanthium often prolonged beyond the ovary, lined below with nectariferous
ssue which is expanded above into (4-) 5 lobes alternating with the stamens,
ie lobes resembling minute petals; tepals (4-) 5; ovary 2/3 inferior; fruit
ut-like. (Gr. coma, tuft of hairs, aner, man, referring to the tuft of hairs
ometimes on the anthers.)

C. umbellata (L.) Nutt. (incl. C. richardsiana Fern.). Plants 1-4 dm
igh from a rhizome; leaves oblong to oval, 2-4 cm long; flowers whitish.
lesic to damp open soil, throughout the state.

LORANTHACEAE ----- MISTLETOE FAMILY

Shrubby or woody-based half-parasites attached to the branches of
ees and shrubs but with chlorophyll; leaves usually opposite or whorled;
owers bisexual or unisexual, regular; perianth of 1 or 2 whorls, when 2
ot differentiated into calyx and corolla; tepals 2-6, the stamens as many
s these and opposite them; ovary inferior, 1-locular; placentas and ovules
aly partly differentiated; fruit berry-like or drupe-like.

ARCEUTHOBIUM ----- SMALL MISTLETOE*

Dioecious dwarf yellowish woody-based herbs with opposite scale-like
onnate leaves, parasitic on the branches of conifers; flowers single or few in
ie leaf axils; staminate perianth 2-5-lobed; pistillate perianth 2-lobed; fruit
compressed 1-seeded berry. (Gr. arkeuthos, the juniper, bios, life.)

A. pusillum Peck. Plants 5-20 mm high; leaves semi-circular, 1 mm
ide; flowers minute. Chiefly on black spruce, rarely on white spruce or
irch; from Becker and Clearwater to Aitkin and St. Louis counties.

ARISTOLOCHIACEAE ----- BIRTHWORT FAMILY

Shrubby vines or perennial herbs, often aromatic; leaves alternate or
asal, entire; flowers bisexual, axillary, regular to zygomorphic; perianth
sually undifferentiated, 3-lobed, colored; stamens 6-many; ovary 1/2 to fully

101

inferior, with (4-5) 6 united carpels (rarely free); ovules many, axile or sometimes parietal; fruit a capsule.

A-Low creeping herbs with regular flowers . . . . ASARUM
A-High-climbing woody-based vines with zygomorphic flowers
. . . . ARISTOLOCHIA

ARISTOLOCHIA ----- BIRTHWORT; PIPE VINES

Herbs or vines, usually with broad palmately veined leaves; perianth tubular, zygomorphic, S-shaped or pipe-shaped and 3-lobed, or straight and 1-lobed; stamens 6, the anthers united to the stigma; ovary partly or wholly inferior, 6-locular. (Gr. aristos, best, locheia, birth.)

A. macrophylla Lam. (A. durior Hill). Dutchman's Pipe; cultivated. High-climbing twiner; leaves round-cordate, 10-20 cm long; perianth pipe-shaped, 3-6 cm long, the limb dark purple. Mountains of e. North America.

ASARUM ----- WILD GINGER *

Aromatic creeping herbs, the rhizome bearing 1 or 2 broad leaves and a single terminal flower; perianth regular, 3-lobed, sometimes with an alternating inner series of 3 rudimentary petals; stamens 12; ovary 6-locular, partly to wholly inferior. (Gr. asaron, name of a plant.)

A. canadense L. Leaves round-cordate to cordate-kidney shaped, mostly 8-12 cm wide at anthesis, larger at maturity; flower at ground level, reddish; petals none; ovary fully inferior. Mesic to moist usually deciduous woods, throughout most of the forested zone.

A-Sepals with a narrow tail-like tip 3-20 mm long; Houston to Mower
    Co., n. to Redwood, Becker, e. Roseau, and Cook counties
    . . . . A. c. var. acuminatum Ashe.
A-Sepals without such tips, short-pointed at most; Mower Co.
    . . . . A. c. var. reflexum (Bickn.) Robins.

POLYGONACEAE ----- BUCKWHEAT FAMILY

Herbs to trees or vines; stipules usually sheathing the stem; flowers bisexual or unisexual, regular; perianth of 3-6 parts, differentiated or undifferentiated; stamens mostly 4-9; ovary superior, 1-locular, of 2-3 (-4) united carpels, the styles as many and usually united at base; ovule 1, basal; fruit an achene.

A-Leaves cordate-ovate, 20 cm or more wide . . . . RHEUM
A-Leaves lanceolate to ovate, much narrower.
    B-Perianth parts 6, the outer 3 shorter and usually narrower than
        the inner, the inner enlarging further in fruit . . . . RUMEX
    B-Perianth parts 5, the outer ones at least as large as the inner in
        flower and fruit . . . . POLYGONUM

POLYGONUM ----- KNOTWEED, SMARTWEED

Herbs or rarely shrubs; leaves alternate, the stipules forming tubular sheaths (ocreae) around the stem; tepals 5 (4-6), the outer ones at least as large as the inner; fruit 3-angled or lens-shaped. (Gr. <u>poly</u>, many, and <u>gonu</u>, knee or joint, from the thickened joints of the stem.)

A-Ocreae mostly with reflexed bristles at base; achenes shiny black;
   styles separate, divergent . . . . P. cilinode
A-Ocreae smooth; achenes dull black; styles united . . . . P. convolvulus

P. <u>cilinode</u> Michx. Bindweed, Climbing Buckwheat. Perennial, twining or trailing to occasionally erect; leaves ovate to triangular-ovate, cordate at base; flowers white to pink-tinged, 1.5-2 mm long. Dry thickets, slopes, and edges of woods, Cook to Lake of the Woods Co., s. to Clearwater, Mille Lacs, and Ramsey counties.

P. <u>convolvulus</u> L. Black Bindweed, Climbing Buckwheat. Annual; twining or trailing; leaves arrow-shaped to triangular-cordate;flowers green to white to purplish-tipped, 1.5-2 mm long. Introduced from Europe, a widespread weed of disturbed ground, throughout the state.

RHEUM ----- RHUBARB, PIE PLANT

Perennial herbs with large alternate leaves and tall flowering stems; flowers bisexual, greenish or whitish, numerous in panicled racemes or fascicles, the perianth not much enlarging in fruit, 6-parted, the outer parts reflexed; stamens mostly 9; styles 3; achene becoming strongly winged. (Gr. <u>rha</u>, rhubarb.)

R. <u>rhaponticum</u> L. Cultivated. Leaves mostly basal, cordate-ovate, 30-45 cm or more long, 20 cm or more wide; flowering stems to 2 m high; fruit 6-12 mm long. From Siberia. Variable with several distinct forms. Some doubt exists as to whether the rhubarb represents a natural species or a hybrid or abnormal variant of some kind.

RUMEX ----- DOCK, SORREL

Ours annual or perennial herbs with alternate simple leaves, the stipules forming tubular sheaths ("<u>ocreae</u>") around the stem; flowers greenish to yellowish or reddish, bisexual or unisexual, in small whorls in a compound inflorescence; perianth parts 6, here termed tepals, the outer 3 shorter and usually narrower than the inner, the inner enlarging further in fruit and often developing a warty outgrowth (the "<u>grain</u>") on the back; stamens 6; styles 3; ovary and fruit 3-angled. Fruit is necessary for accurate identification. (The classical Latin name.)

A-Leaves all or some of them with 2 basal lobes; plants dioecious;
   leaves acid to the taste . . . . R. acetosella
A-Leaves without basal lobes; flowers all or mostly bisexual; leaves
   seldom acid.
  B-Edges of inner tepals with 2-4 spine-like teeth . . . . R. obtusifolius
  B-Edges of tepals without spine-like teeth.
    C-The longer pedicels 2-5 times as long as the inner tepals in
     fruit; grains 3, projecting ca. 0.5 mm below the tepals
     . . . . R. verticillatus
    C-Pedicels seldom over twice as long as the inner tepals in
     fruit; grains 1-3, not projecting below the inner tepals.
      D-Leaves conspicuously crinkle-edged; grains mostly 2/3-
       3/4 as wide as long. . . . . R. crispus

D-Leaves flat or nearly so; grains up to 1/2 as wide as long.
  E-Inner tepals in fruit triangular-ovate to triangular, acute
      or nearly so; plump grains 3 . . . . R. mexicanus
  E-Inner tepals in fruit broadly round-ovate to ovate-triangular,
      the tip usually blunt; plump grain 1 (-3). . . . . . R. altissimus

R. acetosella L. Sheep, Common, or Red Sorrel. Annual or perennial to 4 dm high; inner tepals 1.5-2 mm long, not enlarging in fruit, without grains. Introduced from Eurasia; widespread weed of disturbed ground and acid soils, recorded from Cook to Kittson Co. and s. to Clearwater, Kandiyohi, Olmsted, and Houston counties, and in Traverse and Cottonwood counties.

R. altissimus Wood. Water or Pale Dock. Perennial to 1 m high; leaves ovate to lance-ovate, acute to obtuse at base, the main ones 2.5-7 cm wide; pedicels 3-5 mm long; inner tepals in fruit 4-6.5 mm long and wide. Wet soil, Houston to Jackson Co., n. to Hennepin and Brown counties, and in Aitkin Co.

R. crispus L. Yellow or Sour Dock. Perennial to 1 m high; pedicels 5-10 mm long; inner tepals in fruit 4-5 mm long and wide; grains 3, often unequal, the larger 1/2 as long as the tepal. Introduced from Europe; widespread weed of disturbed ground, throughout the state.

R. mexicanus Meissn. Perennial to 1 m high; leaves pale green, narrowly lanceolate, acute to acuminate at base, the main ones 1.5-3.5 cm wide; pedicels 2-4 mm long; inner tepals in fruit 3-6 mm long and wide. Moist soil, throughout the state.

R. obtusifolius L. Bitter Dock. Perennial to 12 dm high; lower leaves cordate at base; pedicels 1 1/2-2 1/2 times as long as the fruiting tepals, these 3-5 mm long, one with a grain, the others only with a slightly thickened midrib. Introduced from Europe; disturbed ground, recorded from Houston, Winona, s. St. Louis, and Lake counties.

R. verticillatus L. Swamp or Water Dock. Perennial to 1 m high; pedicels 10-15 mm long; inner tepals in fruit 3.5-5 mm long, as wide or nearly so. Swamps and wet lowlands woods, Winona, Mower, and Blue Earth counties

NYCTAGINACEAE ----- FOUR O'CLOCK FAMILY

Herbs (ours) or shrubs or trees with alternate or opposite usually entire leaves; flowers bisexual or rarely unisexual, regular, 1-several often borne within a calyx-like involucre, when only 1 the flower and involucre easily mistaken for a flower with both calyx and corolla; perianth undifferentiated, the tepals typically 5, fused, often corolla-like; stamens 3-5 in ours, hypogynous; carpel 1, with 1 erect ovule; fruit achene-like, sometimes enclosed in the perianth tube.

MIRABILIS ----- WILD FOUR-O'CLOCK, UMBRELLA-WORT

Perennial herbs with opposite leaves; flowers rose to pink-purple, open in the morning, numerous in panicles, 1-4 in each involucre, the involucre 5-lobed; perianth tube narrowed above the ovary, the ovary thus seemingly (not acutally) inferior; style slender; fruit 5-ribbed. (L. for wonderful.)

M. nyctaginea (Michx.) MacM. (Oxybaphus nyctagineus (Michx.) Sweet). Leaves ovate-oblong to triangular-ovate, the margin often somewhat irregular, entire or minutely toothed; involucre ca. 1 cm wide; perianth pink-purple, ca. 1 cm long. Dry soil, and disturbed ground, Houston to Rock Co., n. to s. St. Louis, Beltrami, Lake of the Woods, and Kittson counties.

PORTULACACEAE ----- PURSLANE FAMILY

Herbaceous (or rarely somewhat woody) plants, often with somewhat thickened and fleshy parts; leaves usually opposite; flowers bisexual, regular or nearly so; sepals usually 2, rarely more; petals (2-) 4-5 (-6), usually free; stamens 4-30, free or nearly so; ovary superior (except Portulaca), 1-locular with 2-many ovules on a basal or free-central placenta; fruit a capsule, circumscissile or opening lengthwise.

A-Flowers sessile or nearly so; ovary partly inferior; capsule circum-
    scissile; cultivated . . . . PORTULACA
A-Flowers pedicelled; ovary superior; capsule opening lengthwise; native.
  B-Leaves flat, 1-few at the base and 2 on the stem . . . . CLAYTONIA
  B-Leaves cylindrical or nearly so, numerous and crowded at or
    near the base . . . . TALINUM

CLAYTONIA ----- SPRING BEAUTY *

Perennial herbs, ours from slightly flattened corms; leaves 1-few at the base and 2 in an opposite pair on the stem; flowers in a raceme, white to rose with deeper pink veins; sepals 2, ovate; petals 5; stamens 5, adhering to the bases of the petals; style 3-cleft; ovules 6; capsule opening by 3 in-rolling segments. (Named for John Clayton, an American botanist.)

A-Blades of stem leaves 2.3-4.7 times as long as wide, 6-23 mm
    wide, the petiole well distinguished. . . . . C. caroliniana
A-Blades of stem leaves 5.3-15 times as long as wide, 3-10 mm
    wide, the petiole hardly distinguished . . . . C. virginica

C. caroliniana Michx. Stem leaves 3-6 (-9) cm long; petals 9-15 mm long. Woods and thickets in St. Louis Co. Similar broad-leaved plants have been found in Hennepin and Rice counties, doubtfully of this species.

C. virginica L. Stem leaves 5-15 cm long; petals as above. Rich soil in moist woods and clearings, Houston to Mower Co., n. to Blue Earth, Morrison, and s. St. Louis counties.

PORTULACA ----- PURSLANE, ROSE-MOSS *

Ours fleshy annuals with mostly alternate leaves, the upper leaves crowded and forming an involucre to the flowers; flowers sessile or nearly so; sepals 2; petals 4-6, mostly 5; stamens 7-20; style deeply 3-9-cleft; ovary partly or wholly inferior, with basal placentas; fruit circumscissile. (L. portulaca, of uncertain meaning.)

A-Flowers 5-10 mm wide, yellow; leaves flat, broadly linear to
    obovate . . . . P. oleracea
A-Flowers 20-40 mm wide, variously colored; leaves cylindrical
    . . . . P. grandiflora

P. grandiflora Hook. Rose-moss, Sun Plant; cultivated. Plants densely hairy at the nodes. From Argentina.

P. oleracea L. Purslane; cultivated. Plants glabrous or nearly so. Of uncertain origin, perhaps native to w. Asia, perhaps a cultigen. Often escaped in open or disturbed ground over most of the state.

TALINUM ----- FAMEFLOWER *

Glabrous fleshy herbs, ours perennial with many nearly cylindrical leaves crowded at or near the base; flowers cymose, white or pink, open for only a few hours in full sun; sepals 2, not long persistent; petals 5 (rarely more); stamens 5-45; style 3-lobed; ovary 3-locular only at the base, with a free-central placenta; fruit 3-segmented, many-seeded. (Apparently taken from the native Senegal name.)

A-Stamens usually 5 (4-8); stigmas ovate, ca. 0.5 mm long T. parviflorum
A-Stamens 10-25; stigmas lance-linear, 1-1.5 mm long. . . T. rugospermum

T. parviflorum Nutt. Petals 4-7 mm long, white to pale pink. Thin soil on rocks and sterile sandy soil, Rock to Blue Earth Co., n. to w. Benton and Big Stone counties.

T. rugospermum Holz. Petals 6-8 mm long, pink. Thin soil on sandstone and sandy soil, Winona, Goodhue, and Chisago counties.

CARYOPHYLLACEAE ----- PINK FAMILY

Annual or perennial herbs, sometimes woody at base; leaves opposite (except for 1 genus, not ours) or occasionally whorled, entire; flowers in cymose inflorescences or single, usually bisexual, hypogynous or sometimes perigynous, regular; sepals 4-5; petals 4-5 (rarely none), free; stamens 1-10, usually twice the petals; ovary 1-5-locular, mostly 1-locular with free-central placentation or with partitions only below; styles and stigmas 2-5; fruit a capsule.

A-Sepals free or nearly so.
   B-Petals entire to barely notched at the apex. . . . . ARENARIA
   B-Petals notched 1/3 or more of their length (when cleft to the
      base appearing to be 10 in number).
      C-Fruit ovoid to oblong, opening by twice as many lengthwise
         segments as there are styles; styles 3 (rarely 4 or 5) . .STELLARIA
      C-Fruit cylindric, often bent near the apex or curved, opening
        only at the apex by twice as many teeth as there are styles;
        styles 5 (rarely 4 or 3) . . . . CERASTIUM
A-Sepals united into a tube, their tips usually free.
   D-Flowers all staminate, styles and functioning ovary absent. . LYCHNIS
   D-Some or all of the flowers with styles and ovaries.
      E-Styles 5 (in some species occasionally 4 or very rarely 3
        (L. viscaria) but mostly 5) . . . . LYCHNIS
      E-Styles 2 or 3.
        F-Styles 3; flowers not subtended by bracts. . . . . SILENE
        F-Styles 2; flowers each subtended by 1-3 pairs of bracts .DIANTHUS

ARENARIA ----- SANDWORT*

Low annual or perennial herbs; flowers single or in terminal cymes; sepals 5; petals 5, entire or barely notched, white or rarely pink, rarely none; stamens normally 10; ovary 1-locular; ovules many; styles normally 3; segments of the capsule as many as the styles or twice as many. (L. arena, sand, the habitat of many species.)

A-Leaves narrowly linear, 1.5 mm wide or less. .A. stricta ssp. dawsonensis
A-Leaves lanceolate to ovate to oblanceolate, 2 mm or more wide.
    B-Leaves 2-7 mm long; taprooted annual. . . . . .A. serpyllifolia
    B-Leaves 7-70 mm long; rhizomatous perennials.
        C-Sepals 2-3 mm long, the petals 1/2 again as long or longer;
           leaves 7-35 mm long, blunt or slightly acute . . . . . A. lateriflora
        C-Sepals 2.5-6 mm long, the petals about as long or shorter;
           leaves 15-60 mm long, acute to acuminate. . . . . . A. macrophylla

A. lateriflora L. Leaves usually ovate to elliptic-oblong. Openings or edges of woods, Houston to Jackson Co., n. to Lake, Lake of the Woods, and Kittson counties.

A. macrophylla Hook. Leaves lanceolate to oblanceolate. Cliffs and rocky slopes, Lake and Cook counties.

A. serpyllifolia L. Leaves ovate, acute; sepals 2.5-3.5 mm long; petals usually shorter than the sepals. Introduced from Eurasia; sandy or gravelly areas, recorded from Hubbard and Clearwater counties.

A. stricta subsp. dawsonensis (Britt.) Maguire (A. dawsonensis Britt.). Leaves 5-15 mm long; sepals 3.5-6.5 mm long, the petals somewhat longer. Rocky and gravelly places, Houston and Fillmore counties, Goodhue to Chisago Co., and Lake of the Woods and Roseau counties.

CERASTIUM ----- MOUSE-EAR CHICKWEED*

Low annual or perennial usually pubescent herbs; flowers single or in terminal cymes; sepals 5 (rarely 4); petals as many as sepals, white, 2-lobed or 2-cleft (when cleft to the base appearing to be double the true number) or sometimes lacking in cleistogamous flowers; stamens 10 (rarely fewer); styles as many as the sepals and opposite them, rarely 3; capsule cylindric, often bent near the apex or curved, opening at the apex by twice as many teeth as there are styles. (Gr. keration, little horn, from the shape of the fruit.)

A-Petals 2-3 times as long as the sepals; leaf axils often with bunches
    of smaller leaves or short shoots; leaves linear to narrowly ovate,
    0.5-13 mm wide . . . . C. arvense
A-Petals 7/8-1 7/8 times as long as the sepals; leaf axils usually without leaf clusters; leaves lance-ovate to ovate to oblanceolate, 3-15
    mm wide.
    B-Petals about as long as the sepals or shorter; pedicels in fruit
        4-14 mm long; plants perennial . . . . C. vulgatum
    B-Petals 1 1/4-1 7/8 times as long as the sepals; pedicels in
        fruit 5-40 mm long; plants annual . . . . C. nutans

C. arvense L. Matted or tufted perennial; leaves 1-7 cm long; sepals 5-8 mm long. Rocky, gravelly, or sandy places, often a weed in fields, scattered over most of the state, especially the w. 1/3, unrecorded from many counties.

<u>C</u>. nutans Raf. Leaves narrowly lance-oblong to oblanceolate, 1-7 cm long, 5-15 mm wide; sepals 4-5 mm long. The typical form has pedicels in fruit 1.5-4 cm long; plants with shorter pedicels, mostly 5-15 mm long, often narrower and of drier habitats, have been given the name <u>C</u>. nutans var. brachypodum Engelm. Moist to mesic woods and open places, Houston to Pipestone Co., n. to Big Stone, Lake of the Woods, and Cook counties.

<u>C</u>. vulgatum L. Leaves lance-ovate to ovate to oblong, 1-3 cm long, 3-15 mm wide; sepals 4.5-6 mm long. Introduced from Eurasia; widespread in disturbed ground throughout the state, common as a lawn weed.

DIANTHUS ----- PINK, SWEET WILLIAM

Annual to perennial herbs; flowers terminal, single or in panicled cymes; flower subtended by 1-3 pairs of bracts; calyx tubular, 5-toothed, with 20 or more nerves; petals 5, with long narrow bases, entire to fringed or toothed; stamens 10; styles 2; capsule opening by 4 or 5 teeth at the top. (Gr. <u>dio-</u>, of Jupiter, <u>anthos,</u> flower.)

A-Flowers several to many in a dense round-topped cluster surrounded
    by an involucre-like series of narrow leafy bracts; pedicels less than
    1 cm long. . . . .<u>D</u>. barbatus
A-Flowers 1-5 in an open inflorescence without an involucre-like
    series of bracts; pedicels 1-4 cm long.
    B-Calyxes mostly 10-15 mm long; petals toothed, the teeth not over
       1/4 the length of the limb; basal leaves oblanceolate . . .<u>D</u>. deltoides
    B-Calyxes 18-25 mm long; petals fringed, cut about 1/3
       the length of the limb; leaves linear. . . . .<u>D</u>. plumarius

<u>D</u>. barbatus L. Sweet William; cultivated. Leaves lanceolate to oblanceolate, 4-10 cm long; bracts of each flower equalling the calyx; calyx 12-18 mm long; petals white to dark red, 15-25 mm long. From Eurasia.

<u>D</u>. deltoides L. Maiden Pink; cultivated. Leaves 1.5-3 cm long; bracts about 1/2 as long as the calyx; petals white to dark rose to purple, 15-20 mm long. From Eurasia.

<u>D</u>. plumarius L. Cottage Pink; cultivated. Leaves 2-8 cm long; bracts 1/4-1/3 as long as the calyx; petals white to red, 30-40 mm long; flowers very fragrant. Austria to Siberia.

LYCHNIS ----- CAMPION

Annual or perennial herbs; flowers single or in cymes, bisexual or unisexual; calyx tubular, 5-toothed; petals 5, with sharply narrowed bases, usually with a pair of small appendages on the inner face at junction of narrow and broad parts, entire, 2-cleft, or fringed; stamens 10; ovary 1-locular or incompletely 3-5-locular; styles 5 (in some species occasionally 4 or very rarely 3 but mostly 5); capsule opening by as many or usually twice as many apical teeth as there are styles. (Gr. lychnos, lamp, referring to the flame-colored flowers of some species.)

A-Calyx 10-12 mm long; petals 13-18 mm long; leaves narrowly
    oblanceolate (at least 9 times as long as wide); flowers bisex-
    ual; cultivated . . . . .L. viscaria
A-Calyx 15-20 mm long; petals 20-40 mm long; leaves lanceolate to broadly
    elliptic (not over 6 times as long as wide); flowers unisexual; naturalized.

B-Flowers usually white and fragrant, opening in the evening; capsule
  conic-ovoid, its teeth erect or only slightly spreading . . . . L. alba
B-Flowers mostly red-purple to pink (rarely white), almost odorless,
  opening in the morning; capsule globose, its teeth recurved. L. dioica

L. alba Mill. White Campion. Dioecious annual or perennial; leaves 3-10
m long; calyx teeth lance-linear, attenuate. Introduced from Eurasia; established
ι disturbed ground throughout the state. Perhaps better placed under Silene.

L. dioica L. Red or Morning Campion. Similar to preceding; calyx teeth
·iangular-lanceolate, acute. Introduced from Eurasia; found as a weed in
ittson Co. Perhaps better placed under Silene.

L. viscaria L. German Catchfly; cultivated. Perennial; leaves to 12 cm
·ng; sticky patches present on the stem below the inflorescence; petals purple,
ɛd, pink, or rarely white. From Eurasia.

SILENE ----- CATCHFLY, CAMPION

As described for Lychnis except the ovary 1-locular or incompletely 3-
·cular and the styles 3 (rarely 4, not in ours). (Gr. Seilenos, a companion
· Bacchus.)

-Calyx 6-12 mm long, glabrous; flowers in cymes.
 B-Stems puberulent at base; leaves fringed with hairs at very
   base; upper internodes usually with sticky bands. . . . . . . S. antirrhina
 B-Plants glabrous throughout; sticky bands none. . . . . S. cserei
-Calyx 13-22 mm long, glabrous or hairy; flowers in cymes or axillary.
 C-Flowers in an open cyme; calyx with prominent green ribs,
   pale between; calyx lobes long-acuminate. . . . . S. noctiflora
 C-Flowers mostly single in the upper leaf axils; calyx light
   green, the ribs not prominent; calyx lobes broadly acute. . . . S. nivea

S. antirrhina L. Sleepy Catchfly. Annual or biennial; leaves tapering to
ɩse, not clasping, 2-10 mm wide; calyx 6-8.5 mm long, with prominent
reen ribs; petals 7-11 mm long, pink to whitish. Open rocky or sandy soil
· disturbed ground, throughout the state.

S. cserei Baumg. Smooth Catchfly. Biennial; leaves 0.5-3 cm wide, the pair
ιasping the stem; calyx 8.5-12 mm long, not green-ribbed, often pinkish; petals
3-18 mm long, white to pinkish. From se. Europe; open disturbed ground over
ιost of the state, unrecorded from the sw. corner, Cook, Lake, and other counties.

S. nivea (Nutt.) Otth. Snowy Campion. Perennial, glabrous to puberulent;
owers white. Woods, Houston and Fillmore counties to Goodhue Co.

S. noctiflora L. Night-flowering Catchfly. Annual or winter-annual, sticky-
ιbescent; flowers often unisexual with the female ones uppermost, opening at
ιght; petals white to pink. Introduced from Europe; disturbed ground, widely
:attered across the state, unrecorded from many counties.

STELLARIA ----- CHICKWEED, STARWORT, STITCHWORT *

Low annual or perennial herbs; flowers small, single or in terminal
·mes; sepals (4-) 5; petals (4-) 5, cleft, when cleft to the base appearing
· be 10 in number, or sometimes petals none; stamens (2-) 10; ovary 1-
cular; styles 3 or less often 4 or 5; capsule ovoid to oblong, opening usually
· twice as many lengthwise segments as there are styles. (L. stella, a star.)

-Styles normally 5; leaves 10-30 mm wide, mostly sessile . . . S. aquatica

A-Styles normally 3; leaves 1.5-20 mm wide, if more than 10 mm wide
  then the middle and lower leaves distinctly petioled.
  B-Leaf blades 1-2 3/4 times as long as wide, the middle and lower
    ones distinctly petioled; stems usually not angled . . . . . . S. media
  B-Leaf blades 2 1/2-25 times as long as wide, mostly sessile or
    essentially so; stems 4-angled.
    C-Flowers usually solitary in the forks of the stem or terminal,
      or if forming an inflorescence then the bracts mostly all green.
      D-Petals shorter than the sepals or none; seeds only obscurely
        sculptured; principal leaves 15-50 mm long, 2-8 mm wide
        . . . . S. calycantha
      D-Petals present and exceeding the sepals; seeds wrinkled;
        principal leaves 4-25 mm long, 0.8-3 mm wide . . S. crassifolia
    C-Flowers in cymes, the bracts whitish to brownish or sometimes
      with a green midrib.
      E-Petals shorter than the sepals or none; median leaves 2 1/2-
        9 times as long as wide.
        F-Seeds essentially smooth; cymes terminal; principal leaves
          15-50 mm long . . . . S. calycantha
        F-Seeds strongly pebbled; cymes soon appearing lateral due
          to continued growth of stem; principal leaves 9-22 mm
          long . . . . S. alsine
      E-Petals as long as or longer than the sepals; median leaves
        7-25 times as long as wide,
        G-Older pedicels and branches of the inflorescence ascending,
          each diverging 45° or less from its respective axis (or the
          imaginary extension of that axis); stems mostly erect; leaves
          ascending; fruit deep brown to blackish . . . . S. longipes
        G-Older pedicels and often the branches of the inflorescence
          spreading to recurved, each diverging 60° or more from its
          respective axis; stems erect to reclining; leaves ascending
          to widely spreading; fruit pale brown to sometimes dark.
        H-Sepals 2.5-3.5 (-4) mm long, weakly 3-nerved or not
          nerved; fruit pale to dark; seeds essentially smooth
          . . . . S. longifolia
        H-Sepals (3.5-) 4.5-5.5 mm long, strongly 3-nerved; fruit
          pale; seeds finely wrinkled or roughened . . . . S. graminea

S. alsine Grimm. Annual or biennial, reclining to ascending; leaves 2 1/2-
6 times as long as wide; sepals 2-3.5 mm long. Cold springs and stream
borders; one locality in Winona Co.

S. aquatica (L.) Scop. (Myosoton aquaticum (L.) Moench). Sprawling
perennial; leaves 2-8 cm long, 2-2 1/2 times as long as wide; sepals 5-6
mm long in flower, the petals longer. Stream banks and wet places, Houston
to Blue Earth Co., widely scattered n. to Benton, St. Louis, and Lake counties.

S. calycantha (Ledeb.) Bongard. Perennials with weak stems; leaves 4-9
times as long as wide; bracts when present occasionally whitish; sepals 2-4
mm long. Moist and usually shaded places, Cook to Cass and Lake of the
Woods counties, and in Hennepin Co.

S. crassifolia Ehrh. Low perennial; leaves 3-8 times as long as wide;
sepals 2.5-4 mm long; fruit pale. Springs and cold moist situations; widely
scattered, Goodhue to Chippewa Co., n. to Kanabec, Cass, Clearwater,
and Wilkin counties.

S. graminea L. Perennial; leaves 1.5-4 cm long, 1.5-8 mm wide. Introduced from Europe; grassy places and disturbed ground, Houston and Winona
counties, Washington Co., and Carlton, St. Louis, and Lake counties.

<u>S</u>. <u>longifolia</u> Muhl. Perennial; leaves 1.5-5 cm long, 1-5 mm wide. Moist places, throughout most of the state, unrecorded se. of a line through Goodhue, Waseca, and Jackson counties.

<u>S</u>. <u>longipes</u> Goldie. Perennial; leaves 10-35 mm long, 1-3 mm wide; sepals 3-4.5 (-5.5) mm long, slightly nerved; seeds slightly pebbled. Mesic to moist sandy or gravelly places, Otter Tail to Kittson counties.

<u>S</u>. <u>media</u> (L.) Vill. Annual; leaves 1-3 (-6) cm long, 4-20 mm wide; sepals 3-5.5 mm long, the petals shorter; seeds strongly roughened. Highly variable. Introduced from Eurasia; a common weed found in a wide variety of habitats, throughout the state.

NYMPHAEACEAE ----- WATER LILY FAMILY

Aquatic herbs mostly from rhizomes; floating or emergent leaves peltate or cordate; flowers at the surface of the water, bisexual, regular, hypogynous to epigynous; sepals and petals together 5-many, in some genera hardly differentiated; stamens 5-many; carpels few to many, free or united; fruit various.

NUPHAR ----- YELLOW POND LILY, SPATTER-DOCK

Rhizomes very large, horizontal; floating leaves large, cordate, with a deep basal notch; flowers large, yellow to purplish or red; sepals 5-6, concave; petals many, much smaller than the sepals, usually shorter than the stamens, thought to be derived from them; stamens many; carpels fused, the compound style short and thick, the stigma broad; seeds many, parietal. (The Arabic name for the water lily.)

<u>N</u>. <u>variegatum</u> Engelm. Floating leaves 10-25 cm long, 2/3 as wide; flowers 3-5 cm thick, yellow, the inner sepals usually red to purple inside at base. Lakes and ponds, throughout the state.

RANUNCULACEAE ----- BUTTERCUP or CROWFOOT FAMILY

Herbs or rarely shrubs or climbing vines; flowers hypogynous, mostly regular, typically bisexual, the parts separate (rarely the carpels fused); perianth differentiated or not; tepals when present 3-15, often petal-like; sepals and petals when present mostly 3-5; stamens 5-many; carpels 1-many; ovules 1-many per carpel; fruit various.

A-Leaves all simple or once compound.
  B-Stem leaves opposite or whorled, sometimes much reduced in size
     from the basal ones (when sessile sometimes resembling an involucre
     or calyx placed below the flower).
    C-Climbing or trailing vines, more or less woody . . . . . . CLEMATIS
    C-Upright herbs.
      D-Leaves 3-lobed, the margins entire . . . . HEPATICA
      D-Leaves variously lobed, the margins toothed to cleft . . ANEMONE
  B-Stem leaves alternate or the leaves all basal or not yet developed.
    E-Flowers yellow to greenish-yellow (the perianth parts 5 or
      more, persisting through flowering).
      F-Leaf blades narrowly to broadly linear, entire.

G-Flowers yellow, the sepals not spurred, the receptacle
short-cylindric. . . . . RANUNCULUS
G-Flowers greenish-yellow, the sepals each prolonged below
into a short spur, the receptacle very elongate . . MYOSURUS
F-Leaf blades broader, entire to toothed or compound.
H-Perianth of well-developed sepals and petals
(the sepals sometimes falling early). . . . . RANUNCULUS
H-Perianth undifferentiated, with or without a series of
small narrow staminodes outside of the stamens.
I-Leaves entire to dentate, not lobed . . . . CALTHA
I-Leaves lobed to divided . . . . TROLLIUS
E-Flowers white to pink to blue-purple or greenish-white (if
greenish-white then the perianth of 3 early deciduous tepals).
J-Basal leaves not yet developed, the apparent calyx consisting
of many narrow silky divisions . . . . ANEMONE
J-Basal leaves present, calyx otherwise if present.
K-Leaves 3-lobed, the margins entire . . . . HEPATICA
K-Leaves otherwise.
L-Leaves compound with 3 leaflets . . . . COPTIS
L-Leaves simple, palmately 5-7-lobed. . . . . HYDRASTIS
A-Leaves, at least the basal ones, twice or more compound (including
leaves deeply cleft into many narrow divisions).
M-One or more sepals or petals prolonged backward into a long spur.
N-Each of the 5 petals spurred. . . . . AQUILEGIA
N-Upper sepal and 2 upper petals spurred, both petal spurs inside
the sepal spur . . . . DELPHINIUM
M-No perianth parts spurred.
O-Flowers many in a raceme or panicle.
P-Flowers white; leaflets sharply toothed . . . . ACTAEA
P-Flowers greenish to yellowish to purplish; leaflets bluntly
toothed or lobed. . . . . THALICTRUM
O-Flowers solitary or few, terminal, in the leaf axils, or umbellate.
Q-Leaflets or finest leaf divisions narrowly lanceolate, wedge-
shaped, or linear.
R-Plants aquatic, the leaves usually submerged . . . RANUNCULUS
R-Plants terrestrial. . . . . ANEMONE
Q-Leaflets ovate to obovate to nearly round.
S-Stem leaves alternate, the leaflets obovate, the flowers
axillary. . . . . ISOPYRUM
S-Stem leaves opposite or whorled, the leaflets ovate to
roundish, the flowers umbellate . . . . ANEMONELLA

ACTAEA ----- BANEBERRY

Perennial herbs; leaves alternate, large, 2-3 times ternately compound, the leaflets sharply toothed and cleft; flowers white, in terminal
racemes; sepals 3-5, early deciduous; petals 4-10, obovate to narrowly
oblong; stamens many; carpel 1, fruit a berry. (Gr. _aktea_, elder.)

A-Pedicels slender, 0.4-0.7 mm thick in fruit; ovary wider than
stigma; fruit red, rarely white . . . . A. _rubra_
A-Pedicels thick, 1-2 mm thick in fruit; stigma wider than ovary;
fruit white, rarely red. . . . . A. _pachypoda_

A. _pachypoda_ Ell. (A. _alba_ (L.) Mill.). White Baneberry, White Cohosh.
4-8 dm high; petals 2.5-4 mm long. Rich soil in moist woods and thickets,
Hennepin, Carlton, s. St. Louis, and s. Lake counties.

A. rubra (Ait.) Willd. Red Baneberry. Similar to above. The white-fruited form has been called A. r. forma neglecta (Gillman) Robins. Rich soil in moist woods and thickets, throughout the state, unrecorded in a few counties.

ANEMONE ----- ANEMONE, WINDFLOWER*

Erect perennial herbs with lobed, divided, or dissected basal leaves and 2-3 opposite or whorled stem leaves subtending 1 or more elongate peduncles; peduncles 1-flowered; tepals 4-20, white to blue or red or green-ish; stamens many; carpels many; ovules 1 per carpel; fruit an achene, some-times with a long feathery persistent style attached. (Gr. anemone, windflower.)

A-Stem leaves sessile (when deeply divided their divisions sometimes sur-
    rounding the stem, resembling an involucre or calyx placed below
    the flower).
  B-Tepals mostly 10-20. . . . . A. caroliniana
  B-Tepals mostly 4-8.
    C-Leaves deeply parted into 3-7 oblong, oblanceolate, or wedge-
        shaped primary divisions, these in turn with 2 or 3 divisions
        or only irregularly cut and toothed; tepals white, 8-25 mm
        long . . . . A. canadensis
    C-Leaves deeply 2-3 times dissected into many narrow linear,
        lanceolate, or wedge-shaped divisions; tepals variously colored,
        20-35 mm long.
      D-Plants densely silky-hairy when young; styles conspicuously
          hairy, 2-4 cm long and plumose in fruit; native . . . . . A. patens
      D-Plants pubescent to glabrous, not densely silky; styles not
          elongate nor plumose in fruit; cultivated . . . . A. coronaria
A-Stem leaves petioled.
  E-Tepals glabrous on the back; flowering plant without basal leaves
      . . . . A. quinquefolia var. interior
  E-Tepals hairy on the back; flowering plant with both basal and
      stem leaves.
    F-Leaves deeply cut into many linear-oblong to narrowly lanceolate
        divisions . . . . A. multifida var. hudsoniana
    F-Leaves rather coarsely cut into 2-5 broad toothed to cleft divisions.
      G-Stem leaves (3-) 5-9; peduncles mostly leafless; leaflets
          lobed or cleft for 1/2-2/3 of their length, their lobes
          linear-oblong to narrowly obtriangular; fruiting head of
          achenes 2-4.5 cm long, 6-10 mm thick, cylindric, 2 or
          more times as long as wide . . . . A. cylindrica
      G-Stem leaves 2-3 (-5); all but the first peduncle usually with
          a pair of stem leaves; leaflets lobed for 1/3-1/2 of their
          length, the lobes broadly oblong to triangular; fruiting head
          of achenes 1.5-3 cm long, 7-15 mm thick, cylindric to
          ovoid or ellipsoid, less than twice as long as wide.
        H-Anthers 0.7-1.2 mm long; fruiting heads 7-11 mm thick
            . . . . A. riparia
        H-Anthers 1.2-1.6 mm long; fruiting heads 12-15 mm thick
            . . . . A. virginiana

A. canadensis L. Canada Anemone. Plants 2-7 dm high, slightly hairy; sepals 5, hairy on the back; fruiting heads spherical. Low ground in woods, meadows, and ditches, throughout the state.

A. caroliniana Walt. Carolina Anemone. Plants 7-18 cm high, sparsely hairy; leaflets 3, these variously cleft; tepals 10-22 mm long, white to rose or purple; fruiting head ellipsoid. Dry prairies in the s. third of the state, from Pipestone, Blue Earth and Goodhue counties n. to Swift, Hennepin, and Washington counties.

A. coronaria L. Poppy Anemone; cultivated. Plants 15-45 cm high; flower single, tepals blue to red to white; anthers blue. From the Mediterranean region.

A. cylindrica Gray. Thimble Weed. Plants 3-10 dm high, slightly hairy; flowers 2-6; tepals 5, greenish to greenish-white, hairy below. Mesic to dry open areas, Houston to Pipestone Co., n. to Washington, Crow Wing, Clearwater, Roseau, and Kittson counties, and in St. Louis and Lake counties.

A. multifida var. hudsoniana DC. Plants 1-6 dm high, usually silky-hairy; flowers 1-3, all but the first peduncle with a pair of leaves; tepals 5-8, whitish to yellowish to red; fruiting head subglobose to short-cylindric. Gravelly and rocky places, found to date only in Mahnomen Co.

A. patens L. Pasque Flower, Wild Crocus . Plants 1-4 dm high; tepals 5-7, white to purplish blue; blooming before or as the basal leaves develop. Prairies and open hillsides, Houston to Rock Co., n. to Washington, Anoka, Otter Tail, Roseau, and Kittson counties, and in Crow Wing Co.

A. quinquefolia var. interior Fernald. Wood Anemone. Plants 1-2 dm high, glabrous or nearly so; leaflets 3-5, irregularly cut; tepals usually 5, whitish, tinged with red below; fruiting head spherical. Mesic to moist woods, Houston to Freeborn Co., n. to Clay, Kittson, and Cook counties.

A. riparia Fernald. Thimble Weed. Similar to A. virginiana; divisions of stem leaves tending to be wedge-shaped at base with straight sides; flowers usually whitish, less often greenish, rarely red. Moist to somewhat dry open woods, thickets, and prairies, Houston to Martin Co., n. to St. Louis, Crow Wing, Clearwater, and Polk counties.

A. virginiana L. Thimble Weed. Plants 4-9 dm high, lightly hairy; divisions of stem leaves mostly convex at base; flowers mostly 2-7; tepals 5, greenish, greenish-yellow, or greenish-white, less often white, rarely tinged with red; fruiting heads thick-cylindric. Moist to mesic open woods, Houston to Martin Co., n. to Clay, Polk, Kittson, and Cook counties.

ANEMONELLA ----- RUE ANEMONE [*]

Perennial glabrous herbs from a cluster of tuberous-thickened roots; leaves ternately compound, the basal ones 2-3 times ternate, the 2 or 3 opposite or whorled stem ones once ternate and sessile and appearing as a whorl of simple leaves; flowers few in an umbel; tepals 5-10, petal-like; stamens many; carpels 4-15; achenes ovoid, 8-10-ribbed. (Diminutive of Anemone.)

A. thalictroides (L.) Spach. Plants 1-2 dm high; leaflets broadly ovate to roundish, 1-3 cm long, 3-toothed on the end; tepals 5-15 mm long, white to pink or pink-purple. Mesic or usually dry somewhat open woods, se. Minnesota, from Houston and Fillmore counties n. to Rice, Hennepin, and Chisago counties.

AQUILEGIA ----- COLUMBINE*

Perennial herbs with alternate 2-3 times ternately compound leaves; leaflets lobed; sepals 5, colored; petals 5, each prolonged backward into a hollow spur; stamens many with an inner series of staminodes; carpels usually 5, each forming a many-seeded follicle. (The name of uncertain origin.)

A-Flowers red and yellow; native . . . . A. canadensis
A-Flowers white, blue, purple, or yellow; cultivated.
  B-Spur strongly hooked, 10-20 mm long . . . . A. vulgaris
  B-Spur straight to slightly incurved, 25-65 mm long.
    C-Stamens not or scarcely exserted; sepals mostly blunt; flowers
      blue and white to white to yellowish-white . . . . A. caerulea
    C-Stamens plainly exserted; sepals sharp-pointed;flowers clear
      yellow. . . . . A. chrysantha

A. caerulea James. Cultivated. Sepals 2-4 cm long; spurs 25-60 mm long. From the Rocky Mountains. This species hybridized with A. chrysantha and others has produced many of the long-spurred hybrids of cultivation and is now outnumbered by them in gardens. The cv. Clematiflora is a spurless form derived from one of these hybrids.

A. canadensis L. Plants 3-20 cm high; leaflets broadly obovate to round-ish; sepals red, 10-20 mm long; petals with yellow blade and nearly straight red spur, the spurs 10-25 mm long; flowers rarely all yellow or salmon-colored. Mesic to moist wooded slopes and rocky cliffs and ledges, through-out the state.

A. chrysantha Gray. Cultivated. Sepals 15-35 mm long; spurs 30-65 mm long. From the Rocky Mountain region and Texas. See A. caerulea.

A. vulgaris L. Garden or European Columbine; cultivated. Flowers blue to purple, white, or pink; sepals 20-30 mm long. From Eurasia.

CALTHA ----- MARSH MARIGOLD

Glabrous perennial herbs with alternate simple broad leaves; tepals 5-9, petal-like; stamens many, staminodes none; carpels 4-many; fruits somewhat flattened, many-seeded. (L. caltha, marigold.)

C. palustris L. Plants 2-6 dm high; leaves broadly heart-shaped, entire to toothed; tepals bright yellow, 12-18 mm long; carpels 4-12. Wet places, throughout most of the state, unrecorded sw. of a line from Traverse to Martin Co. and a few other places.

CLEMATIS ----- CLEMATIS, VIRGIN'S BOWER

Perennial erect herbs to woody vines with opposite simple or com-pound leaves, often dioecious, ours vines climbing by the bending or clasping of the petioles of the compound leaves; flowers single to panicled, medium to large; tepals mostly 4, more or less petal-like; stamens many, the outer sometimes modified into small petal-like staminodes; carpels many, the styles elongate and persistent in fruit. (Gr. klematis, a climbing plant.)

C. verticillaris DC. Trailer to climber; leaves trifoliolate; flowers bi-sexual, single; staminodes present; tepals blue-purple, 3-5 cm long. Rocky woods and thickets, Houston, Wabasha, Carlton, St. Louis, Lake, and Cook counties.

COPTIS ----- GOLDTHREAD*

Low perennial herbs with basal evergreen ternately compound leaves and erect peduncles with whitish flowers; tepals 5-7, petal-like; stamens 15-25; staminodes 5-7, outside and shorter than the stamens, club-shaped, hollow and nectar-bearing at the roundish summit, 1/3-1/2 as long as the tepals; carpels 3-7, on slender stalks, follicles in fruit. (Gr. koptos, cut, from the leaves.)

C. trifolia var. groenlandica (Oeder) Fassett (C. groenlandica (Oeder) Fern.). Rhizomes slender, golden yellow; leaflets 3, toothed; flowers solitary, white, 12-16 mm wide. Damp mossy woods and bogs, Cook to Lake of the Woods Co., s. to Becker, Crow Wing, Hennepin, and Chisago counties, and in Blue Earth Co.

DELPHINIUM ----- LARKSPUR

Erect annual or perennial herbs with alternate palmately lobed or divided leaves; flowers in racemes or panicles, zygomorphic; sepals 5, unequal, somewhat petal-like, the upper one prolonged backward into a spur; petals mostly 4, in 2 unlike pairs, those of the upper pair each with a long spur extending into the spurred sepal; petals sometimes united; stamens many; carpels 1-5, becoming many-seeded follicles. (L. delphin, dolphin, from the shape of the flower.)

D. virescens Nutt. Prairie Larkspur. Perennial 3-15 dm high; stem hairy; leaves deeply cleft into many narrow linear or narrowly lanceolate divisions; flowers in a raceme, greenish-white to white to bluish-white. Grasslands and open woods, Houston to Rock Co., n. to Chisago, Crow Wing, Becker, and Polk counties.

HEPATICA ----- HEPATICA, LIVERLEAF

Low perennial herbs with basal 3-lobed leaves that persist through the winter; flowering stalks 1 or several, each with a calyx-like whorl of 3 simple entire bracts immediately below the single flower; tepals 5-12, petal-like; stamens many, staminodes none; carpels several to many, 1-ovuled, becoming achenes. (L. hepaticus, referring to the liver, from the shape of the leaves.) It has been asserted by J. A. and C. S. Steyermark that our two plants are best considered as varieties of the European H. nobilis Schreb., a disposition not followed here for various reasons. Depth of leaf cutting as used below is measured against the central lobe.

A-Leaves cut 0.62-0.8 of the way to the base, the lobes acute . . H. acutiloba
A-Leaves cut 0.3-0.57 of the way to the base, the lobes blunt
    or rounded . . . . H. americana

H. acutiloba DC. Sharp-lobed Hepatica. Plants 5-15 cm high; leaves occasionally 5-7-lobed; tepals bluish to white to pink to purplish, 6-15 mm long. Mesic to moist wooded slopes, preferring the more neutral to basic

116

soils, Houston to Mower Co., n. to Nicollet, Hennepin, e. Stearns, Morrison, Becker, and Washington counties.

H. americana (DC.) Ker. Round-lobed Hepatica. Similar to H. acutiloba; leaves 3-lobed. Mesic to moist wooded slopes, preferring the more acid soils, from Lake to Koochiching and se. Polk counties, s. to Otter Tail, Ramsey, Wabasha, Olmsted, and Fillmore counties.

HYDRASTIS ----- GOLDEN SEAL, ORANGE-ROOT*

Erect perennial herbs with alternate leaves from a knotty, yellow rhizome; flowers single, terminal; tepals 3, petal-like; stamens many; carpels many, each with 2 ovules, forming in fruit a small head of 1-2-seeded berries resembling a raspberry. (Name of doubtful origin.)

H. canadensis L. Plants 1.5-3.5 dm high with 1 basal leaf and 2 smaller stem leaves, leaves 5-7-lobed, doubly serrate; flowers greenish-white. Rich moist soil in woods, Winona Co.

ISOPYRUM*

Slender glabrous perennial herbs; leaves alternate and basal, 1-3 times ternately compound; flowers axillary and terminal, 1 or 2 together; tepals mostly 5, petal-like; stamens many, staminodes in ours none; carpels 3-6 or more, becoming 2-several-seeded follicles. (Gr. isopyron, name of a plant similar to this one.)

I. biternatum (Raf.) T. & G. False Rue Anemone. Roots with small tuber-like thickenings; plants to 4 dm high; stem leaves progressively reduced upwards in size and number of divisions; leaflets broadly obovate, 2-3-lobed; flowers white, 1.5-2 cm wide; follicles mostly 4. Moist rich soil in woods in the southeast. Houston to Mower Co., n. to Blue Earth, Hennepin, Ramsey, and Washington counties.

MYOSURUS ----- MOUSE TAIL*

Small annuals with linear basal leaves and 1-flowered leafless peduncles; sepals 5, each spurred at the base; petals 5 (or none) with a nectariferous pit at the summit of the long slender base; stamens 5-20; carpels many on a long slender receptacle which elongates greatly in fruit, the achenes closely packed. (Gr. myos, of a mouse, oura, tail.)

M. minimus L. Plant 3-15 cm high; leaves linear or nearly so; flowers yellowish-green; sepals 4.5-7.5 mm long including the spur; receptacle to 6 cm long in fruit. Moist open areas and edges of rocky pools, Rock, Pipestone, Big Stone, Chippewa, and Nicollet counties.

RANUNCULUS ----- BUTTERCUP, CROWFOOT*

Annual or perennial herbs with alternate leaves; flowers yellow, white, or rarely red (not ours); sepals (3-) 5, rarely more; petals mostly 5, each with a nectariferous pit and small scale on the upper surface near the base; stamens mostly many; carpels many, 1-ovuled; fruit an achene bearing the hardened and often enlarged style, the "beak". (L. ranunculus, little frog.)

An irritating juice has been found in several species; of ours, these are R.
abortivus, acris, cymbalaria, flammula, repens, and sceleratus.

A-Petals white, sometimes tinged with yellow at the base; plants aquatic.
  B-Petiole above the stipules about as long as the stipular part; leaves soft,
    tending to collapse when taken from water; achenes 10-20 (-40), beak
    0.2-0.5 mm long, pedicels not recurved . . R. aquatilis var. capillaceus
  B-Petiole above the stipules none or much shorter than the stipular
    part; leaves less apt to collapse when taken from water; achenes
    (7-) 15-45 (-80), beak 0.2-1.1 mm long; pedicels recurved or not.
    C-Beak of achene 0.2-0.5 mm long; achenes 30-45 (-80); mature
      pedicels tending to be recurved . . . . R. circinatus var. subrigidus
    C-Beak of achene 0.7-1.1 mm long; achenes (7-) 15-25; pedicels
      not recurved . . . . R. longirostris
A-Petals yellow; plants terrestrial or aquatic.
  D-Leaves all entire to strongly crenate.
    E-Leaves linear to narrowly elliptic to lanceolate . . . . . R. flammula
    E-Leaves cordate-ovate to ovate or kidney-shaped . . . . R. cymbalaria
  D-Leaves all or some of them deeply lobed, dissected, or compound.
    F-Basal leaf blades all or some cut less than 1/4 of the way to
      the base, the stem leaves much more deeply cut.
      G-Petals 1.5-3.5 mm long; plants glabrous to puberulent
        . . . . R. abortivus
      G-Petals 5-9 mm long; plants mostly spreading-hairy. R. rhomboideus
    F-Basal leaf blades cut about 1/2 or more of the way to the base,
      the stem leaves similar or more deeply cut, or no separation
      into basal and stem leaves possible.
      H-Either submerged or floating aquatics, or the plants with
        prostrate running stems eventually rooting at the nodes.
        I-Plants terrestrial, in mesic to wet grasslands and road-
          sides, usually with hairy runners; central division of
          the leaves on a definite unwinged stalk; achenes some-
          what flattened. . . . . R. repens
        I-Plants aquatic or terrestrial on mud banks or in swamps
          or bogs, usually with glabrous runners; emergent leaves
          with the central division winged to the base with blade
          tissue, the submerged leaves if any deeply dissected into
          linear segments 1-4 mm wide; achenes plump.
          J-Flowers single on erect stalks; sepals 3 (-4); achenes
            3.5-5 mm long including the beak; submerged leaves
            none; teeth of the leaf lobes very blunt. . . . . . R. lapponicus
          J-Flowers often more than one, the stalks not always erect;
            sepals 5; achenes 1.5-3.5 mm long including the beak;
            submerged leaves present or absent; teeth of leaf lobes
            often acute.
            K-Segments of submerged leaves mostly 1-2 mm wide;
              petals mostly 6-14 mm long; margins of achenes be-
              low the middle thickened and corky; achenes 2-3.5
              mm long including the beak, the beak 0.7-1.5 mm
              long . . . . R. flabellaris
            K-Segments of submerged leaves mostly 2-4 mm wide;
              petals 3.5-8 mm long; margins of achenes not con-
              spicuously corky; achenes 1.2-2 mm long including
              beak, the beak 0.4-0.7 mm long . . . . R. gmelini
      H-Terrestrial plants with mostly erect stems, often in wet places.
      L-Petals 2-7.5 mm long, if over 5.5 mm then the achene beak
        0.5-1.2 mm long and the receptacle in fruit 4-8 mm long.

M-Central division of basal leaves and often of the stem leaves
winged to the base with blade tissue; either the styles and
achene beaks hooked back and down or the achenes 0.8-1.2
mm long excluding the beak.
  N-Plants usually glabrous; styles and achene beaks straight
to somewhat curved, not hooked; achenes 0.8-1.2 mm
long excluding beak; petals 2-4.5 mm long . . <u>R</u>. <u>sceleratus</u>
  N-Plants hairy; styles and achene beaks strongly hooked
back and down; achenes 2-2.7 mm long excluding beak;
petals 3.5-6 mm long . . . . <u>R</u>. <u>recurvatus</u>
M-Central and often the lateral divisions of basal and larger
stem leaves on definite unwinged stalks; styles and
achene beaks straight to somewhat curved, not hooked;
achenes 1.7-3.3 mm long excluding beak.
  O-Petals shorter than to equaling the sepals, 1.3-3.2 mm
wide; carpels in flower 1-1.4 mm long; head of achenes 5-
8 mm thick, 1.2-2.2 times as long as thick . . . <u>R</u>. <u>pensylvanicus</u>
  O-Petals equaling to longer than the sepals, 2.5-6.5 mm
wide; carpels in flower 1.3-2.5 mm long; head of achenes
7-9 mm thick, 1-1.3 times as long as thick . . . . . . <u>R</u>. <u>macounii</u>
L-Petals 7-17 mm long, either beak or receptacle not as above.
  P-Styles slightly curved, stigmatic only at the tip, mostly
0.8-1.6 mm long; achene beaks 1.4-3 mm long.
    Q-Lateral leaflets on definite wingless stalks; lateral
lobes of leaflets 5-25 mm wide, oblanceolate to obovate
to broadly oblong; petals 5-12 mm wide; thickened roots
mostly more than 5 cm long . . . . <u>R</u>. <u>septentrionalis</u>
    Q-Lateral leaflets sessile, winged to the base; lateral lobes
of leaflets 2-5 mm wide, oblanceolate to linear to narrowly oblong to lanceolate; petals 3-6 mm wide; thickened
roots 5 cm or less long . . . . <u>R</u>. <u>fascicularis</u>
  P-Styles outcurved, stigmatic along the upper (inner) side,
0.3-0.6 mm long; achene beaks 0.4-1.4 mm long.
    R-Leaves with 3-5 palmate divisions, the divisions usually
but not always winged to the base, usually much cleft
into linear to lanceolate lobes; achene beaks 0.4-1.0
mm long . . . . <u>R</u>. <u>acris</u>
    R-Leaves once or twice ternately divided, the terminal
and often the lateral divisions on definite wingless
stalks, the divisions obovate to roundish, mostly
cleft into ovate to oblong lobes; achene beaks 0.8-
1.4 mm long . . . . <u>R</u>. <u>repens</u>

<u>R</u>. <u>abortivus</u> L. Small-flowered Crowfoot. Erect mostly glabrous plants;
sal leaves roundish, mostly only crenate, some cleft; petals pale yellow,
orter than the sepals; achenes 1.2-1.5 mm long. Mostly on damp ground,
roughout the state.

<u>R</u>. <u>acris</u> L. Tall or Meadow Buttercup. Plants glabrous, or hairy below;
tals bright yellow, twice as long as the sepals; achenes 2-3 mm long ex-
uding beak. Introduced from Europe; in fields and roadsides, e. of a line
rough (and including) Houston, Scott, Kandiyohi, Polk, and Lake of the Woods
unties.

<u>R</u>. <u>aquatilis</u> var. <u>capillaceus</u> (Thuill.) DC. (<u>R</u>. <u>trichophyllus</u> Chaix).
hite Water-crowfoot. Submerged aquatic, the leaves finely dissected into
near segments; flowers at the surface of the water, 1-1.5 cm wide; achenes
2.5 mm long excluding beak. Lakes and streams, throughout the state.

R. circinatus var. subrigidus (Drew) Benson (R. subrigidus Drew). White Water-crowfoot. Very similar to R. longirostris, and in at least parts of our area not clearly distinguished from it. Lakes, streams, and other aquatic habitats, widely scattered nw. of a line through (and including) Rock and St. Louis counties, unrecorded from many counties.

R. cymbalaria Pursh. Seaside Crowfoot. Plants glabrous, 5-15 cm high; leaves mostly basal; petals 3-5 mm long, hardly exceeding the sepals; achenes ca. 1.5-2 mm long excluding beak. Wet soil, especially in alkaline places, sw. of a line through (and including) Goodhue, Wadena, and Roseau counties, and in St. Louis and Lake counties.

R. fascicularis Muhl. Early Crowfoot. Some roots slender, some thickened and up to 5 cm long; plants pubescent; achenes 1.5-3.2 mm long excluding beak. Prairies and dry woods, Houston to Pipestone Co., n. to Renville, Stearns, and Chisago counties.

R. flabellaris Raf. Yellow Water-crowfoot. Emergent leaves (when present) triternately cleft and lobed; flowers few, mostly terminal. Quiet water and muddy shores over most of the state, unrecorded from Roseau to Itasca and Koochiching counties and from Rock to Faribault to Wabasha Co. and southward.

R. flammula L. Creeping Spearwort. Leaves entire or slightly toothed; petals 3-7 mm long; achenes 1.3-1.7 mm long excluding beak. Muddy to gravelly shores.

A-Basal leaf blades 0.5-1.5 mm wide; Cook to Lake of the Woods Co., s. to Clearwater, Mille Lacs, Hennepin, Blue Earth, and Dakota counties. . R. f. var. filiformis (Michx.) Hook. (R. reptans L.).
A-Basal blades 1.5-7 (-20) mm wide; St. Louis Co. . . . .
. . . . R. f. var ovalis (Bigel.) Benson.

R. gmelini DC. Yellow Water-crowfoot. Similar to R. flabellaris. Seldom completely emergent. Shallow water and muddy shores.

A-Plants glabrous or nearly so; sepals 4-6 mm long; petals mostly 4-8 mm long; St. Louis to Kittson Co., s. to Clearwater, Morrison, Scott, and Blue Earth counties . . . R. g. var. hookeri (D. Don) Benson.
A-Plants tending to be hairy; sepals 2.5-3 mm long; petals 3.5-4 mm long; Aitkin and St. Louis counties . . . . . . R. g. var. gmelini.

R. lapponicus L. Rhizomes slender, elongate, bearing 1 or 2 basal leaves and a flowering stalk at each node. Wooded swamps and bogs, St. Louis to Aitkin to Koochiching Co.

R. longirostris Godr. White Water-crowfoot. Submerged aquatic, the leaves finely dissected into linear segments; flowers at the surface of the water, 1-1.5 cm wide; achenes 1.3-1.7 mm long excluding beak. Very similar to R. circinatus var. subrigidus, and at least in parts of our area not clearly distinguished from it. Lakes, streams, and other aquatic habitats throughout the state except for Cook and Lake counties.

R. macounii Britt. Plants usually hairy, stems sometimes rooting; petals 3.5-7.5 mm long; achene body 2.6-3.4 mm long. Marshes and wet meadows Kittson to Lake of the Woods, Beltrami, and Clay counties, and in Cook Co.

R. pensylvanicus L. Bristly Crowfoot. Plants hairy; petals 2-5 mm long; achene body 1.7-2.7 mm long. Marshes, ditches, and damp low ground throughout the state.

R. recurvatus Poir. Hooked Crowfoot. Leaves 3-cleft, the basal ones sometimes cut only about half way to the base; petals pale yellow. Moist to mesic woods, Houston and Fillmore counties n. to Blue Earth, Hennepin, ne. Todd, and Lake counties.

R. repens L. Creeping Buttercup. Usually creepers with hairy runners, sometimes erect; sepals 5; petals 8-15 mm long; achenes 2-3.5 mm long excluding beak. From Europe; mesic to wet grasslands and roadsides, recorded from Winona and s. St. Louis counties.

R. rhomboideus Goldie. Prairie Crowfoot. Plants erect; basal leaves ovate to ovate-oblong or rhombic, mostly crenate; achenes in a globose head, 2-2.8 mm long excluding beak. Mesic to dry grasslands and open woods, Houston to Rock Co., n. to Washington, Crow Wing, Lake of the Woods, and Kittson counties.

R. sceleratus L. Cursed Crowfoot. Basal leaves often cut only about half way to the base, the stem leaves more deeply cut. Streambanks and other damp locations, Kittson to Rock Co., e. to Jackson, Wabasha, Crow Wing, and Lake of the Woods counties, and in the Duluth area. Two varieties are supposed to exist in our area, R. s. var. sceleratus with the primary divisions of the basal leaves only lobed and the central achene surfaces minutely ridged, and R. s. var. multifidus Nutt. with the primary divisions usually deeply cleft into oblong to lanceolate lobes and the achene surfaces smooth except for a circle of tiny pin-point depressions. In most of our plants the achene surfaces are smoothish while in a few they are ridged, but there is little or no correlation between ridging and depth of lobing of the basal leaves.

R. septentrionalis Poir. (including R. carolinianus DC.). Swamp Buttercup. Plants more or less hairy; usually developing stolons; roots somewhat thickened or not; achenes 3-4.5 mm long excluding beak. Moist places in woods and grasslands, throughout most of the state, unrecorded from Cook and several other counties.

THALICTRUM ----- MEADOW RUE*

Erect perennial herbs with alternate, 2-4 times ternately compound leaves, the stem leaves with expanded sheathing bases; flowers bisexual or unisexual, our species dioecious or polygamo-dioecious; inflorescence a much-branched panicle; flowers greenish, yellowish, purplish or whitish; tepals 4-5, soon falling; stamens many; carpels 4-15, becoming veined or ribbed achenes. (A name of some plant mentioned by Dioscorides.)

A-Leaflets usually longer than wide, mostly with 3 entire lobes; middle
    and upper stem leaves sessile or subsessile . . . . T. dasycarpum
A-Leaflets as wide as long or broader, many or all with 4 or more
    teeth or lobes, these usually taking the form of 3 lobes each with
    1-3 teeth; at least the middle stem leaves petioled.
  B-Upper stem leaf (at base of inflorescence) with petiole 2-6 cm long;
    leaves barely expanded as flowers appear; stem from a short thick
    rootstock . . . . T. dioicum
  B-Upper stem leaf sessile or the petiole up to 1 cm long; leaves
    well formed as flowers appear; stem from a stout horizontal
    rhizome.
    C-Stems mostly 3-7 dm high; leaflets of the larger leaves mostly
      1-3 cm wide; anthers 2-3.5 mm long, with a tip 0.1-0.4 mm
      long; stigma 1-2.5 mm long; achene body 3-4 mm long
      . . . . T. venulosum
    C-Stems to 10 dm high; leaflets of the larger leaves mostly 1.5-
      4 cm wide; anthers 2-4 mm long, with a tip 0.4-1 mm long;
      stigma 2-5 mm long; achene body 4-6 mm long . . . . . T. confine

T. confine Fern.   Petioles of lower leaves to 10 cm long; fruiting pedicels 8-25 mm long.   Rocky and sandy soil, especially along streams, in the s. 1/2 of St. Louis Co.   Our material doubtfully distinguished from T. venulosum.

T. dasycarpum Fisch. & Ave-Lall.   Tall Meadow Rue.   Stem from a short thick rootstock with short offshoots; lowest stem leaves with petioles to 11 cm long; leaflets usually puberulent beneath; anthers 1.5-3.5 mm long, with a tip 0.1-0.4 mm long; stigmas 2-4.5 mm long, about equalling the body of the carpel; achenes 4-6 mm long.   Rich moist soil, throughout the state.   Plants glabrous throughout are called T. d. var. hypoglaucum (Rydb.) Boivin; our only record for this var. is from Fillmore Co.

T. dioicum L.   Early Meadow Rue.   Petioles of lower stem leaves to 20 cm long; anthers 2-3.5 mm long; stigmas 1.5-3 mm long; achenes 2.6-4.5 mm long.   Mesic to moist woods, throughout the state except for the extreme sw. and nw. corners and Cook Co.

T. venulosum Trel.   Petioles of lower leaves to 10 cm long; fruiting pedicels 3-15 mm long.   Sandy or rocky soil in prairies or open woods, St. Louis to n. Otter Tail, Clay, and Kittson counties.

TROLLIUS ----- GLOBE FLOWER

Perennial herbs with alternate palmately cut leaves; flowers terminal, mostly single, large, yellow to whitish to purplish; tepals 5-15, petal-like; stamens many, surrounded by a series of 5-many narrow staminodes (sometimes interpreted as petals) each with a nectar pit at base; carpels 5-many, becoming a cluster of follicles.   (From the Ger. common name, Trollblume.)

T. europaeus L.   Cultivated.   Basal leaves petioled, stem leaves sessile, 5-parted or compound, the divisions toothed; flowers lemon-yellow; staminodes about as long as the stamens; tepals 10-15.   From Europe.

PAEONIACEAE ----- PEONY FAMILY

Perennial herbs or subshrubs; leaves alternate and basal, ternately, twice ternately, or pinnately compound or cleft, the leaflets entire to many times dissected; flowers bisexual, regular, hypogynous, large and showy, usually terminal and solitary but sometimes clustered, red, purple, white, or yellow; sepals 5, free, unequal; petals 5 or sometimes 6-10; stamens many, free, the innermost developing first; carpels 2-5, free, on a fleshy receptacle, becoming follicles; seeds large, wholly or partly covered with an additional tissue layer, the "aril".

PAEONIA ----- PEONY

Characters those of the family.   (Ancient name, said to commemorate a physician Paeon.)

A-Plant shrubby; receptacle enlarging in fruit, becoming 19 mm wide
    or wider . . . . P. suffruticosa
A-Plants herbaceous; receptacle enlarging only slightly or not at all.
    B-Leaflets glabrous above, the divisions acute . . . . P. tenuifolia
    B-Leaflets sparsely hairy along the nerves above, the divisions
        acute to long-attenuate . . . . P. anomala

P. anomala L. Cultivated. Root tuberous; stolons absent; leaves biternate, the leaflets many times cleft into narrow divisions; outer sepals often extended into lobed leaf-like ends; petals 8-10, obovate to oblong, crimson to magenta. Eurasia.

P. suffruticosa Haw. Tree Peony; cultivated. Shrub to 17 dm high; leaves biternate, their smallest divisions ovate to broadly elliptic and mostly 3-5-lobed, whitish below, sparsely pubescent; petals 8 or more, obovate, crenate or irregularly toothed, red or rose-red to white. China.

P. tenuifolia L. Cultivated. Roots large, clustered; stolons produced; leaves ternate, cut into many narrow divisions; petals 8-10, elliptic-wedge-shaped, dark crimson to purple. Se. Europe and the Caucasus.

BERBERIDACEAE ----- BARBERRY FAMILY

Herbs or shrubs with alternate or basal or in Podophyllum a pair of opposite leaves, leaves simple to compound; flowers 1 to many, bisexual, regular, all parts free, tending to be trimerous; perianth differentiated or not; sepals 4 or 6, sometimes early deciduous; petals as many as the sepals or more; stamens 4-18, hypogynous, either as many as the petals and opposite them, the anthers opening by uplifting flaps, or (in Podophyllum) twice as many with anthers opening lengthwise; pistil 1, 1-locular, thought to be 1 carpel; ovules 1-many; fruit a berry or capsule.

A-Spiny shrubs . . . . BERBERIS
A-Herbs.
  B-Flowers several, yellow-green to greenish-purple . . CAULOPHYLLUM
  B-Flower single, white.
    C-Flowering stem with one pair of opposite leaves . . PODOPHYLLUM
    C-Leaves all basal . . . . JEFFERSONIA

BERBERIS ----- BARBERRY

Shrubs, usually spiny, the primary leaves of the shoots often modified into spines, with axillary clusters of small leaves; flowers yellow, in racemes, umbel-like clusters, or single; sepals 6, with 2 or 3 outer bractlets tending to grade into the sepals; petals 6, usually smaller than the sepals and each with 2 basal glands; stamens 6; ovules 1-few; fruit a berry. (The Arabic name for the fruit.)

B. thunbergii DC. Japanese Barberry; cultivated. To 2 m high; spines usually simple; leaves obovate to oblanceolate, entire; flowers single or a few in umbel-like clusters, 8 mm wide; fruit bright red. From Japan. Forms with deep purple to bronze-red leaves have been termed **B. t.** cv. Atropurpurea.

CAULOPHYLLUM ----- BLUE COHOSH*

Erect glabrous perennial herbs; leaves triternate but sessile, thus resembling 3 biternate leaves; flowers in panicles or rarely racemes; sepals 6, petal-like, with 3 or 4 outer sepal-like bractlets; petals 6, much shorter than the sepals, thick and gland-like; stamens 6; ovules 2, bursting and exceeding the ovary wall in growth, ripening into 2 globose stalked blue seeds resembling berries. (Gr. kaulos, stalk, phyllon, leaf, the stem seeming to be the stalk of the leaf.)

C. thalictroides (L.) Michx. 3-8 dm high; leaflets obovate-oblong, 2-5-lobed above the middle, 5-8 cm long; flowers yellow-green or greenish-purple, 8-9 mm wide. Rich soil in mesic to moist woods, throughout the state except n. and e. of an arc through s. Lake, s. Itasca, and Lake of the Woods counties and the w. tier of counties except Clay, and several others interspersed.

JEFFERSONIA ----- TWINLEAF*

Glabrous perennial herbs with long-petioled deeply 2-parted basal leaves; flowers single on leafless stalks; sepals usually 4, early deciduous; petals usually 8; stamens 8; ovules many; fruit a capsule, splitting halfway around horizontally. (Named for Thomas Jefferson.)

J. diphylla (L.) Pers. Leaf blades eventually 8-15 cm long; flowering stalk 1-2 dm high; flowers white, 2-3 cm wide. Rich soil in mesic to moist woods, Houston and Winona counties.

PODOPHYLLUM ----- MAY APPLE*

Erect perennial herbs from rhizomes; leaves palmately lobed; flowering stem with one pair of opposite leaves and a single terminal flower between them; flower bud with 3 green bractlets which fall early; sepals 6, falling early; petals 6-9; stamens (in ours) twice as many as the petals; fruit a large fleshy many-seeded berry. (Gr. podos, foot, phyllon, leaf.)

P. peltatum L. Basal leaves peltate; stem leaves half-round to peltate; flower nodding, white, 3-5 cm wide; fruit yellow, 3-5 cm long, edible; seeds and herbage poisonous. Rich soil in open woods or at edges of woods, from Houston to Freeborn, Steele, Rice, and Goodhue counties.

MENISPERMACEAE ----- MOONSEED FAMILY

Dioecious twining vines with alternate simple mostly palmately veined leaves; flowers in racemes or panicles, mostly trimerous, regular, hypogynous; perianth not sharply differentiated, its parts usually in 4 alternating whorls, the outer 2, the "calyx", exceeding the inner 2, the "corolla", or the corolla absent; stamens usually 6 (3-many), free or fused; carpels separate, typically 3, sometimes fewer or more; ovule 1, pendulous; fruit a drupe.

MENISPERMUM ----- MOONSEED*

Leaves peltate near the margin; sepals 4-8; petals 4-8; stamens 12-24; carpels 2-4; drupe nearly spherical, its stone flattened and roundish or half-moon-shaped. (Gr. mene, moon, and sperma, seed.)

M. canadense L. Leaves broadly ovate to nearly round, entire to shallowly 3-7-lobed, 10-15 cm wide and long; flowers greenish-white, small; fruit bluish-black, its stone flat and roundish. Mesic to moist thickets and open woods, Hou ton to Pipestone Co., n. to Ramsey, Meeker, Clearwater, and Kittson counties.

MAGNOLIACEAE ----- MAGNOLIA FAMILY

Trees or shrubs with alternate simple leaves; flowers large, regular, mostly bisexual, hypogynous; perianth mostly of 3 or more whorls of 3 free members each, the outer one usually somewhat differentiated from the inner; stamens many, free; carpels many, spiralled, on an elongate axis (receptacle), free or somewhat united; ovules 1-few per carpel; fruit various.

MAGNOLIA

Flowers solitary, bisexual; perianth of 9-15 members (in 3-5 whorls); filaments short, anthers long and introrse; fruiting gynoecium a cone-like cluster of carpels, each splitting down the outer side, the fleshy seeds remaining attached for a while by slender threads. (Named for Pierre Magnol, French botanist.) A few species besides the following are sometimes grown in Minnesota.

M. acuminata L. Cucumber Tree; cultivated. Tree to 25 m high; leaves oblong to elliptic, 10-20 cm long; perianth parts 9, greenish-yellow, the inner ones 5-8 cm long. S. Ontario, and e. and s. United States.

PAPAVERACEAE ----- POPPY FAMILY

Herbs or rarely shrubs or trees, usually with milky or colored sap; leaves mostly alternate; flowers bisexual, regular, hypogynous; sepals 2 or 3, mostly early deciduous; petals 4-12, separate, often twice as many as the sepals; stamens mostly many; carpels fused, the ovary 1-locular with many ovules on parietal placentas, or rarely 2- or more-locular through the production of secondary partitions; fruit usually a capsule.

A-Leaves palmately lobed; petals 8-16, white; native . . . . . SANGUINARIA
A-Leaves pinnately lobed to divided; petals 4-6, white, yellow, or
  red; cultivated.
  B-Flowers single on long stalks; stigmas 4 or more, united into
    a disk. . . . . PAPAVER
  B-Flowers in stalked umbels; stigma 2-lobed . . . . CHELIDONIUM

CHELIDONIUM ----- CELANDINE

Biennial herbs with acrid yellow sap; leaves alternate, once or twice pinnately cleft; flowers yellow, in few-flowered stalked umbels; sepals 2; petals 4; stamens 16-24; ovary 1-locular, of 2 carpels with a 2-lobed stigma; capsule linear, separating into 2 segments from the base upward. (Gr. chelidon, the swallow, of varying interpretation.)

C. majus L. Cultivated. 3-8 dm high; petals ca. 1 cm long; fruit 3-5 cm long. From Eurasia.

PAPAVER ----- POPPY

Annual, biennial, or perennial herbs with milky juice; leaves alternate, lobed or dissected; flowers single on usually long stalks, large and showy; sepals 2 (rarely 3), falling as the flower opens; petals 4 (-6); stamens many; carpels fused, 4-many; stigmas as many, united into a flat-topped "disk"; ovary 1-locular with parietal placentas, rarely some placentas meeting in the center; fruit a many-seeded capsule, opening by pores near the top. (The Latin name of the poppy.)

A-Flowers on leafless stems, white, yellow, orange, or reddish
. . . . P. nudicaule
A-Flowers on leafy stems, scarlet with usually a dark violet spot at
base . . . . P. orientale

P. nudicaule L. Iceland Poppy; cultivated. Leaves pinnately lobed or parted, the blades 4-8 cm long; flowers fragrant, 2.5-8 cm across; capsule ca. 15 mm long. Arctic regions in both hemispheres.

P. orientale L. Oriental Poppy; cultivated. Leaves pinnately parted, to 40 cm long; flowers 10-15 cm across; capsule ca. 25 mm long. Mediterranean region to Iran.

SANGUINARIA ----- BLOODROOT*

Low perennial herb from a thick rhizome with orange-red sap; leaves basal, palmately veined and lobed; flower single on a leafless stalk; sepals 2, falling as flower opens; petals 8 (-16); stamens many; ovary 1-locular, of 2 fused carpels, with 2 parietal placentas, fruit a many-seeded capsule, its 2 halves falling away from the persistent placentas. (L. sanguinarius, bleeding, from the color of the sap.)

S. canadensis L. Leaf roundish in overall outline, to 2 dm wide at maturity 3-9-lobed; flowers white or rarely pink, 2-5 cm wide; fruit 3-5 cm long. Rich soil in mesic to moist woods, throughout the state except for Cook and n. Lake counties and many counties along or near the w. border of the state.

FUMARIACEAE ----- FUMITORY FAMILY

Glabrous herbs with dissected or compound leaves and watery sap; flowers in racemes or panicles, bisexual, hypogynous, with bilateral symmetry; sepals 2, falling early; petals 4, usually lightly fused, 1 or 2 of the outer ones spurred or saccate at base, the inner ones narrow below, more or less enlarged above; stamens 4 or 6, if 6 then in 2 groups of 3, each group with 1 4-sporangiate stamen and 2 2-sporangiate ones; ovary 1-locular with 2 parietal placentas; ovules 2-many; fruit a capsule or nut.

A-Flowers laterally compressed; 2 petals with short spurs or pouches at
base, the flowers 2-spurred or heart-shaped as seen from the side
. . . . DICENTRA
A-Flowers not compressed; 1 petal spurred . . . . CORYDALIS

CORYDALIS*

Annual, biennial, or perennial herbs with alternate twice pinnately dissected leaves; flowers in racemes or panicles, yellow to pink-purple; uppermost petal with a short spur at base; stamens 6; capsule slender, many-seeded. (Gr. korydalis, a crested lark.)

A-Flowers pinkish or greenish-purple, with yellow tips . . . . C. sempervirens
A-Flowers yellow.
  B-Outer petals each folded near the end into a lengthwise hollow keel
    or ridge; spurred petal 13-16 mm long; fruit 15-30 mm long
    . . . . C. aurea ssp. aurea

B-Outer petals each with a narrow but distinct flat lengthwise wing
    along the center line near the end; spurred petal 11-15 mm
    long; fruit 10-15 (-20) mm long . . . . . . C. micrantha ssp. micrantha

C. aurea Willd., subsp. aurea. Annual or biennial; flowers in racemes,
often exceeded by the leaves; spur 3.5-5 mm long; fruiting pedicels 4-10 mm
long; cleistogamous flowers rare; seeds nearly 2 mm thick. Rocky banks or
sandy or gravelly soil, Cook to Kittson Co., s. to Clay, Stevens, Redwood,
Blue Earth and Houston counties.

C. micrantha (Engelm.) Gray, subsp. micrantha. Annual; flowers in
racemes, usually exceeding the leaves; spur 4.5-6 mm long; fruiting pedicels
2-5 mm long; cleistogamous flowers common; seeds ca. 1.5 mm thick.
Sandy, gravelly, or rocky soil, Houston to Nobles and Pipestone counties, n.
to Brown and Hennepin counties and in Chippewa Co.

C. sempervirens (L.) Pers. Biennial; flowers in racemes or panicles;
spurred petal 10-15 mm long; spur 2.5-4 mm long; seeds ca. 1 mm thick.
Rocky places and openings in the woods, Cook to Lake of the Woods Co., s.
to Clearwater, Morrison, and Chisago counties.

DICENTRA ----- BLEEDING HEART, DUTCHMAN'S BREECHES*

      Perennial herbs often with rhizomes, tubers, or bulblets formed from
modified petiole bases; leaves basal or alternate, several times compound;
flowers white to red, single or in racemes or panicles, appearing laterally
compressed; sepals minute; petals weakly united, the outer 2 large, spurred
or saccate at base; stamens 6; fruit a 10-20-seeded capsule. (Gr. dis, twice,
and kentron, spur.)

A-Leafy stem present, the inflorescence terminal or axillary on it;
    cultivated . . . . D. spectabilis
A-Leaves all basal, the inflorescence on a leafless stem; native or
    cultivated.
  B-Flowers in a raceme, white or whitish tinged with rose; native.
    C-Spurs mostly 6-10 mm long, 2/5-3/5 the length of the flower
    . . . . D. cucullaria
    C-Spurs mostly 3-5 mm long, ca. 1/5 as long as the flower
    . . . . D. canadensis
  B-Flowers in a panicle, rose-purple to pink (rarely white);
    cultivated . . . . D. eximia

D. canadensis Walp. Squirrel Corn. Plants from short rootstocks; bulblets yellow, pea-shaped; flowers 10-20 mm long, nodding, very fragrant.
Rich soil in mesic deciduous woods, often in rocky places, Winona Co.

D. cucullaria (L.) Bernh. Dutchman's Breeches. Plants from short
rootstocks; bulblets white to pink, tear-shaped (about half as large as in D.
canadensis); flowers 10-20 mm long, pendent. Rich soil in mesic deciduous
woods, Houston to Rock Co., n. to Big Stone, Otter Tail, Beltrami, and s.
St. Louis counties.

D. eximia (Ker) Torr. Wild Bleeding Heart, Turkey Corn; cultivated.
Plants from stout scaly rhizomes, without bulblets or tubers; flowers 15-
30 mm long, 8-14 mm wide, pendent, the spurs 2-3 mm long. Mountains of
e. North America.

D. spectabilis (L.) Lam. Bleeding Heart; cultivated. Plants from taproots, without bulblets or tubers; flowers in racemes, rose-purple to pink

(rarely white), pendent, 20-30 mm long, 16-22 mm wide, the spurs 3-7 mm long. E. Asia.

BRASSICACEAE (CRUCIFERAE) ----- MUSTARD FAMILY

Ours all annual to perennial herbs; leaves exstipulate, simple to compound, mostly alternate; flowers usually in bractless racemes, bisexual, mostly regular, hypogynous; sepals 4, free; petals 4 (rarely 0), free; stamens 6 (very rarely fewer or more), 4 long and 2 shorter; ovary usually of 2 united carpels, 2-locular with parietal placentas at the outer edges of the partition; stigmas 2 or 1; ovules 1-many per locule; fruit usually a capsule (sometimes indehiscent) opening by the separation of the two outer halves or "valves" from the partition; fruit often tipped by the persistent style and its broadened base, together termed the "beak", the beak usually sharply narrowed from the dehiscent body of the fruit containing the seeds (rarely a few seeds present in the base of the beak itself). Fruit often necessary for accurate identification.

A-Petals yellowish to orange.
  B-Leaves all or some pinnately compound or cleft at least halfway to
    the midrib, at least at the base of the blade.
    C-Leaves, at least the lowermost ones, 2 or more times finely cleft.
      D-All leaves cleft at least once . . . . DESCURAINIA
      D-Middle and upper stem leaves entire (except for their large
        basal lobes) . . . . Lepidium perfoliatum
    C-Leaves once cleft to once compound.
      E-Stem leaves, at least the middle and upper ones, with short
        lobes at base, one on each side of the stem.
        F-Upper leaves sessile, entire to shallowly toothed; beak of
          ovary 1.5-3 mm long, of fruit 8-15 mm long .. Brassica rapa
        F-Upper leaves sessile or petioled, wavy-edged to usually
          sharply toothed or pinnately cleft at least at base; beak of
          ovary 0.2-1.8 mm long, of fruit 0.3-3 mm long.
          G-Terminal lobe of basal leaves 2.5-8 times as wide as the
            lateral lobes, oblong to roundish, broadly rounded; fruits
            8-25 times as long as wide, the seeds in 1 row per locule
            . . . . BARBAREA
          G-Terminal lobe of basal leaves only rarely as wide as above;
            fruits 1.5-6 times as long as wide, the seeds in 2 rows
            per locule. . . . . RORIPPA
      E-Stem leaves unlobed at base.
        H-Fruits 2-6 mm thick, with a beak 1.5-18 mm long, if the
          beak less than 4.5 mm long then the upper leaves toothed,
          not cleft; petals 6.5-14 mm long . . . . BRASSICA
        H-Fruits 1-1.3 mm thick; beak 0.5-3 mm long; upper leaves
          mostly pinnately cleft or deeply lobed at least at base of
          blade; petals 2.5-9 mm long.
          I-Annuals or biennials of dry and disturbed ground; fruits
            10-100 mm long, straight or very slightly curved, each
            valve with 3 fine lengthwise nerves; seeds in 1 row per
            locule . . . . SISYMBRIUM
          I-Perennial of damp habitats; fruits 5-14 mm long including
            beak, usually upwardly curved, each valve nerveless or
            with a very obscure midnerve; seeds in 2 rows per locule
            . . . . Rorippa sinuata
  B-Leaves simple, entire or toothed, cut less than half way to the midrib.

J-Stem leaves all or some with short backwardly directed lobes at
    base, one on each side of the stem.
  K-Basal lobes and apex of leaf broadly rounded; definite basal
      leaf rosettes absent; fruits elongate . . . . CONRINGIA
  K-Basal lobes and apexes pointed; either basal rosettes (see
      below) or short broad fruits present.
    L-Compact radiating tufts of leaves, "rosettes", at base of
        flowering stems or on basal offshoots; fruits 3 cm or more
        long, many times as long as wide . . . . ARABIS
    L-Rosettes absent; fruits to 1 cm long, 1.4-2 times as long as
        wide . . . . CAMELINA
J-Stem leaves without backwardly directed lobes at base.
  M-Fruits distinctly flattened, to 8 times as long as wide, if over
      2 times then basal leaf rosettes present (compact radiating
      tufts of leaves).
    N-Plants from basal leaf rosettes; fruits 3-8 times as long as
        wide . . . . DRABA
    N-Rosettes absent; fruits about as wide as long . . . . ALYSSUM
  M-Fruits angular to round in section, not flattened, 5 or more
      times as long as wide; basal leaf rosettes absent.
    O-Plants more or less pubescent with 2-4-branched hairs
      . . . . ERYSIMUM
    O-Plants pubescent with unbranched hairs, or glabrous. BRASSICA
A-Petals white to pink to purple (sometimes yellow at base), or absent.
  P-Leaves, at least the basal ones, pinnately compound or cleft at least
    halfway to the midrib, at least at the base of the blade.
    Q-Stem leaves 2 or 3 in a whorl or near-whorl, palmately compound
      or cleft; petals 12-19 mm long. . . . . DENTARIA
    Q-Stem leaves often more, not whorled, pinnately cut to entire; petals
      0.5-13 mm long or absent.
      R-Fruits 2-8 mm long, 1-1.5 times as long as wide, the undeveloped
        ovary either strongly flattened or ellipsoid.
        S-Petals 5-8 mm long; style distinct; fruit subglobose to ellip-
          soid to obovoid, the undeveloped ovary ellipsoid . . . ARMORACIA
        S-Petals 0.5-4 mm long or absent; style minute or none; fruit
          and undeveloped ovary strongly flattened.
          T-Fruits oval to elliptic, rhombic-elliptic, round, or obovate
            in outline, the ovary similar; petals 0.5-3 mm long or
            absent . . . . LEPIDIUM
          T-Fruits, and undeveloped ovary, inverted-triangular;
            petals 2-4 mm long. . . . . CAPSELLA
      R-Fruits 10-45 mm long, 6-many times as long as wide, the un-
        developed ovary slenderly linear, flattish or not.
        U-Pinnately cut leaves usually confined to the basal leaf tuft,
          if on the lower stem, the stem leaves 1-8 mm wide . . ARABIS
        U-Pinnately cut leaves present on the stem as well as at the
          base, 5-50 mm wide, if less than 15 mm wide then the
          pinnate leaves found throughout the plant.
          V-At least the upper leaves undivided, the others tending
            to be divided only at the base of the blade . . . . . IODANTHUS
          V-All leaves divided for their full length.
            W-Petals 4-5 mm long; lateral leaflets ca. 2 times as long
              as wide . . . . NASTURTIUM
            W-Petals either 1.5-3 or 8-13 mm long; lateral leaflets
              of middle and upper stem leaves 3-6 times as long as
              wide . . . . CARDAMINE

P-Leaves simple, entire or toothed, cut less than halfway to the midrib.
X-Stem leaves, at least the lower or upper, with short backwardly
    directed lobes at base, one on each side of the stem.
    Y-Fruit flattened, 2-18 mm long, 1-1.5 times as long as wide, the
        undeveloped ovary more or less flattened.
        Z-Fruits, and undeveloped ovary, inverted-triangular; larger
            leaves in a basal tuft, the stem leaves reduced .. CAPSELLA
        Z-Fruits oval to elliptic or rhombic-elliptic, round, or obovate
            in outline, the undeveloped ovary similar; stem leaves often
            the largest.
            AA-Plants usually pubescent; petals 0.5-2 mm long or absent;
                fruits 2-6 mm long, 1-or 2-seeded . . . . LEPIDIUM
            AA-Plants glabrous; petals 3-4.5 mm long; fruits 10-18 mm
                long, several-seeded . . . . THLASPI
    Y-Fruit flattened or not, 12-120 mm long, 10 or more times as
        long as wide, the undeveloped ovary slenderly linear.
        BB-Leaves, all or some, toothed.
            CC-Stem leaves mostly sessile, if petioled then the blades
                1-8 mm wide; plants mostly with compact radiating tufts
                of leaves at base ("rosettes") . . . . ARABIS
            CC-Middle and lower stem leaves with a distinct petiole-like
                base, the blades 18-50 mm wide; rosettes absent . IODANTHUS
        BB-Leaves all entire.
            DD-Stem leaves broadly rounded at apex, 15-50 mm wide;
                plants glabrous . . . . CONRINGIA
            DD-Stem leaves acute, often narrower than above; plants
                usually pubescent . . . . ARABIS
X-Stem leaves without lobes at base.
    EE-Fruits 5-100 mm long, 3 or more times as long as wide; un-
        developed ovary slenderly linear or cylindric or ovoid, not
        strongly flattened.
        FF-Fruits flattened, linear to elliptic in section; basal leaves
            usually forming a compact radiating tuft or "rosette", or
            rosettes borne on basal offshoots.
            GG-Fruits 12-100 mm long, 10 or more times as long as wide;
                anthers much longer than broad; petals 3-9 mm long . ARABIS
            GG-Fruits 5-20 mm long, 3-8 times as long as wide; anthers
                oval to oblong; petals 2-6 mm long, or none . . . . . . DRABA
        FF-Fruits not flattened, round to 4-angled in section; rosettes
            absent.
            HH-Petals 15-25 mm long, purple to white . . . . . . HESPERIS
            HH-Petals 5-12 mm long, white.
                II-Stem leaf blades ovate to round, oblong, or lanceolate
                    . . . . Cardamine bulbosa
                II-Stem leaf blades broadly triangular . . . . ALLIARIA
    EE-Fruits 2-9 mm long, 1-2 times as long as wide; undeveloped
        ovary roundish to ovate or elliptic in outline, often strongly
        flattened.
        JJ-Petals deeply 2-parted . . . . BERTEROA
        JJ-Petals entire.
            KK-Fruits obovoid to ellipsoid, not flattened; undeveloped
                ovary not flattened; lower stem leaves petioled, the blades
                cordate at base; plants glabrous . . . . ARMORACIA
            KK-Fruits strongly flattened; undeveloped ovary flattened or
                not; leaves often sessile, the blades not cordate; plants
                often pubescent.

LL-Petals 6-15 mm long . . . . IBERIS
LL-Petals 0.5-5 mm long, or none.
   MM-Petals 0.5-2 mm long, or none; plants puberulent with
     unbranched hairs or glabrous; fruit flattened at right
     angles to the partition . . . . LEPIDIUM
   MM-Petals 2.5-5 mm long; plants pubescent with branched
     hairs; fruit flattened parallel with the partition.
     NN-Pubescence of 2-branched hairs lying lengthwise
       with the stems and leaves; fruit ca. 1.5 times as
       long as wide . . . . LOBULARIA
     NN-Pubescence of star-like several-branched hairs;
       fruit as wide as long or nearly so . . . . ALYSSUM

ALLIARIA ----- GARLIC MUSTARD*

Erect biennials or perennials with the odor of garlic; leaves simple, broad; petals white; ovary cylindric; fruits linear, 4-angled, each valve with a conspicuous midnerve and smaller lateral nerves. (Name from Allium, onion or garlic, from the odor.)

A. petiolata (Bieb.) Cav. & Grande. (A. officinalis Andrz.) Biennial to 1 m high; lower leaves kidney-shaped, the others broadly triangular, 3-6 cm long and wide, coarsely toothed; petals 5-6 mm long; fruits 30-60 mm long. Naturalized from Europe, a weed in disturbed ground and moist woods, recorded from Clay and Hennepin counties.

ALYSSUM ----- MADWORT*

Low annual or perennial herbs, more or less pubescent with star-like several-branched hairs; leaves entire or toothed; petals yellow to white; ovary short, somewhat flattened; fruit flattened parallel to the partition, elliptic to round in outline, each locule with 1-few seeds. (Gr. alyssos, curing madness, supposed to cure hydrophobia.)

A-Leaves 7-25 cm long; fruits pubescent . . . . A. alyssoides
A-Leaves 30-80 mm long; fruits glabrous. . . . . A. saxatile

A. alyssoides L. Annual; leaves entire, 2-3 mm wide, linear to oblanceolate; petals pale yellow to whitish, 3-4 mm long; fruit 3-4 mm long, notched at the apex. Naturalized from Europe, now a weed in disturbed ground, recorded from Wabasha, Hennepin, and Ramsey counties.
A. saxatile L. Cultivated. Perennial; leaves toothed to entire, 4-10 mm wide, oblanceolate to obovate-oblong; petals yellow, 3-5 mm long; fruit 5 mm long, not notched at the apex. S. Europe.

ARABIS ----- ROCK CRESS*

Annual to perennial herbs, usually pubescent with branched or unbranched hairs; compact radiating tufts of leaves, "rosettes", usually present at base of flowering stem or on basal offshoots; leaves entire to pinnately cleft; flowers in racemes or panicles; petals white to pink or purplish, or yellowish; anthers much longer than broad; ovary cylindric; fruit linear, 10 or more times as long as wide, usually moderately to strongly flattened, each valve often with a midnerve; seeds in 1 or 2 rows in each locule. (Referring to Arabia.)

A-Petals 9.5-18 mm long; stem pubescent; stem leaves cordate-ovate,
  toothed; cultivated . . . . A. caucasica
A-Petals 2-10 mm long, if more than 9 mm then the stem glabrous
  at least above and the stem leaves lanceolate to narrowly oblong
  and entire or nearly so; native.
  B-Stem leaves without lobes at base.
    C-Larger stem leaves 2-8 mm wide; stems usually branching from
      the base; fruits 0.5-1 mm wide, ascending . . . . A. lyrata
    C-Larger stem leaves 10-40 mm wide; stems usually unbranched;
      fruits 2.2-3.1 mm wide, spreading to pendulous . . . A. canadensis
  B-Stem leaves, at least some, with backwardly directed lobes at base,
    one on each side of the stem.
    D-Pedicels and fruits at maturity erect or nearly so, mostly diver-
      ging 0-30⁰ from the vertical.
      E-Stems usually hairy 1/2 or more of the way to the inflores-
        cence; fruits 2-5 cm long, 0.7-1.2 mm wide, the stigma
        0.3-0.4 mm wide. . . . . A. hirsuta var. pycnocarpa
      E-Stems glabrous or hairy less than 1/4 of the way to the
        inflorescence; fruits 4-10 cm long, if 0.7-1.2 mm wide
        then the stigma 0.5-1 mm wide.
        F-Petals creamy to yellowish, 2.5-6 mm long; fruits roundish
          or 4-angled to elliptic in section, 0.7-1.3 mm wide,
          the stigma 0.5-1 mm wide. . . . . A. glabra
        F-Petals white to pinkish, 6-10 mm long; fruits strongly
          flattened, narrowly elliptic to linear in section, 1.3-
          3.3 mm wide, the stigma 0.4-0.5 mm wide. . . A. drummondii
    D-Pedicels and fruits at maturity ascending to pendulous, diver-
      ging 30-180⁰ from the vertical.
      G-Pedicels and fruits pendent, mostly diverging 135-180⁰ from
        vertical . . . . A. holboelii var. retrofract
      G-Pedicels and fruits ascending to spreading, mostly diver-
        ging 30-120⁰ from vertical.
        H-Middle and upper stem pubescent; stem leaves 2-4.5 times
          as long as wide . . . . A. perstellata var. shortii
        H-Middle and upper stem glabrous; stem leaves 4.5-16 times
          as long as wide.
          I-Basal leaves with star-like several-branched hairs on
            both sides; petals 5-9 mm long . . . . A. divaricarpa
          I-Basal leaves glabrous or with unbranched hairs; petals
            3-5 mm long . . . . A. laevigata

A. canadensis L. Sickle-pod. Biennial 3-9 dm high; stem leaves more or
less pubescent, 5-15 cm long, toothed to nearly entire; lower stem sparsely
pubescent; petals 3-6 mm long; fruits 4-8 cm long, flat, mostly curved, mostly
diverging 100-160⁰ from vertical. Woods, thickets, and bluffs, Houston and
Fillmore counties nw. to Hennepin and Lyon counties.

A. caucasica Willd. Wall Rock Cress; cultivated. Perennial 15-30 cm
high; white-hairy; basal leaves oblong-obovate, toothed; stem leaves cordate-
ovate, toothed, sessile, with clasping basal lobes; petals white. E.
Mediterranean to Asia Minor.

A. divaricarpa Nels. Biennial 2-9 dm high; stem leaves 4.5-11 times as
long as wide, glabrous or slightly pubescent, entire or nearly so; petals
whitish or pink, turning pink-lavender in age; fruits 30-90 mm long; pedicels
and fruits diverging 30-120⁰ from the vertical. Rocky or sandy places, over
most of the state.

A. drummondii Gray. Similar to A. divaricarpa. Seeds in 2 rows per
locule. Dry rocky and sandy places, recorded only from Cook to St. Louis

Co. and in Hubbard, Yellow Medicine, Wabasha, and Olmsted counties.

A. glabra (L.) Bernh. Tower Mustard. Biennial 6-12 dm high; stem hairy at base, glabrous above; basal leaves pubescent or glabrous, entire or toothed; stem leaves mostly glabrous and entire; seeds in 1 or 2 rows per locule. Rocky places and dry soil, very widely scattered from Lake to Kittson Co. and s. to Becker, Kanabec, Hennepin, Olmsted, and Houston counties.

A. hirsuta var. pycnocarpa (Hopkins) Rollins. Resembling A. glabra; plants 1.5-8 dm high; flowers often in panicles; petals whitish to somewhat yellowish or pinkish; fruits flattened; seeds in 1 row per locule. Rocky and gravelly places, throughout the state. One specimen from Waseca Co. has been identified as A. h. var. adressipilis (Hopkins) Rollins, in which the stem hairs are appressed and mostly 2-branched rather than spreading and mostly unbranched, and in which the stem leaves are glabrous or nearly so rather than at least the lower ones being hairy.

A. holboelii var. retrofracta (Graham) Rydb. Biennial or perennial; stems 1-several, 2-8 dm high, pubescent with branched hairs below; basal leaves entire or slightly toothed, pubescent; stem leaves entire, at least the lower pubescent; petals white to pink, 7-10 mm long; fruits 35-80 mm long. Dry rocky or gravelly soil, Cook and Kittson counties.

A. laevigata (Muhl.) Poir. Biennial 3-9 dm high; stem leaves 6-16 times as long as wide, glabrous, entire or toothed; petals white; fruits 50-100 mm long, often strongly recurved, their pedicels diverging 30-90° from the vertical. Woods and hillsides, Houston, Hennepin, ne. Todd, and Clearwater counties.

A. lyrata L. Biennial or perennial 1-3.5 dm high; stems hairy below; basal leaves entire to usually pinnately lobed, hairy at least below; stem leaves entire to lobed; petals usually white, 3-8 mm long; fruits 12-45 mm long, diverging 0-60° from vertical on pedicels diverging 30-80° from vertical. Dry rocky, gravelly, or sandy soil, e. edge of the state from Houston and Fillmore counties to Morrison, Itasca, and Cook counties, unrecorded from Lake Co. and a few others.

A. perstellata var. shortii Fern. (A. shortii (Fern.) Gl.). Biennial or perennial 2-6 dm high; basal leaves toothed to pinnately lobed, stem leaves irregularly toothed, both pubescent at least beneath; petals white, 2-3 mm long; fruit 15-40 mm long, diverging 60-120° from the vertical. Moist woods and rocky places, Houston and Fillmore counties to Blue Earth, Redwood, Hennepin, and s. Washington counties.

ARMORACIA *

Glabrous perennials; leaves entire to pinnately cleft, submerged leaves (when present) finely cleft; petals white; ovary ovoid to ellipsoid; fruits obovoid to ellipsoid, each valve with an inconspicuous midnerve. Seeds in 2 rows per locule. (Ancient name of the Horseradish.)

A. rusticana Gaertn. (A. lapathifolia Gilib.). Horseradish; cultivated. Lower leaves long-petioled, the blade 1-3 dm long, cordate at base; upper leaves reduced; petals 5-8 mm long; fruits obovoid, 4-6 mm long. From se. Europe and w. Asia.

BARBAREA ----- WINTER CRESS, YELLOW ROCKET*

Biennial to sometimes perennial, with overwintering basal leaf clusters, glabrous or nearly so; basal leaves pinnately cut, the terminal lobe largest, in ours 2.5-8 times as wide as the lateral lobes and broadly rounded; stem leaves pinnate to entire, with a lobe on each side of the stem at base; flowers yellow; fruits linear, round or somewhat 4-angled in section, in ours 8-26 times as long as thick, each valve with a midnerve; seeds in 1 row per locule. (Named for St. Barbara.)

A-Petals bright yellow, 5-8 mm long; beak 1.5-3 mm long . . . B. vulgaris
A-Petals pale yellow, 2.5-5 mm long; beak 0.5-1.3 (-2) mm long
. . . . B. orthoceras

B. orthoceras Ledeb. Basal leaves entire or with 1 or 2 lateral leaflets; uppermost leaves pinnately cleft; fruits erect and appressed or strongly ascending, 21-36 mm long excluding beak, 15-26 times as long as wide. Swamps and other wet places, Cook to Carlton Co. and in Mille Lacs and Anoka counties.

B. vulgaris R. Br. Basal leaves entire or usually with 2-6 lateral leaflets; uppermost leaves wavy-edged or sometimes pinnately cleft; fruits usually wide-spreading, sometimes strongly ascending, 12-28 mm long excluding beak, 8-17 times as long as wide. From Europe, naturalized in wet meadows and damp disturbed ground, Cook to Itasca Co., s. to Morrison, Blue Earth, Fillmore, and Houston counties, and in Pipestone and Clay counties.

BERTEROA*

Annual or perennial herbs, pubescent with star-like branched hairs; leaves mostly entire; petals white or sometimes yellow, deeply 2-lobed; ovary ellipsoid; fruit elliptic or oval in outline, ellipsoid or flattened parallel to the partition, few-seeded. (Named for C. G. Bertero, Italian botanist.)

B. incana (L.) DC. Hoary Alyssum. Annual; leaves entire, lanceolate; petals white; fruit ellipsoid, only slightly flattened, 5-8 mm long. Naturalized from Europe; disturbed ground throughout most of the state.

BRASSICA ----- MUSTARD, TURNIP*

Annuals or biennials; basal leaves pinnately compound or cleft, stem leaves compound or cleft to entire; petals yellow in ours, often drying white; ovary nearly cylindric; fruits more or less elongate, roundish to 4-angled in section, with a relatively large beak sometimes containing a basal seed; valves of fruit each with 1-5 lengthwise nerves (in addition to the lateral ribs marking their junction); seeds in 1 row per locule. (Latin name of the cabbage.

A-Upper leaves sessile and with short backwardly directed lobes at base,
one on each side of the stem . . . . B. rapa
A-Upper leaves petioled to sessile, not lobed at base.
  B-Valves of fruit with 3 strong parallel nerves that extend onto the
    beak, the nerves often late to appear, sometimes completely
    obscured on the body by dense hairs; beak 1/4-1 2/3 as long
    as the body, 4-angled to flattened, 1.8-4.6 mm long in mid-
    flower, often containing a seed in its base.

C- Fruit glabrous or sometimes with some hairs; beak 1/4-1 times
   as long as the body, roughly diamond-shaped in section, the 3
   nerves more widely spaced than below; seeds mostly 8-18 per
   fruit . . . . B. kaber
C- Fruit body bristly-hairy at least when young; beak 3/4-1 2/3 as
   long as the body, strongly flattened, the 3 nerves forming a
   narrow central band not over 1/4 the width of the beak; seeds
   mostly 4-8 per fruit . . . . B. hirta
B- Valves of fruit strongly 1-nerved, the other nerves if any much
  weaker, not continuously parallel to the midnerve and often
  joining others; fruit glabrous; beak 1/6-1/3 as long as the body,
  round in section or somewhat 4-angled or 2-edged, 1-3.2 mm
  long in mid-flower, without seeds.
D- Fruits usually erect and often appressed to the stem, 10-22 mm
   long including beak, the beak 1.5-4 mm long, ca. 1/6-1/4
   as long as the body . . . . B. nigra
D- Fruits erect or diverging to 60° from vertical, not appressed
   to the stem, 30-50 mm long including beak, the beak (4.5-)
   6-10 mm long, 1/4-1/3 as long as the body . . . . B. juncea

B. hirta Moench. White Mustard. Annual, green, hairy; lower and often
the upper leaves pinnately cleft or compound; petals 8-10 mm long; body of
fruit 6-18 mm long, beak 10-18 mm long, the beak 1.8-3.4 mm long in mid-
flower; ovules 2-4 per locule. From Eurasia; plants of disturbed ground,
unrecorded but to be expected.

B. juncea (L.) Cosson. Brown, Chinese, or Indian Mustard. Annual,
glabrous or with scattered hairs only below, usually somewhat whitened;
lower leaves pinnately cleft to compound, the upper toothed to entire, on
short petioles; petals 8-10 mm long; body of fruit 25-40 mm long; beak 1-
3.2 mm long in mid-flower. From Eurasia, established in disturbed ground,
recorded from Winona, Chippewa, Hennepin, Clay, s. St. Louis, and
Hubbard counties.

B. kaber (DC.) Wheeler. Charlock. Annual, green, hairy at least below
and usually above; lower leaves toothed or sometimes lobed or compound,
the upper toothed, sessile or nearly so; petals 10-14 mm long; body of fruit
12-35 mm long, beak 7-14 mm long, the beak 2.4-4.6 mm long in mid-flower;
ovules 4-9 per locule. From Eurasia; in disturbed ground, throughout the
state.

B. nigra (L.) Koch. Black Mustard. Annual, green or sometimes
slightly whitened, hairy below, glabrous above; leaves all petioled, the
lower usually lobed or compound, the upper unlobed; petals 7-9 mm long;
body of fruit 9-18 mm long, the beak 1-2.5 mm long in mid-flower. From
Eurasia, in disturbed ground, recorded from Houston to Blue Earth Co.,
n. to Hennepin and Scott counties.

B. rapa L. (B. campestris L.) Glabrous or nearly so; lower leaves pinnately cleft, the upper entire to shallowly toothed; petals 6.5-10 mm long;
fruit body 30-50 mm long, each half 1-nerved, the beak 8-15 mm long. From
Eurasia.

A- Annual with thin tap root; established as a weed in disturbed ground,
   recorded from Houston, Blue Earth, Lincoln, Hennepin, St. Louis,
   and Lake counties . . . .
   . . . . B. r. var. silvestris (Lam.) Briggs. Field Mustard, Rape.
A- Biennial with thick fleshy root; cultivated . . . . B. r. var. rapa. Turnip.

CAMELINA ----- FALSE FLAX *

Annuals or winter-annuals with both simple and branched hairs; leaves entire or toothed, those on the middle and upper stem lobed at base, one on each side of the stem; petals small, yellow, often drying white; fruits obovoid or pear-shaped, slightly flattened parallel to the partition. (Gr. chamai, dwarf, and linon, flax.)

A-Plants hairy, the branched hairs short and exceeded 1-2 mm by the
    simple ones; fruits 5.5-8 mm long, 3-4.5 mm wide . . . . . C. microcarpa
A-Plants glabrous or sparsely hairy, the branched hairs not exceeded
    by the simple ones; fruits 7-10 mm long, 5-7 mm wide . . C. sativa

C. microcarpa Andrz. From Europe, established in disturbed ground, mostly southern, scattered n. to Kanabec, Clearwater, and Clay counties.

C. sativa (L.) Crantz. From Europe, established in disturbed ground, southern, recorded from Houston, Brown, Hennepin, Chisago, and Pope counties.

CAPSELLA ----- SHEPHERD'S PURSE *

Annual or biennial herbs, pubescent with branched hairs; leaves mostly in a basal tuft, the stem leaves reduced with a lobe at the base on each side of the stem; petals white; ovary flat, obovate to inverted-triangular; fruit flat, obcordate to inverted-triangular. (Diminutive of L. capsa, box, referring to the fruit.)

C. bursa-pastoris (L.) Medic. Annual; basal leaves usually pinnately cleft; petals 1.5-4 mm long; fruit 4-8 mm long. From Europe, established in disturbed ground throughout the state.

CARDAMINE ----- BITTER CRESS *

Annual to perennial; glabrous or with unbranched hairs; leaves simple to compound; petals white to pink or purple, or none; ovary cylindric; fruit linear, roundish to 4-angled in section or somewhat flattened. Often growing in wet places. (Gr. kardamon, name of a cress-like herb.)

A-Leaves all simple, not pinnately cleft . . . . C. bulbosa
A-Leaves all or mostly compound or pinnately cleft.
  B-Petals 8-13 mm long . . . . C. pratensis var. palustris
  B-Petals 1.5-3.5 mm long.
    C-Stem leaves mostly 4-8 cm long; terminal leaflets of lower and
      middle stem leaves 2-3 times as wide as the lateral ones, the
      lateral ones linear-oblanceolate to obovate, usually webbed to
      the leaf axis; stem often hairy at or above the base . . C. pensylvanica
    C-Stem leaves mostly 2-4 cm long; terminal leaflets of stem leaves
      1-1.5 times as wide as the lateral ones, the lateral ones linear
      to narrowly elliptic, usually not webbed to the axis; stem glabrous
      . . . . C. parviflora var. arenicola

C. bulbosa (Schreb.) BSP. Spring Cress. Perennial; stems from a short thick tuber, glabrous; leaves entire to toothed; petals white, 7-14 mm long; fruit 15-25 mm long. Around springs or in wet meadows or woods, throughout the state except ne. of a line from Pine to Beltrami to Kittson Co.

C. parviflora var. arenicola (Britt.) Schulz. Annual or biennial; petals white; fruits 15-30 mm long. Usually in dry soil, from Cook to St. Louis Co. and s. to Chisago and Stearns counties.

C. pensylvanica Muhl. Annual or biennial; petals white; fruits 10-30 mm long. Springs and wet places, throughout the state.

C. pratensis var. palustris Wimm. & Grab. Cuckoo-flower, Marsh Bitter Cress. Perennial; leaflets of basal and sometimes lower stem leaves rounded and stalked, of the upper leaves oblong to linear; petals white; fruits 25-40 mm long. Springs, bogs, and wet places, Clearwater, s. St. Louis, and n. Lake counties.

CONRINGIA ----- HARE'S-EAR MUSTARD *

Annual or biennial glabrous herbs; leaves entire, at least the upper leaves cordate at base with a basal lobe on each side of the stem; petals yellow to nearly white; ovary cylindric; fruit elongate, roundish to 4-angled in section. (Named for H. Conring, German botanist.)

C. orientalis (L.) Andrz. Annual to 8 dm high; stem leaves oval to oblong, broadly rounded at apex; petals pale yellow, 10-13 mm long; fruits 7-11 cm long, 2-2.5 mm wide, 4-angled. From Eurasia, naturalized in disturbed ground, recorded from Goodhue, Hennepin, Chippewa, and St. Louis counties.

DENTARIA ----- TOOTHWORT, PEPPERROOT *

Perennials from often fleshy rhizomes; stem leaves few, opposite or closely grouped at or above the middle, palmately cleft or compound; petals white or purple; ovary cylindric; fruit lanceolate, flattened. (L. dens, tooth, presumably from the toothed rhizomes of some species.)

D. laciniata Muhl. Stems 2-4 dm high; stem leaves usually 3 in a whorl above the middle, deeply 3-cleft or compound, the lanceolate divisions sometimes further divided to produce a 5-parted leaf, each segment nearly entire or toothed; petals white or purplish, 12-19 mm long; fruit 25-50 mm long including the beak. Rich soil in moist woods, the se. half of the state, from Houston Co. w. and n. to Murray, Morrison, and s. St. Louis counties.

DESCURAINIA ----- TANSY MUSTARD *

Annuals or biennials, more or less pubescent, some or all of the hairs branched; leaves 1-3 times pinnately cleft or divided into many small divisions; petals yellow; ovary cylindric; fruits linear or club-shaped, round to somewhat 4-angled in section, each valve with a midnerve. (Named for F. Descourain, French botanist.)

A-Axis of inflorescence with very short globular-tipped hairs ("glandular" hairs); fruits 1-2 mm wide, the seeds usually in 2 rows per locule
. . . . D. pinnata var. brachycarpa
A-Axis of inflorescence pubescent but without glandular hairs; fruits 0.5-1.2 mm wide, the seeds usually in 1 row per locule.
B-Fruits 5-12 mm long, 6-12 times as long as wide . . . . . D. richardsonii

B-Fruits 15-25 mm long, 19-36 times as long as wide. . . . . D. sophia

D. pinnata var. brachycarpa (Richards.) Fern. Fruits 6-13 mm long, 3.5-8 times as long as wide, the midnerve prominent; smaller fruits sometimes with 1 row of seeds per locule. Sandy and rocky soils, often a weed in disturbed ground, Houston to Rock Co., n. to Hennepin, Mille Lacs, Todd, Clearwater, and Kittson counties, and in Cook Co.

D. richardsonii (Sweet) Schulz. Fruits 0.7-1.2 mm wide, the midnerve nearly invisible to moderately developed; larger fruits sometimes with 2 rows of seeds per locule. Gravelly and sandy soils, western, Lincoln to Polk Co., e. to Pope Co. and in the Duluth area.

D. sophia (L.) Webb. Herb-Sophia. Fruits 0.5-1 mm wide; seeds in 1 row per locule. From Eurasia, established as a weed in disturbed ground, recorded at wide intervals from Pipestone to Kittson Co., and e. to Faribault and Dakota counties.

DRABA

Annual to perennial herbs, sometimes woody at base; compact radiating tufts of leaves, "rosettes", usually present at base of flowering stem or on basal offshoots; pubescence of simple or branched hairs; leaves entire or toothed; petals yellow or white; anthers oval to oblong; ovary ovoid; fruit flattened parallel to the partition, ca. 2-8 times as long as wide, sometimes twisted; seeds in 2 rows in each locule. (Gr. drabe, ancient name for some plant of the Brassicaceae.)

A-Perennial,usually with additional rosettes on basal offshoots, leafy for 1/2-3/4 the height of the plant; fruit 2.3-3.5 mm wide, twisted; petals 4-6 mm long. . . . . D. arabisans
A-Annuals or winter-annuals without basal offshoots, leafy to 1/2 the height of the plant; fruits 1.4-2 mm wide, not twisted; petals 2-5 mm long or none.
  B-Leaves entire or nearly so; petals white, 3.5-5 mm long or none
  . . . . D. reptans
  B-Leaves usually toothed; petals yellow, ca. 2 mm long . . D. nemorosa

D. arabisans Michx. Petals white; fruit 5-12 mm long. Rocky places, Cook and s. Lake counties.

D. nemorosa L. Plants leafy 1/5-1/2 of their height; fruits 5-10 mm long, 1.4-1.9 mm wide; pedicels 7-25 mm long, 1-3 times as long as the fruit. Dry open soil, Kittson to Pipestone Co., e. to Lake of the Woods, Stearns, and Cottonwood counties, and in Cook Co. Forms with glabrous fruits rather than pubescent are sometimes distinguished as D. n. var. lejocarpa Lindbl.

D. reptans (Lam.) Fern. Plants leafy to 1/3 their height; fruits 8-18 mm long, 1.5-2 mm wide; pedicels 2-9.5 mm long, 1/5-3/4 as long as the fruit. Dry ledges and sandy places, Houston to Pipestone Co., n. to Washington, Nicollet, Chippewa, and Kittson counties. Forms with pubescent fruits rather than glabrous are sometimes distinguished as D. r. var. micrantha (Nutt.) Fern.

ERYSIMUM ----- TREACLE MUSTARD *

Annuals to perennials, more or less pubescent with 2-4-branched hairs; leaves narrow, entire to pinnately cleft; petals in ours yellow to orange; ovary

linear-cylindric, hairy; fruits linear, more or less 4-angled in section, each
valve with a prominent midnerve; seeds in 1 row per locule. (Of Gr. origin
but of varying interpretation.)

A-Petals 15-25 mm long; sepals 8-12 mm long. . . . . E. asperum
A-Petals 3-11 mm long; sepals 2-7 mm long.
  B-Petals 3-5.5 mm long; sepals 2-3 mm long . . . . . E. cheiranthoides
  B-Petals 6-11 mm long; sepals 4-7 mm long. . . . . . . E. inconspicuum

    E. asperum (Nutt.) DC. Western Wallflower. Biennial or short-lived per-
ennial; fruits 5-11 cm long. Dry grasslands and sandy places, s. Lake, Ramsey, Anoka, Morrison, Clay and Mahnomen counties.

    E. cheiranthoides L. Wormseed Mustard. Annual or winter annual; fruits
12-25 mm long. Of disputed origin, perhaps native, perhaps introduced from
the Old World; in mesic to damp meadows and disturbed ground, throughout
the state except for Cook Co.

    E. inconspicuum (Wats.) MacMill. Perennial; fruits 15-45 mm long. Mostly
dry to mesic grasslands and sandy or rocky places, Pipestone to Blue Earth and
Goodhue counties, n. to Morrison, Roseau, and Kittson counties, and in St. Louis
Co.

HESPERIS ----- ROCKET *

    Biennials or perennials; pubescence of both simple and branched hairs;
petals purple to pink to white; ovary cylindric; fruit linear, round in section or
nearly so, the valves obscurely 1-nerved; seeds in 1 row per locule. (Gr. hes-
peros, evening or evening star, from the evening fragrance of the flowers.)

    H. matronalis L. Dame's Violet; cultivated. Mostly biennial, to 10 dm
high; leaves lanceolate to deltoid- or oblong-lanceolate, toothed; flowers fragrant, purple to pink or white, 15-25 mm long; fruits 50-100 mm long. From
Eurasia; often escaping, recorded at wide intervals over most of the state.

IBERIS ----- CANDYTUFT

    Annuals or perennials, glabrous or pubescent with unbranched hairs;
stems leafy; leaves entire to pinnately cleft; petals white, rose, or violet, the
2 outer ones larger than the 2 inner, often several times larger in the marginal flowers of the inflorescence; fruit strongly flattened at right angles to
the partition, roundish to ovate to somewhat rectangular in outline, winged
around the edge or not; seeds 1 per locule. (Iberia, ancient name of Spain.)

A-Outer petals 5-9 mm long . . . . I. amara
A-Outer petals 10-15 mm long . . . . I. sempervirens

    I. amara L. Rocket Candytuft; cultivated. Annual, or rarely biennial,
sparsely pubescent; leaves oblanceolate to spoon-shaped, toothed or seldom
entire, 2.5-9 cm long; petals white, the outer twice as long as the inner;
fruit 4.5-7 mm long, roundish. From Europe.

    I. sempervirens L. Edging Candytuft; cultivated. Perennial, woody at
base, glabrous; leaves linear-oblong, entire, 1.5-3 cm long; petals white or
sometimes rose, the outer 3 times as long as the inner; fruit ca. 7 mm long,
ovate to rectangular. From s. Europe.

IODANTHUS ----- PURPLE ROCKET *

    Perennial; petals violet to almost white; ovary cylindric; fruits linear,
roundish in section or slightly flattened, each valve with a prominent midnerve;

seeds in 1 row per locule. 1 species. (Gr. _iodes_, violet-colored, and _anthos_, flower.)

I. _pinnatifidus_ (Michx.) Steud. Glabrous or nearly so; leaves roundish to ovate to lanceolate, toothed or some of them pinnately cleft at base of blade, with short backwardly-directed lobes at base, one on each side of the stem; petals 8-13 mm long; fruits 18-35 mm long. Rich soil in moist bottomland woods, Houston, Fillmore, and Goodhue counties.

LEPIDIUM ----- PEPPERGRASS, PEPPERWORT*

Annual to perennial herbs, glabrous or pubescent; leaves entire to pinnately cleft; flower small; petals whitish or greenish to reddish or rarely yellowish; ovary flat; fruit strongly flattened at right angles to the partition, roundish to ovate, elliptic, rhombic-elliptic, or obovate in outline, often notched at the apex, often with a marginal wing; seeds 1 per locule. (Gr. _lepidion_, little scale, referring to the fruit.)

A-Stem leaves (at least the middle and upper) sessile with basal lobes, one on each side of the stem.
  B-Leaves all entire to once pinnately cleft into a few broad divisions; petals white . . . . L. campestre
  B-Basal and lower stem leaves 2 or more times dissected into linear-oblong divisions; petals pale yellow . . . . L. perfoliatum
A-Stem leaves without basal lobes, sessile or not.
  C-Middle and upper stem leaves pinnately dissected into a few linear, oblong, or oblanceolate lobes; stamens 6; fruits 5-7 mm long . . . . L. sativum
  C-Middle and upper stem leaves toothed to entire, not deeply dissected; stamens 2 (-4); fruits 2-4 mm long.
    D-Petals none or shorter than the sepals; fruits 2-3.3 mm long . . . . L. densiflorum
    D-Petals present, as long as to twice as long as the sepals; fruits 2.5-4 mm long . . . . L. virginicum

L. _campestre_ (L.) R. Br. Field Cress, Cow Cress. Annual or biennial, hairy; leaves oblanceolate to oblong or lanceolate; petals slightly exceeding sepals; fruits oblong-ovate, 5-6 mm long. From Europe, established as a weed in disturbed ground, recorded from Houston and Nobles counties.

L. _densiflorum_ Schrader. Annual or biennial, thinly pubescent; leaves oblanceolate to linear, the basal ones toothed to pinnately cleft, the stem ones entire to toothed or rarely the lower ones cleft; pedicels in fruit wide-spreading to moderately ascending; fruits roundish; embryo folded double so that the back of one cotyledon lies against the embryonic root. Dry or moist disturbed ground; perhaps introduced from Europe. Throughout the state.

L. _perfoliatum_ L. Glabrous to pubescent annual; middle and upper stem leaves broadly ovate to roundish, entire, the basal lobes about as long as the rest of the blade; petals 1-1.5 mm long; fruit rhombic-elliptic, 3.5-4 mm long. From Europe, established as a weed in disturbed ground, recorded only from Clay Co.

L. _sativum_ L. Garden Cress; cultivated. Glabrous to pubescent annual; leaves all once or twice pinnately cleft; petals 2-3 mm long, white to pink; pedicels closely ascending in fruit. Sometimes escaping in disturbed ground, so recorded from Hennepin Co. and Duluth.

L. virginicum L. Annual or biennial, puberulent to nearly glabrous; leaves oblanceolate to linear, the basal ones toothed to pinnately cleft, the stem ones entire to toothed; pedicels in fruit wide-spreading to moderately ascending; fruits roundish; embryo folded double so that the edges of both cotyledons lie against the embryonic root. Dry to moist open soil and disturbed ground, recorded from Anoka, Hennepin, Scott, and Rice counties.

LOBULARIA ----- SWEET ALYSSUM *

Annuals or perennials, more or less pubescent with 2-branched hairs; leaves entire; petals white to purple; ovary ovoid; fruit strongly flattened parallel to the partition, round to ovate in outline; seeds 1-5 per locule. (L. lobulus, little lobe, probably referring to the 2-branched hairs.)

L. maritima (L.) Desv. Cultivated. Annual to perennial; leaves linear to linear-oblanceolate, 10-70 mm long, 1.5-10 mm wide; flowers white to purple, fragrant; petals 2.5-4 mm long; fruit elliptic, 3-3.5 mm long; seeds 1 per locule. Canary, Madeira, and Azores Islands, and occasionally escaped.

NASTURTIUM ----- WATER CRESS *

Perennial herbs of wet places, usually glabrous; leaves pinnately cleft to compound; petals white (sometimes fading violet); ovary cylindric; fruits linear, short to long, round in section or nearly so; seeds in 1 or 2 irregular rows per locule. (L. nasus, nose, tortus, twisted, referring to the effect of the pungent properties of the plants.)

N. microphyllum Boenn. ex Reichb. Similar to the following; fruits (14-) 17-26 mm long; face of seed with ca. 150 pits; tetraploid. From Europe; recorded from Winona to Jackson, Hubbard, and St. Louis counties.

N. officinale R. Br. Leaves compound, of 3-9 blunt leaflets, the terminal usually much the largest; petals 4-5 mm long; fruits 10-15 (-20) mm long; face of seed with 35-45 pits; diploid. Herbage with a sharp peppery taste, used in salads. From Europe, naturalized in springs, brooks, and wet places, recorded from Houston and Fillmore to Stearns and Hubbard counties.

RORIPPA ----- YELLOW CRESS, MARSH CRESS

Annuals to perennials; pubescence of simple hairs or none; leaves toothed to pinnately cleft; petals yellow; ovary cylindric; fruit subglobose to cylindric, roundish in section; seeds many, in 2 rows per locule. (Old Saxon Rorippen, name for these plants.)

A-Petals 1.7-2 mm long; fruits 1.5-3 times as long as wide . . R. islandica
A-Petals 5-7 mm long; fruits 4-6 times as long as wide . . . . R. sinuata

R. islandica (Oeder) Borbas. Annual or biennial; at least the lower leaves pinnately cleft, leaves with a short basal lobe on each side of the stem. Shores and wet openings.
A-Plants glabrous or rarely the stem hairy below; fruits mostly 4.5-6
    mm long, 2-3.4 times as long as wide. Throughout the state.
    . . . . R. i. var. fernaldiana Butters & Abbe.
A-Base of stem or lower leaves usually hairy; fruits mostly 3-4
    mm long, 1.1-2.2 times as long as wide. Throughout the state
    except for the se. corner . . R. i. var. hispida (Desv.) Butters & Abbe.

R. sinuata (Nutt.) Hitchc. Perennial, spreading by roots; leaves pinnately cleft, more or less lobed at the base; fruits 5-14 mm long. Moist soil, especially sandy and rocky places, widely scattered in the s.1/3 of the state, n. to Meeker and Hennepin counties.

SISYMBRIUM*

Ours annual or winter-annual herbs, more or less pubescent with un-branched hairs; at least the lower leaves pinnately cleft; petals small, yellow-ish, often fading white on drying; ovary cylindric; fruits elongate, cylindric or long-tapering to a point, roundish to slightly 4-angled in section, each valve with 3 fine lengthwise nerves; seeds in 1 row per locule. (Latinized from an ancient Greek name for some plant of this family.)

A-Petals 2.5-3.5 mm long; pedicels in fruit 2-3 mm long . . . S. officinale
A-Petals 5-9 mm long; pedicels in fruit 5-10 mm long.
  B-Fruits 50-100 mm long, their pedicels as thick as the fruits or
    nearly so . . . . S. altissumum
  B-Fruits 12-35 mm long, their pedicels much narrower than the
    fruits. . . . . S. loeselii

S. altissimum L. Tumble Mustard. Segments of leaves elongate-linear; petals pale yellow, 6-9 mm long; fruits glabrous. From Eurasia, established in disturbed ground throughout most of the state, not recorded from Cook and several other counties.

S. loeselii L. Lobes of leaves triangular to ovate; petals 5-7 mm long; fruits glabrous or with a few hairs toward the base. Se. Europe and w. Asia; found in open ground in Big Stone Co.

S. officinale (L.) Scop. Hedge Mustard. Leaf segments oblong to ovate or the terminal one round; upper leaves sessile or nearly so and sometimes entire; petals bright yellow; fruits 10-17 mm long, long-tapering to the tip, pubescent or not. From Europe, established in open disturbed ground, Houston to Pipestone Co., n. to Carlton, Morrison, and Chippewa counties.

THLASPI ----- PENNY CRESS*

Annuals to perennials, usually glabrous; leaves entire to pinnately cleft, mostly with basal lobes, one on each side of the stem; petals in ours white, in others to pink or blue; ovary ellipsoid to obovoid, moderately to strongly flattened; fruits strongly flattened at right angles to the partition, roundish to obovate to obcordate in outline, notched at the apex; seeds 1-8 per locule, usually about 5. (Gr. thlaein, to crush, apparently from the flattened fruit.)

T. arvense L. Glabrous annual; leaves entire to toothed, with basal lobes; petals 3-4.5 mm long; fruits round to broadly elliptic, 10-18 mm long. From Europe; widely established in disturbed ground throughout most of the state.

CAPPARIDACEAE ----- CAPER FAMILY

Herbs (ours) to trees; leaves mostly alternate, simple to (in ours) palmately compound; flowers hypogynous, mostly bisexual, regular to zygomorphic; sepals usually 4; petals 4-many (or none), free; stamens 6-many (rarely fewer), not 6 of unequal lengths as in the Brassicaceae; ovary typically 2-carpellate, often on a stalk, usually 1-locular with 2 parietal placentas; fruit usually a berry or (in ours) a capsule dehiscent in 2 parts; seeds few to many.

POLANISIA ----- CLAMMY WEED *

Annuals with sticky hairs and a disagreeable odor; leaves trifoliolate; flowers in racemes; sepals 4; petals 4, white to pinkish, notched at the apex; stamens 8-32, of unequal lengths; ovary sessile or short-stalked; fruit linear to oblong, many-seeded. (Gr. polys, many, and anisos, unequal, apparently referring to the stamens.)

P. dodecandra (L.) DC. (P. graveolens Raf.). Leaflets 2-5 cm long; petals 4-8 mm long; stamens about 11. Dry sandy or gravelly soil, especially along streams, in the s. 2/3 of the state, n. to s. St. Louis, Beltrami, and Clay counties.

SARRACENIACEAE ----- PITCHER PLANT FAMILY

Perennial herbs with hollow pitcher- or trumpet-shaped leaves; flowers bisexual, hypogynous, regular; sepals 4-5; petals 5, free (or none); stamens many; ovary 3-5-locular with axile placentation; fruit a many-seeded loculicidal capsule.

SARRACENIA ----- PITCHER PLANT *

Hollow leaves all basal, with a lengthwise wing along the inner side and a rounded arching hood over the entrance at the top; flowers single, nodding, on a leafless stalk; sepals 5, with 3 bractlets at the base; ovary globose, 5-locular, the short style expanded at the top into a broad 5-angled or lobed umbrella-shaped structure, the 5 stigmas beneath it at the angles. (Named for M. Sarrasin de l'Etang, a Canadian botanist.)

S. purpurea L. Leaves 1-2 dm long, slightly curved; flowers 5-7 cm wide, the petals dark purple or rarely yellowish. Sedge mats and bogs in the ne. 1/2 of the state, w. and s. to Lake of the Woods, Clearwater, Pope, and Scott counties, and reliably reported from Rice Co.

SAXIFRAGACEAE ----- SAXIFRAGE FAMILY

Herbs, shrubs, or seldom trees; leaves usually without stipules, alternate or opposite, simple to less often compound; flowers mostly bisexual, regular or nearly so, more or less perigynous to epigynous; sepals and petals (4-) 5 or rarely 7-10, or rarely the petals absent; petals free; stamens usually as many or twice as many as the petals, sometimes many; carpels typically 2 (-3-5 or rarely 10), nearly free to fused, often separate above; placentation axile or parietal, ovules few to many; fruit a berry, capsule, or group of follicles.

A-Shrubs.
  B-Leaves alternate or in alternate clusters; stamens 5; native . . . RIBES
  B-Leaves opposite; stamens 20-40; cultivated . . . . PHILADELPHUS
A-Herbs.
  C-Petals absent; sepals 4 . . . . CHRYSOSPLENIUM

C-Petals present; sepals 5.
  D-Stamens 10.
    E-Petals fringed or cleft . . . . MITELLA
    E-Petals entire . . . . SAXIFRAGA
  D-Stamens 5.
    F-Hypanthium plus calyx (4-) 6.5-10 mm long; lower axis of in-
      florescence with very short globular-tipped hairs much over-
      topped by ordinary hairs . . . . HEUCHERA
    F-Hypanthium plus calyx 2.5-4 mm long; axis only with globular-
      tipped hairs . . . . SULLIVANTIA

CHRYSOSPLENIUM ----- GOLDEN SAXIFRAGE*

Perennial herbs of moist situations; leaves opposite or alternate, roundish, crenate; flowers small, greenish; hypanthium adnate to the ovary; calyx lobes 4; petals none; stamens (4-) 8; carpels 2, united below into a 1-locular ovary with 2 parietal placentas. (Gr. chrysos, golden, splen, the spleen, probably from some supposed medicinal properties.)

C. americanum Schw. Plants to 2 dm high; leaves all opposite or the uppermost sometimes alternate, 5-15 mm long, entire to toothed; flowers single in the leaf axils. Springs and cool wet places, from Cook Co. w. and s. to St. Louis, Aitkin, Hennepin, and Washington counties.

HEUCHERA ----- ALUM ROOT*

Perennial herbs; leaves palmately veined and lobed, long-petioled, mostly basal, the stem leaves alternate; flowers paniculate, greenish or purplish, sometimes white or red; hypanthium saucer-shaped to tubular, often somewhat zygomorphic, adnate to the lower part of the carpels; calyx lobes 5; petals 5, small, occasionally absent; stamens 5; carpels 2, united below into a 1-locular ovary with 2 parietal placentas; fruit a 2-beaked capsule. (Named for J. H. Heucher, a German botanist.)

H. richardsonii R. Br. Petioles hairy; leaf blades cordate-ovate; stem with ordinary hairs much overtopping very short globular-tipped hairs ("glandular" hairs), these more abundant above; hypanthium plus calyx (4-) 6.5-10 mm long; petals 3-4 mm long. Mesic to dry prairies and dry woods.

A-Stamens well exserted from the perianth; capsules more or less exserted; Houston, Winona, and Olmsted counties . . . .
  . . . . H. r. var. grayana Rosend., Butt., & Lak.
A-Stamens barely exserted; capsules included.
  B-Petioles and stems densely hairy with hairs 2-3.5 mm long; leaf
    blades 4-8 cm wide; throughout the state . . . .
    . . . . H. r. var. hispidior Ros., Butt. & Lak.
  B-Petioles and stems with hairs up to 1.5 mm long; leaf blades 2-6
    cm wide; Cook to Lake of the Woods Co., and s. to Polk and
    Stearns counties . . . . H. r. var. richardsonii.

MITELLA ----- BISHOP'S CAP, MITREWORT*

Perennial herbs with long-petioled, ovate, or roundish basal leaves, the stems leafless or 1-2-leaved; flowers in racemes, white, greenish, or purplish; hypanthium saucer-shaped to obconic, adnate to the base of the carpels; calyx lobes and petals 5, the petals fringed or cleft (in ours) to entire; stamens 10 (in ours) or 5; carpels 2, fused into a 1-locular ovary with parietal placentas; fruit a capsule. (Diminutive of Gr. mitra, cap, in reference to form of the young fruit.)

A-Flowering stem with 2 opposite leaves; flowers white . . . . . M. diphylla
A-Flowering stem leafless or with 1 small leaf; flowers yellowish-
    green . . . . M. nuda

M. diphylla L. Petals deeply fringed or cleft, ca. 2 mm long. Rich soil in moist woods, from Houston to Mower Co. and w. and n. to Blue Earth, Mahnomen, and s. St. Louis counties.

M. nuda L. Petals deeply pinnately cleft, 3-5 mm long. Bogs and wet woods, usually with mosses, Cook to Roseau Co. and s. to Becker, Douglas, and Rice counties.

PHILADELPHUS ----- MOCK ORANGE

Shrubs with simple opposite exstipulate leaves, entire to toothed; flowers showy, single or in few-flowered cymes, sometimes appearing racemose or paniculate; hypanthium top-shaped, adnate to the ovary; calyx lobes and petals 4 (-5-6) or sometimes in cultivated forms the petals double in number or nearly so; stamens 20-40; ovary half to fully inferior, 4- (3-5-) locular, placentation axile; styles as many as the locules or united; fruit a many-seeded capsule. (Said to be named for Ptolemy Philadelphus, Egyptian king of the 3rd century B. C.) Hybridization and selection have produced many cultivars which cannot be referred to any one original species or which are not normal for that species.

A-Pedicels, hypanthium, and outer side of sepals pubescent; petals
    usually double the sepal number . . . . P. X virginalis
A-Pedicels, hypanthium, and outer side of sepals glabrous; petals the
    single number.
  B-Flowers 1-3 on a branchlet.
    C-Leaf blades on flowering branchlets 2-4 cm long; flowers very
      fragrant; pedicels 2-4 mm long; petals 10-18 mm long; bark
      peeling from 2 year old branches. . . . . P. X lemoinei
    C-Leaf blades on flowering branchlets 4-8 cm long; flowers scent-
      less or slightly fragrant; pedicels 3.5-7 mm long; petals 14-30 mm
      long; bark peeling from the previous year's twigs . . .
      . . . . P. inodorus var. grandiflorus
  B-Flowers 5-9 on a branchlet.
    D-Shrub to 2 m high; leaf blades on flowering branchlets 2-4 cm
      long, entire to toothed; bark peeling from 2 year old branches;
      pedicels 2-4 mm long . . . . P. X lemoinei
    D-Shrub to 4 m high; leaf blades on flowering branchlets 4-8 cm
      long, toothed; bark peeling from the previous year's twigs;
      pedicels 2-10 mm long . . . . P. coronarius

P. coronarius L. Cultivated. Flowers very fragrant; petals 12-17 mm long. From Europe and sw. Asia.

P. inodorus var. grandiflorus (Willd.) Gray. Cultivated. Shrub 2-3 m high; flowers rarely 5 to a branchlet. Pennsylvania to Alabama.

P. X lemoinei Lemoine (P. microphyllus X P. coronarius). Cultivated.
Shrub to 2 m high; flowers very fragrant, 3-7 on the branchlets; petals 10-
18 mm long.

P. X virginalis Rehd. (hybrid between P. X lemoinei and P. X nivalis cv.
Plenus). Cultivated. Tall shrub; bark of previous year's twigs usually
peeling; leaf blades 4-10 cm long, pubescent beneath; flowers 3-7 on the
branchlets; petals ca. 1-2 cm long.

RIBES ----- CURRANTS AND GOOSEBERRIES *

Shrubs, often spiny or prickly; leaves alternate, often densely clustered in short shoots, more or less palmately veined and lobed; flowers bisexual in ours except for the cultivated R. alpinum, single or in small
corymb-like clusters of 2-5 or in racemes; hypanthium extending beyond the
ovary, saucer-shaped to tubular; sepals, petals, and stamens 5, the sepals
longer than the petals; ovary half to fully inferior, 1-locular with 2 parietal
placentas; styles free or fused; fruit a berry. (Of disputed origin, perhaps the
Arabic name.)

A-Flowers single or in small corymb-like clusters of 2-4; pedicel not
    jointed at base of flower; plants usually prickly: the Gooseberries.
    B-Ovary bristly, becoming a prickly fruit; sepals shorter than to
        rarely as long as the hypanthium (the part above the ovary);
        styles weakly united for more than 3/4 of their length . . R. cynosbati
    B-Ovary glabrous or pubescent with plain or globular-tipped hairs,
        these never enlarging to prickles in fruit; sepals about as long
        as to longer than the hypanthium; styles usually united for 1/3-
        3/4 of their length.
      C-Stamens 8-12 mm long . . . . R.   missouriens
      C-Stamens 2.5-5 mm long.
        D-Stamens shorter than the sepals, usually ca. equalling the
          petals . . . . R. oxyacanthoide
        D-Stamens nearly or quite equalling the sepals, 1.5-2 times
          as long as the petals.
          E-Hypanthium above the ovary not or very slightly constricted
            at base; hypanthium and ovary glabrous or with a few
            scattered hairs or rarely lightly pubescent; native. R. hirtellum
          E-Hypanthium abruptly constricted at base; hypanthium and
            ovary pubescent; cultivated . . . . R. grossularia
A-Flowers in racemes; pedicels jointed at base of flower; plants not
    prickly except in R. lacustre: the Currants.
    F-Stems very prickly; ovary with globular-tipped bristles . . R. lacustre
    F-Stems without prickles; ovary without bristles except in R. glandulosum.
      G-Flowers golden yellow; hypanthium above the ovary 10-15 mm
        long . . . . R. odoratum
      G-Flowers white, greenish-white, or greenish-yellow to purplish;
        hypanthium 0.5-5 mm long.
        H-Leaves dotted with tiny yellow resinous "glands" at least beneath.
          I-Bracts of the raceme 5-8 mm long, much longer than the
            pedicels . . . . R. americanum
          I-Bracts (except the lowest) 1-3 mm long, much shorter than
            the pedicels.
            J-Racemes erect or ascending; hypanthium above the ovary ca.
              1 mm long; native . . . . R. hudsonianum
            J-Racemes somewhat drooping; hypanthium ca. 3 mm long;
              cultivated . . . . R. nigrum

            H-Leaves without such glands.
                K-Ovary (and fruit) bristly with globular-tipped hairs . R. glandulosum
                K-Ovary (and fruit) glabrous, or the flowers staminate.
                    L-Racemes erect or ascending; bracts of the raceme 2.5-
                        5 mm long, nearly as long to longer than the pedicels
                        . . . . R. alpinum
                    L-Racemes ascending to usually drooping; bracts (except
                        the lowest) 1-2 mm long, much shorter than the pedicels.
                        M-Flowers greenish-purple; pedicels usually with globular-
                            tipped hairs; pollen sacs almost in contact with each
                            other; native . . . . R. triste
                        M-Flowers greenish to yellow-green; pedicels without
                            globular-tipped hairs; pollen sacs separated by a
                            connective as wide as the sac; cultivated . . . . . R. sativum

R. alpinum L. Mountain Currant; cultivated. Plants polygamo-dioecious;
peduncles and pedicels with sessile to stalked globular "glands"; flowers
greenish-yellow; hypanthium above the ovary 0.5-1 mm long; sepals 1-1.5
mm long, nearly 4 times as long as the petals; berry black. From Europe.

R. americanum Mill. Wild Black Currant. Flowers greenish-white,
pubescent on the outside; hypanthium above the ovary 3-5 mm long; sepals
4-5 mm long, ca. 1 3/4 times as long as the petals; ovary half-inferior;
berry black. Mesic to moist woods and thickets throughout the state except
Cook Co.

R. cynosbati L. Prickly Gooseberry, Dogberry. Prickles and nodal
spines usually present, sometimes absent; flowers greenish-white; ovary
rarely nearly glabrous; hypanthium above the ovary 3-5 mm long, glabrous
to lightly pubescent; sepals 3.5-4 mm long, 1.5-3.5 times as long as the
petals; berry reddish-purple. Mesic to moist woods and thickets throughout
the state except the sw. corner and Cook and Lake counties and a few other
parts of the extreme north.

R. glandulosum Grauer. Skunk Currant. Foliage ill-smelling; bracts
shorter than the pedicels; flowers yellowish-green to somewhat purplish;
hypanthium above the ovary 1 mm or less long, glabrous; sepals 2-2.5 mm
long, ca. twice as long as the petals; berry dark red. Swamps and wet woods
from Cook to Lake of the Woods Co. and s. to Clearwater, Todd, Isanti, and
Pine counties.

R. grossularia L. Garden Gooseberry; cultivated. Stems with 1-3 stout
nodal spines and sometimes some prickles; bracts very short; flowers greenish to purplish; hypanthium above the ovary ca. 3 mm long; sepals 3-4 mm
long, ca. 2 times as long as the petals; fruit green to purple. From Eurasia
and n. Africa.

R. hirtellum Michx. Swamp Gooseberry. Spines present or absent; flowers
greenish; hypanthium above the ovary 2-3 mm long; sepals 2.5-3.5 mm long,
ca. 2 times as long as the petals; berry purple to black. Swamps and moist
woods, from Cook to Kittson Co. and s. to Becker, Meeker, Hennepin, and
Chisago counties.

R. hudsonianum Richards. Northern Black Currant. Foliage ill-scented;
flowers white; hypanthium and sepals pubescent; sepals 3.5-4.5 mm long,
ca. twice as long as the petals; berry black. Cool swamps, from Cook to
Koochiching, Becker, and Carlton counties.

R. lacustre (Pers.) Poir. Swamp Black Currant. Bruised twigs and
berries with a skunk-like odor; flowers greenish to purplish; hypanthium

above the ovary ca. 1 mm long, glabrous; sepals ca. 2 mm long, 1 1/2 times
as long as the petals; berry dark purple to black. Cool moist woods and swamps
from Cook to St. Louis, Koochiching, and Clearwater counties.

R. missouriense Nutt. Missouri Gooseberry. 1-3 nodal spines present,
sometimes smaller prickles also; flowers pale green to nearly white; hypanthium above the ovary 2-2.5 mm long, glabrous or pubescent; ovary glabrous;
sepals 5-7 mm long, 2 times as long as the petals; berry nearly black.
Mesic to moist woods and damp meadows, Houston to Pipestone Co., n. to
Anoka, Morrison, Red Lake, and Norman counties.

R. nigrum L. Black Currant; cultivated. Foliage ill-smelling; flowers
greenish-white to purplish; hypanthium puberulent; sepals ca. 5 mm long, ca.
2 times as long as the petals; ovary half inferior, gland-dotted; berry black.
From Eurasia.

R. odoratum Wendl. Golden Currant, Flowering Currant. Leaves usually
dotted with tiny yellow "resinous glands" on both sides; flowers with fragrance
of cloves or carnation; ovary and hypanthium glabrous; sepals 5-6.5 mm long,
ca. twice as long as the petals; berry black. Perhaps native in the sw.
corner of the state, cultivated elsewhere, often escaping.

R. oxyacanthoides L. Northern Gooseberry. 1-3 nodal spines and other
prickles usually present; flowers greenish to purplish; ovary and hypanthium
glabrous, or rarely with a few bristle-like hairs on the ovary; hypanthium
above the ovary ca. 3 mm long; sepals 3.5-5 mm long, ca. 1 3/4 as long as
the petals. Moist woods, shores, and rocky places, Cook to Lake of the Woods
Co., widely scattered w. and s. to Marshall, Clay, and Yellow Medicine
counties.

R. sativum Syme. Red, White, or Garden Currant; cultivated. Pedicels
glabrous or puberulent; hypanthium above the ovary 0.7-1 mm long; sepals
ca. 3 times as long as the petals; berry red to whitish. From w. Europe.

R. triste Pall. Swamp Red Currant. Low straggling shrub; hypanthium
above the ovary ca. 0.5 mm long; sepals 2 mm long, ca. 2.5 times as long
as the petals; berry red. Bogs, swamps, and moist cool woods, Cook to
Lake of the Woods Co., s. to Clay, Douglas, Hennepin, and Ramsey counties.

SAXIFRAGA ----- SAXIFRAGE

Perennial herbs, the larger leaves usually in a basal tuft or crowded
on basal shoots, the stem leaves mostly alternate; flowers mostly in cymes
or panicled cymes; hypanthium usually adnate to the base of the carpels,
sometimes nearly free; calyx lobes and petals 5 each; stamens 10; carpels
mostly 2, free or fused; placentation axile; fruit a 2-lobed capsule or 2 nearly separate follicles. (L. saxum, stone, frangere, to break, the bulblets of
some species once thought to dissolve urinary stones.)

A-Larger leaves 2-7 cm long; petals white, 4-5.5 mm long . . S. virginiensis
A-Larger leaves 10-20 cm long; petals greenish-white or rarely white,
  2-3 mm long.
  B-Follicles erect for most of their length, the tips usually divergent;
    plants of bogs and wet meadows . . . . S. pensylvanica
  B-Follicles divergent for most of their length; plants of sandstone
    cliffs and wet sandy places . . . . S. forbesii

S. forbesii Vasey. Plants 3-10 dm high; basal leaves entire to faintly
toothed, sparsely hairy; petals lance-ovate, 3-nerved; n = 28. Winona Co.
Similar to the following; perhaps not deserving specific status.

S. pensylvanica L. Swamp Saxifrage. Height and leaves as in S. forbesii.

A-Petals mostly ovate to lance-ovate, 3-nerved; styles mostly less than
    1 mm long; follicles subglobose, appearing inflated throughout;
    leaves mostly ovate to obovate; n=56; Houston, Ramsey, and s.
    Beltrami counties . . . . S. p. subsp. interior Burns.
A-Petals narrowly lanceolate, 1-nerved; styles mostly more than 1
    mm long; follicles inflated only below; leaves mostly lanceolate,
    sometimes lance-ovate.
    B-Mature follicles nearly superior, the upper part stout and
        abruptly tapering, never erect at the tip; n=28; from Houston
        and Olmsted counties w. and n. to Otter Tail, Clearwater,
        Itasca, and St. Louis counties . . . . . . S. p. subsp. pensylvanica.
    B-Mature follicles 1/3-1/2 inferior, the upper part slender and
        long-tapering, the tip erect or divergent; n=42; Carver and
        Clearwater counties. . . . . S. p. subsp. tenuirostrata Burns.

S. virginiensis Michx. Early Saxifrage. Plants 5-35 cm high; basal
leaves crenate to serrate, sparsely hairy; petals oblong to obovate. Rocky
places, Cook to Lake of the Woods Co.

SULLIVANTIA *

Perennial herbs; leaves rounded, palmately veined, mostly basal;
flowers paniculate, white; hypanthium adnate only at the base to the carpels;
calyx lobes, petals, and stamens each 5; carpels 2, fused except at the top;
placentation axile; fruit a many-seeded capsule. (Named for W. S. Sullivant,
American botanist.)

S. renifolia Rosendahl. Leaves round to kidney-shaped, 4-9 cm wide,
cleft into 6-12 shallow lobes, each with 2-3 short teeth; petals 2-3 mm long.
Moist rocky places, Houston, Fillmore, and Winona counties.

PLATANACEAE ----- PLANE-TREE FAMILY

Monoecious trees; star-like branched hairs common on vegetative
parts; leaves alternate, simple, palmately 3-9-lobed, the petioles hollow at
the base and enclosing the axillary bud; male and female flowers densely
crowded in separate round heads arranged along a pendulous stalk; male
flowers several to many per head, each with a cup-like calyx, 3-7 minute
3-toothed petals, 3-7 free stamens with very short or no filaments alternating with the petals, and sometimes staminodes and rudimentary carpels;
female flowers with 3-5 free or fused sepals, several or no petals, staminodes usually in a whorl of 3 or 4, and 5-9 free carpels each with 1 or 2
ovules; fruits achenes or follicles, each fruit subtended by many long hairs.

PLATANUS ----- PLANE TREE, SYCAMORE, BUTTONWOOD

Characters of the family; the only genus. (The ancient name, from
the Gr. platys, broad, apparently referring to the large leaves.)

P. occidentalis L. Sycamore, Buttonwood; cultivated. Tree to 40 m high
or higher; bark scaly, pale; leaves 10-20 cm long, 3-5-lobed, coarsely
toothed, becoming glabrous or nearly so except on the veins beneath. E. N.
America, w. to central Iowa and Texas.

ROSACEAE ----- ROSE FAMILY

Herbs, shrubs, or trees; leaves all or mostly alternate (rarely opposite, not in ours), stipulate, simple or compound; flowers mostly regular, bisexual, perigynous to epigynous, mostly 5-merous; sepals often with 5 bractlets alternating with them; petals separate or rarely absent; stamens (5-) 15-many; carpels 1-many, free or variously united and then the placentation axile and the ovary usually inferior; ovules 1-few per carpel; fruit various.

A-Herbs.
  B-Leaves all basal and with 3 leaflets.
    C-Leaflets entire except for 3 (-5) terminal teeth . <u>Potentilla</u> <u>tridentata</u>
    C-Leaflets many-toothed.
      D-Petals white . . . . FRAGARIA
      D-Petals yellow . . . . WALDSTEINIA
  B-Leaves various, if with 3 leaflets then placed along a stem.
    E-Bractlets absent from the calyx . . . . RUBUS
    E-Sepals alternating with bractlets, these often sepal-like.
      F-Petals yellow or white; styles 0.7-2.5 mm long, not elongating
        after anthesis, often falling . . . . POTENTILLA
      F-Petals whitish-straw-colored, or tan or smoky yellow, to
        purplish; styles 3-4 mm long in early anthesis, rapidly and
        greatly elongating, persistent in fruit . . . . GEUM
A-Low to high shrubs, trees, or woody vines.
  G-Leaves all or mostly compound.
    H-Thornless trees or tree-like shrubs; ovary 1/2-3/4 inferior, of
      2-4 carpels; petals 2.5-5 mm long, white . . . . SORBUS
    H-Usually thorny shrubs or woody vines; ovary superior, usually
      of many carpels, superficially appearing inferior in <u>Rosa</u> but
      then the petals more than 5 mm long; petals white or colored.
      I-Hypanthium globose to urn-shaped, enclosing the carpels . . ROSA
      I-Hypanthium flat to shallowly cup-shaped, plainly exposing
        the carpels . . . . RUBUS
  G-Leaves all simple.
    J-Inflorescences, at least the larger ones, compound.
      K-Leaves entire . . . . COTONEASTER
      K-Leaves toothed at least at apex.
        L-Midrib dotted above with tiny reddish or dark raised
        points, the leaves finely toothed, with 6-16 teeth
        per cm; plants spineless; styles fused at least
        at base . . . . ARONIA
        L-Midrib without raised points, the leaves often
        more coarsely toothed; long smooth spines
        usually present; styles separate. . . . . CRATAEGUS
    J-Inflorescences all simple.
      M-Style (and carpel) 1, the ovary superior. . . . . PRUNUS
      M-Styles (and carpels) 2-many, or if 1 the ovary inferior.
        N-Ovaries separate from each other, superior to 1/3
        inferior.
          O-Stipules or stipule scars present; leaves often
          palmately lobed; nectar glands absent from hypan-
          thium; carpels fully superior . . . . PHYSOCARPUS
          O-Stipules none; leaves seldom lobed; stamens borne
          outside of a series of nectar glands; carpels 1/6-
          1/3 inferior . . . . SPIRAEA
        N-Ovaries fused, 1/2 to fully inferior.

P-Flowers orange-red, sessile or nearly so on
the stem . . . . CHAENOMELES
P-Flowers white to rose-red, pedicelled, single
or in racemes or umbel-like clusters.
  Q-Flowers in racemes or single or in umbel-like
  clusters, if single or in umbel-like clusters
  then the petals 6-9 mm long; petals 2-3. 5 times
  as long as wide; ovary becoming 10-locular through
  the development of 5 secondary partitions . . AMELANCHIER
  Q-Flowers in umbel-like clusters or rounded corymbs,
  the petals 10-28 mm long; petals 1-2. 3 times as
  long as wide; ovary 2-5-locular . . . . PYRUS

AMELANCHIER ----- JUNEBERRY, SERVICEBERRY, SHADBUSH *

Thornless shrubs and small trees; leaves simple, mostly toothed;
tipules falling early; flowers white to seldom pink, in racemes or rarely
-4 in an umbel-like cluster; hypanthium above the ovary obconic, bell-
haped, or saucer-shaped; sepals 5; petals 5, in ours 2-3. 5 times as long
s wide; stamens ca. 20; carpels normally 5 in ours, the ovaries fused,
/2 to fully inferior, the 5 styles free to partly fused; ovules 2 per locule,
oon separated by a secondary partition growing in from the back of the car-
el, the fruit therefore an apparently 10-locular and 10-seeded berry-like
ome. (The Provencal name of a European species.)
The true number of species of serviceberries in our region is by no
leans certain, despite the large amount of study devoted to these plants. A
igh degree of natural variation plus an unknown but presumed high incidence
f hybridization seem to account for this situation, as well as an apparent
endency of some authors to recognize relatively minor characteristics as
aving specific value. Three distinct types of Amelanchier occur in Minnesota:
le non-racemose type (A. bartramiana); the many-toothed racemose type
A. arborea, A. laevis, and the A. intermedia complex); and the few-toothed
acemose type (all other groups). The first is relatively uniform, but the
ther two contain many forms, and the extent to which they should be subdi-
ided is debatable. Introgression between these two racemose types may
ccount for much of the complexity of this genus in our area. The present
axonomic treatment is a compromise.

-Flowers single or in umbel-like or rarely racemose clusters of 2
  or 3; top of ovary (within the hypanthium) conical; leaves overlapping in the bud, wedge-shaped at base . . . . A. bartramiana
-Flowers several to many in racemes; ovary rounded to nearly
  flat on top; leaves folded double lengthwise in bud, rounded or
  slightly heart-shaped at base.
  B-Top of ovary (within the hypanthium) glabrous.
    C-Leaves usually much less than half grown at flowering time,
    densely white-hairy beneath, the blades not purple or
    bronze; sepals broadly oblong-triangular, abruptly pointed;
    fruit somewhat dry, mealy and tasteless . . . . A. arborea
    C-Leaves half-grown at flowering time, purple or bronze or
    rarely bright green, glabrous or nearly so; sepals lanceolate,
    acuminate; fruit sweet and juicy. . . . . A. laevis

151

B-Top of ovary densely to slightly pubescent.
    D-Teeth of average to medium-large leaves 25-50 on a side, 2.1-
       3.8 for each lateral nerve (the average of all teeth and all
       lateral nerves on one side) . . . . A. intermedia complex
    D-Teeth of average to medium-large leaves 0-24 on a side, 1-2
       for each lateral nerve.
      E-Plants spreading by underground offshoots, forming colonies;
        racemes erect; petals 5-11 mm long; hypanthium 1/3-1/2
        as deep as wide . . . . A. spicata complex
      E-Plants mostly single or a few in a clump; racemes ascending
        to drooping; petals 10-20 mm long; hypanthium ca. 1/4
        as deep as wide . . . . A. sanguinea complex

A. arborea (Michx. f.) Fern. Downy Serviceberry. Shrub to small tree;
terminal buds 6-13 mm long; petioles and lower leaf surfaces remaining more
or less pubescent; teeth of average to medium-large leaves 6-10 per cm, 35-
50 on a side, 2.5-3.8 per lateral nerve (see D in key); racemes ascending to
drooping; lower pedicels in flower similar to A. laevis, in fruit perhaps a
few mm shorter; sepals 2-3 (-3.5) mm long; petals 10-18 mm long; hypanthium
2.5-3 (-3.5) mm in diameter. Dry hillsides, Cook to St. Louis Co. and in
Goodhue Co.

A. bartramiana (Tausch) Roemer. Shrub to 2.5 m high; leaves half
grown at flowering time, glabrous or with a few hairs on the petiole when
young; teeth of average to medium-large leaves 6-12 per cm, 20-40 on a
side, 1.8-3.2 per lateral nerve (see D in key); petals 6-9 mm long; top of
ovary woolly. Damp uplands and borders of bogs, Cook to Itasca and Carlton
counties.

A. intermedia complex. Shrubs to small trees to 8 m high; terminal bud
8-13 mm long; leaves soon glabrous; racemes erect to nodding; lower pedicels
10-40 mm long; petals 7-15 mm long; sepals 2-5 mm long. Plants placed in
this complex appear to consist in part of hybrids between A. arborea or
A. laevis and plants of the A. sanguinea or A. spicata complexes. Others
may simply be forms of A. laevis with the top of the ovary pubescent. It is
a moot question whether any plants placed in the A. intermedia complex
represent species separate from the groups mentioned. Distribution of the
complex is from Cook to Clearwater Co. and s. to Becker, Mille Lacs,
Hennepin, Blue Earth, and Houston counties. The following key presents
the "species" sometimes segregated from this group.

A-Leaves typically elliptic or elliptic-obovate, the apex acute, the
    teeth 5-7 per cm; sepals ascending or irregularly revolute.
    Found through most of the above range . . . . A. intermedia Spach.
A-Leaves typically ovate to oblong, the apex mostly acuminate, the
    teeth 4-7 per cm; sepals reflexed from the base.
    B-Leaves flat, the teeth 5-6 (-7) per cm, with rounded sinuses be-
      tween the teeth. Mostly from Mille Lacs Co. and s. in the above
      range . . . . A. interior Nielsen.
    B-Leaves remaining slightly folded at maturity, the teeth 4-5 per
      cm, with sharp sinuses between the teeth. Between L. Superior
      and the divide paralleling it to the nw. . . . . . . A. wiegandii Nielsen.

A. laevis Wieg. Shrub to small tree to 13 m high; terminal buds 13-17
mm long; teeth of average to medium-large leaves 6-8 per cm, 23-50 on a
side, 2.1-3.6 per lateral nerve (see D in key); racemes ascending to drooping; lower pedicels 5-23 mm long in flower, 15-35 mm long in fruit; sepals
3-4 (2.75-4.5)mm long; petals 10-22 mm long; hypanthium 2.75-5 mm in

diameter. Damp wooded slopes and banks, from Cook to Clearwater Co. and s. to Otter Tail, Hennepin, Blue Earth, and Houston counties.

A. sanguinea complex. Shrub to small tree, to 7 m high; racemes 4-7.5 cm long; lowermost pedicel 10-30 mm long. The following key presents the "species" sometimes segregated from this group.

A-Main lateral veins running straight to the apex of the teeth, at least
    in the upper third of the leaf, the teeth 4-5 (-6) per cm; hypanthium
    4-5 mm in diameter; petals linear or narrowly oblanceolate; buds
    dull. Open woods and slopes, Cook to Lake of the Woods Co., s.
    to Otter Tail, Chippewa, Lincoln, Blue Earth, and Houston counties
    . . . . A. sanguinea (Pursh) DC.
A-Main lateral veins curving upward, often forking near the margin,
    the branches running into the teeth, the teeth 3-4 per cm;
    hypanthium 5-7.5 mm in diameter; petals obovate; buds var-
    nished. Open woods and slopes, on calcareous soil or basic
    rocks, Cook to Clearwater to Carlton counties . . A. huronensis Wieg.

A. spicata complex. Low Juneberry. Shrub 1-5 (-7) m high; racemes 1.5-5 cm long; lowermost pedicel 5-15 mm long. The following key presents the "species" often segregated from this group.

A-Leaves mostly unfolded and more than half grown at flowering time,
    the pubescence early deciduous, the leaves soon glabrous or nearly
    so, often whitened beneath, the apex truncate to rounded; sepals
    triangular, 2.5-3 mm long, nearly as wide; Great Plains plants,
    claimed by some and denied by others to occur in western Minnesota
    . . . . A. alnifolia Nutt.
A-Leaves unfolding before or with the flowers, usually about half grown
    at anthesis, the pubescence early or late deciduous, the leaves not
    whitened beneath, the apex usually rounded to acute; sepals tri-
    angular to lanceolate, 2-5.5 mm long.
  B-Leaf teeth 5-8 per cm. Cook, Lake, and St. Louis counties.
    . . . . A. spicata (Lam.) K. Koch (A. stolonifera Wieg.)
  B-Leaf teeth 0-5 (-6) per cm.
    C-Leaves few to many-toothed, elliptic to oblong, not mucronate;
      buds ovate; sepals 2-4 mm long; hypanthium ca. 3-4 mm in
      diameter. Thickets, shores, and rocky places, throughout the
      state . . . . A. humilis Wieg.
    C-Leaves entire or with a few teeth near the tip, narrowly to
      broadly ovate, the apex mucronate; buds ellipsoid; sepals
      3.5-5.5 mm long; hypanthium 4-5 mm in diameter. Cook
      and St. Louis counties . . . . A. mucronata Nielsen.

ARONIA ----- CHOKEBERRY [*]

Thornless shrubs; leaves simple, finely toothed, the midrib on the upper side bearing few to many tiny slender pointed usually reddish structures, "glands"; flowers white or tinted with rose, in rounded to flat-topped simple to usually compound cymes; hypanthium prolonged above the inferior ovary; sepals and petals 5 each, the petals 1.1-1.7 times as long as wide; stamens usually 20; carpels usually 5, the ovaries united, densely woolly on top, the styles as many as the carpels, united at the base; fruit a small globose berry-like pome, the seeds normally 2 per locule. (The name modified from the generic name Aria.) Often combined with Pyrus.

A-Pedicels, younger branches, and lower leaf surfaces soon glabrous or
    nearly so; fruit black; native . . . . A. melanocarpa

A-Pedicels, younger branches, and lower leaf surfaces remaining
    pubescent; fruit red; cultivated . . . . <u>A</u>. <u>arbutifolia</u>

    <u>A</u>. <u>arbutifolia</u> (L.) Ell. (<u>Pyrus</u> <u>arbutifolia</u> (L.) L. f.). Red Chokeberry;
cultivated. Petals 4-6 mm long; fruit 4-6 mm thick. From eastern N. Americ

    <u>A</u>. <u>melanocarpa</u> (Michx.) Ell. (<u>Pyrus</u> <u>melanocarpa</u> (Michx.) Willd.).
Black Chokeberry. Similar to <u>A</u>. <u>arbutifolia</u>; fruit 6-8 mm thick. Bogs, damp
thickets and clearings, from Cook to St. Louis, Todd, Hennepin, and Ramsey
counties.

CHAENOMELES ----- FLOWERING QUINCE

    Shrubs, usually thorny; leaves simple, toothed; flowers brilliant, mostl
opening before the leaves appear, sessile or nearly so; hypanthium and calyx
often colored; sepals and petals 5 each; stamens 20 or more; carpels mostly
5, the ovaries united and inferior, the styles as many and united below; fruit
a pome, the locules many-seeded. (Gr. <u>chainein</u>, to gape or open, <u>melea</u>,
apple, the fruit once thought to split into 5 parts.)

    <u>C</u>. <u>japonica</u> (Thunb.) Lindl. Dwarf Japanese Quince; cultivated. Shrub
1-2 m high; leaves roundish to ovate to obovate, 3-7 cm long; petals orange-
red, 16-28 mm long; fruit 3.5-5 cm in diameter. From Japan.

COTONEASTER

    Shrubs, seldom tree-like, not truly spiny; leaves simple, entire;
flowers white to pink, small, single or in cymose clusters, appearing after
the leaves; hypanthium fused to the ovary; sepals and petals 5 each; stamens
about 20; carpels 2-5, the ovaries fused and inferior, the styles as many
and separate; placentation axile; fruit a small red or black pome with 2-5
stones. (L., quince-like, from the leaves of some species.)

A-Petals pinkish; flowers in 3-12-flowered clusters; fruit black. . <u>C</u>. <u>lucida</u>
A-Petals white; flowers in 6-20-flowered clusters; fruit red . <u>C</u>. <u>multiflora</u>

    <u>C</u>. <u>lucida</u> Schlecht. Cultivated. Shrub 1-2 m high; leaf blades elliptic to
ovate, 2-5 cm long, dark green and shining above; petioles 2-5 mm long;
petals upright, obovate, slightly and irregularly toothed, 2.5-3.5 mm long;
stones of the fruit 3-4. From the Altai Mts. of central Asia.

    <u>C</u>. <u>multiflora</u> Bunge. Cultivated. Shrub to 3 (-4) m high; leaf blades
ovate to broadly elliptic, 2-5 cm long; petioles 3-10 mm long; petals spreading, roundish, 4.5-6 mm long; stones of the fruit 1-2. W. China.

CRATAEGUS ----- HAWTHORN, THORN APPLE*

    Shrubs or small trees, usually thorny, the thorns up to 10 cm long;
leaves simple, toothed and often also lobed, those of the flowering branchlets
(floral leaves) often unlike those of the strictly vegetative branches; flowers
in flat-topped to broadly rounded usually branched cymes; hypanthium cup-
shaped to bell-shaped above the ovary; sepals 5; petals 5, white or rarely to re
nearly round in outline; stamens 5-25; carpels 1-5, the ovaries weakly united,
inferior or free at the tip, the styles as many and free; fruit a pome, the
carpel walls hard and bony when ripe, seed-like, free or coherent within the
fleshy fruit, 1-seeded. (Gr. <u>kratos</u>, strength, from the wood.)

Crataegus has long been known as a "difficult" genus taxonomically. Normal variation plus hybridization, polyploidy, aneuploidy, and apomixis so complicate and obscure the groupings that distinctions are hard to draw. A conservative treatment is given here. Fruits at least partly developed are often needed for identification.

A-Leaves mostly cut more than 1/2 way to the midrib, with 1-3 pairs
    of oblong lateral lobes; carpel and style 1; flowers white to red;
    cultivated . . . . C. monogyna
A-Leaves mostly cut less than 1/2 way to the midrib, the lobes 0-
    several; carpels and styles 2-5; flowers white; native except for
    C. crus-galli.
  B-Stones of the fruit pitted on the inner side.
    C-Fruits purplish black; thorns 0-3 cm long; floral leaves widest
       0.4-0.6 of the way to the apex. . . . . C. douglasii
    C-Fruits red to orange-red; thorns often longer; floral leaves
       widest 0.3-0.55 of the way to the apex.
      D-Young twigs glabrous or nearly so; leaves shining above,
         3-6 cm long, 2-5 cm wide; blades of floral leaves 3-4.5
         times as long as the petioles . . . . C. succulenta
      D-Young twigs hairy; leaves dull above, 5-9 cm long, 4-8
         cm wide; blades of floral leaves 4.5-9.3 times as long as
         the petioles. . . . . C. calpodendron
  B-Stones straight and unpitted on the inner side.
    E-Floral leaves narrowly to moderately acute at base (the included
       angle 40-90°), 1.3-2.4 times as long as wide, widest 0.43-
       0.66 of the way to the apex, tending to be obovate, singly or
       sometimes doubly serrate from the middle upwards, if doubly
       serrate the lower larger teeth mostly 1-3 mm deep and with
       3-9 small teeth; lateral veins 5-8, 1.1-2.3 per cm (no. of
       veins divided by leaf length).
      F-Floral leaves dull above, singly to sometimes doubly ser-
        rate; branches of the inflorescence pubescent; fruit with
        3-5 stones; native . . . . C. punctata
      F-Floral leaves glossy above, singly serrate; branches of
        the inflorescence glabrous or nearly so; fruit with 1-2
        (-3) stones; cultivated. C. crus-galli
    E-Floral leaves moderately acute to truncate or slightly heart-
       shaped at base (the included angle 75-220°), 0.9-1.6 times
       as long as wide, widest 0.25-0.57 of the way to the apex,
       tending to be ovate to elliptic, usually doubly serrate, if
       the angle 90° or less then the lower larger teeth mostly
       4-6 mm deep and with 9-23 small teeth; lateral veins 4-7,
       0.6-1.6 per cm.
      G-Flowers 20-25 mm wide; petioles, main veins of blade be-
        low, branches of the inflorescence, hypanthium, and
        both sides of the sepals densely pubescent even at maturity;
        fruit pubescent at least at the ends, 13-18 mm thick . . C. mollis
      G-Flowers 10-18 mm wide; pubescence usually less than
        above or the plant glabrous; fruit 7-15 mm thick.
        H-Included angle at base of floral leaf blades 75-180°,
          the blades widest below the middle to slightly above
          it, the lobes confined mostly to the apical half; anthers
          mostly white, sometimes pink; fruits in texture from
          sticky as in butter to dry and tough, or at most only
          slightly juicy, in taste from tasteless to bitter; inner

edge of stones broadly acute to blunt; thorns numerous
and very hard to bend . . . . C. rotundifolia complex
H-Included angle at base of floral leaf blades 130-190°,
the blades widest below or at the middle, the lobes
extending from near the base to the apex; anthers
pink to purple-pink to deep red; fruit in texture juicy,
mealy, or mushy, in taste tart or sweetish; inner
edge of stones sharply acute; thorns less numerous,
not difficult to bend as when making a pressed speci-
men . . . . C. macrosperm

C. calpodendron (Ehrh.) Medic. Thorns 3-7 cm long; included angle of base of floral leaf blades 75-135°, blades widest 0.46-0.55 of the way to the apex, tapering into the petiole, singly serrate below the middle, singly or doubly serrate above the middle; flowers 10-17 mm wide; carpels, styles, and stones of fruit 2 or 3; fruit 7-9 mm thick. Open woods and thickets, recorded from Houston, Rice, Hennepin, Chisago, Kanabec, Itasca, and Red Lake counties.

C. crus-galli L. Cockspur Thorn; cultivated. Thorns 3-10 cm long; included angle of base of floral leaf blades 40-70°, blades widest 0.55-0.66 of the way to the apex, glabrous or nearly so, the veins seldom impressed above; flowers 8-18 mm wide; carpels and styles 1-2 (-3); fruit green to red, 6-14 mm thick. From eastern United States.

C. douglasii Lindl. Included angle of base of floral leaf blades 65-115°, the blades singly serrate or doubly serrate above the middle, glabrous to lightly pubescent; inflorescence glabrous; flowers 10-13 mm wide; fruit 8-10 mm thick with 3-5 stones. Open woods and rocky banks, Cook and s. Lake counties.

C. macrosperma Ashe (C. flabellata (Spach) Kirchner). Thorns 2-5 cm long; leaves dull above; stamens 5-10 (-20); carpels, styles, and stones of fruit 3-5; fruit red, 7-15 mm thick. Open woods and thickets, Lake and St. Louis counties to Hennepin and Washington counties and in Hubbard, Clearwater, Winona, and Houston counties. Forms with leaves somewhat smaller than average, more deeply indented and with the lateral lobes relatively few and acute to acuminate, and with relatively small fruits, are sometimes known as C. m. var. roanensis (Ashe) Palmer.

C. mollis (T. & G.) Scheele. Thorns 4-6 cm long; included angle of base of floral leaf blades 135-220°, blades widest 0.25-0.33 of the way to the apex; carpels, styles, and stones of the fruit 3-5; fruit red. Borders of woods and open places, southern, n. to Washington, Hennepin, Brown, and Lincoln counties.

C. monogyna Jacq. English Hawthorn; cultivated. Thorns 1-2 cm long; leaves glabrous to slightly pubescent when young; branches of the inflorescence glabrous; flowers 9-14 mm wide; fruit red, 5-8 mm thick. From Eurasia and the Mediterranean region.

C. punctata Jacq. Thorns 3-10 cm long; included angle of base of floral leaf blades 55-90°, the blades widest 0.43-0.66 of the way to the apex, the upper surface lightly pubescent when young, later glabrous, the lower surface pubescent at least along the veins; veins usually impressed above at maturity; flowers 12-18 mm wide; carpels and styles 3-5;. fruit dull red to bright yellow, 10-17 mm thick. Thickets and open places, Houston to Martin Co., n. to Meeker and Pine counties, and in Otter Tail and Clearwater counties.

C. rotundifolia Moench. Thorns 3-6 cm long; leaves usually very slightly glossy above; stamens 10-20; carpels, styles, and stones of fruit 3-5; fruit red, 7-12 mm thick. Thickets and open places, throughout the state. A complex group, often subdivided as follows:

A-Floral leaves mostly elliptic, acuminate at apex, attenuate at base; vegetative leaves broader than the floral but not almost round
. . . . C. brunetiana Sarg.
A-Floral leaves mostly broadly-or oblong-elliptic, short-pointed; vegetative leaves often nearly round.
   B-Petioles and inflorescence glabrous or sparsely pubescent; fruit remaining hard till late in the season . . . . C. chrysocarpa Ashe.
   B-Petioles and inflorescence abundantly hairy at flowering time; fruit ripening earlier.
      C-Vegetative leaves deeply cut into narrow segments near the base; pubescence of fine long hairs, not matted, often persisting along the veins beneath . . . . C. irrasa Sarg.
      C-Vegetative leaves not cut as above; pubescence of matted hairs; leaves soon glabrous . . . . C. faxoni Sarg.

C. succulenta Link. Thorns 4-8 cm long; included angle of base of floral leaf blades 75-135°, blades widest 0.3-0.5 of the way to the apex, tapering into the petiole, singly serrate below the middle, singly or doubly serrate above the middle; flowers ca. 12-18 mm wide; carpels, styles, and stones of fruit 2-3 (-4); fruit 7-15 mm thick. Edges of woods, thickets, and open places, scattered over most of the state. Forms with leaves with the veins impressed above, relatively pale and pubescent beneath, the stamens 10 instead of the more usual 20, and the fruit pubescent at the ends, have been recognized as C. s. var. permentosa (Ashe) Palmer.

FRAGARIA ----- STRAWBERRY*

    Perennial herbs, often more of less dioecious, usually spreading by stolons; leaves all basal, compound, with 3 leaflets; hypanthium short and flat; sepals 5, alternating with 5 bractlets of nearly equal size; petals 5, white (rarely pink); stamens many; carpels many, borne on the prolonged receptacle; styles lateral, persistent; fruit of many achenes on the greatly enlarged juicy red receptacle. (L. fraga, the strawberry, from the fragrance of the fruit.)

A-Achenes set on the surface of the fruiting receptacle; terminal tooth of leaflets equalling to longer than the adjacent lateral teeth and usually more than 1/2 as wide as them; petals 3-7 mm long . . . . F. vesca var. americana
A-Achenes set in pits in the fruiting receptacle; terminal tooth of leaflets mostly shorter than to equalling the adjacent lateral teeth and usually less than 1/2 as wide as them; petals (4-) 6-10 mm long . . . . F. virginiana

F. vesca var. americana Porter. American Wood Strawberry. Leaflets sessile to short-stalked; main lateral veins diverging from the midrib at an angle of 30-45°; peduncles at first shorter than the leaves, later surpassing them; sepals usually spreading or reflexed in ripe fruit; fruit slenderly ovoid to ellipsoid. Mesic open places, throughout the state except for Roseau and Kittson to Norman counties, Wilkin to Rock, and Rock to Faribault counties.

F. virginiana Duchesne. Virginia Strawberry. Leaflets with short stalks; main lateral veins diverging at an angle of 20-40°; peduncles mostly shorter than the leaves, at first and later; sepals appressed to the fruit; fruit subglobose to ovoid. Mesic open places, throughout the state.

Perennial herbs with lobed or compound leaves, the stem leaves progressively reduced upwards; hypanthium top-shaped to bell-shaped; sepals 5, usually but not always alternating with 5 narrow bractlets; petals 5, whitish to yellowish or suffused with pink or purple; stamens 10-many; carpels many, on a conical or cylindric dry receptacle; achenes tipped by the long persistent styles or their basal halves. (A name used by Pliny.)

A-Widest major divisions of leaves 3-20 mm wide; bractlets longer than
    the calyx lobes . . . . G. triflorum
A-Widest major divisions of leaves 30-120 mm wide; bractlets about
    1/2 as long as the calyx lobes . . . . G. rivale

G. rivale L. Water Avens. Leaves pinnately compound, the terminal leaflets usually abruptly larger than the lower ones; widest divisions of stem leaves 10-50 mm wide; petals tan or smoky yellow to purplish; style at anthesis with an S-shaped joint ca. 1 mm above the base. Wet meadows and bogs, from Cook to Lake of the Woods Co. and s. to Clearwater, Otter Tail, Wright, Anoka, and Chisago counties.

G. triflorum Pursh. Purple Avens. Leaves pinnately compound, the leaflets grading down in size from tip of leaf to base; widest divisions of stem leaves 1-3 mm wide; petals a whitish straw color to purplish; style not jointed. Mesic to dry prairies and openings, from Houston to Rock Co. and n. to Washington, Isanti, Todd, Clearwater, Roseau, and Kittson counties and at one isolated locality in Lake Co.

PHYSOCARPUS ----- NINEBARK [*]

Shrubs with shreddy bark and simple, stipulate, palmately veined, usually lobed leaves; flowers white to pinkish, in umbel-like corymbs; hypanthium shallowly cup-shaped; nectar glands none; sepals and petals 5 each; stamens 20-40; carpels (1-) 3-5, sometimes weakly united below, fully superior; ovules few per carpel; fruit a follicle, appearing inflated, splitting halfway to the base along both edges. (Gr. physa, bellows, and karpos, fruit, from the inflated follicles.)

P. opulifolius (L.) Maxim. Shrub 1-3 m high; bark peeling in narrow strips; flowers 7-12 mm wide; follicles 5-10 mm long, glabrous or with branched hairs. Thickets, rocky slopes, and shores, mostly near Lake Superior from Cook to Carlton Co., in Morrison and Blue Earth counties, and from Chisago, Anoka, and Hennepin counties to Fillmore and Houston counties. Forms with branched hairs on the fruits and usually on the under sides of the leaves have been named P. o. var. intermedius (Rydb.) Robinson. A form with yellow leaves, cv. Luteus, known as Golden Ninebark, is often cultivated.

POTENTILLA ----- CINQUEFOIL, FIVE-FINGER

Annual to perennial herbs or rarely low shrubs; leaves compound; hypanthium short and flat to somewhat cup-shaped; sepals (4-) 5, alternating with as many bractlets, these usually narrower or shorter; petals (4-) 5; stamens 5-many, usually 20; carpels (10-) many, borne on the prolonged receptacle; styles terminal, lateral, or nearly basal, jointed to the ovary;

ovule 1 per carpel; fruit a cluster of achenes. (Diminutive of L. potens, powerful, from the reputed medicinal properties of one species.)

A-Petals white . . . . P. tridentata
A-Petals yellow.
   B-Leaves palmately compound.
      C-Flowers solitary on slender stalks from the nodes; leaflets
         green to slightly whitened beneath . . . . P. simplex
      C-Flowers few to many in a cyme; leaflets densely white-hairy
         beneath . . . . : . . . . P. argentea
   B-Leaves pinnately compound.
      D-Flowers solitary on slender stalks from the nodes, 14-24 mm
         wide . . . . P. anserina
      D-Flowers few to many in a cyme, 5-9 mm wide . . . . . . P. paradoxa

P. anserina L. Silver-weed. Perennial herbs with long stolons; leaflets many, densely white-hairy beneath. Low meadows, marshy shores, river-banks, and sometimes rocky places, Kittson to Pipestone Co., scattered e. to Koochiching, St. Louis, Cass, Hennepin, and Goodhue counties.

P. argentea L. Silvery Cinquefoil. Perennial herbs; larger leaves with 5 leaflets; flowers 7-10 mm wide. Naturalized from Europe; common as a lawn weed and in disturbed ground, recorded from Houston to Blue Earth Co. and n. to Lake, Clearwater, and Clay counties.

P. paradoxa Nutt. Annual to short-lived perennial herb; leaflets 7-11, hairy but not densely whitened beneath. Damp to wet open ground, Roseau to Lincoln Co., e. to Lake of the Woods, Becker, Douglas, Kandiyohi, Hennepin, Dakota, Waseca, and Martin counties.

P. simplex Michx. Old-field Cinquefoil. Perennial herbs; stems at first erect, later sprawling or arching and rooting at the tips; leaflets 5; flowers 10-15 mm wide. Mesic to dry fields and open woods, Houston to Olmsted, Hennepin, Morrison, St. Louis, and Cook counties, and in Renville and Jackson counties.

P. tridentata Soland. Three-toothed Cinquefoil. Perennial herbs from a woody base; leaflets 3, 3-toothed at the tip; flowers several in a flattened cyme. Open rocky, gravelly, and sandy places, from Cook to Roseau to Crow Wing Co. and in Dakota, Fillmore, and Houston counties.

PRUNUS ----- PLUM, CHERRY*

Trees or shrubs, sometimes spiny; leaves alternate (opposite in seed-lings) simple, mostly serrate, often with glandular swellings on the petiole or on the leaf teeth at the base of the blade; flowers solitary or in umbel-like clusters or racemes, white to pink; hypanthium urn-shaped to cup-shaped to obconic; sepals and petals 5 each; stamens 15-30; carpel 1, fully superior; ovules 2, usually only 1 functional; fruit a 1-seeded drupe. (The classical L. name for the plum.)

A-Flowers in elongate racemes, appearing with or after the leaves.
   B-Petals 6-10 mm long; hypanthium woolly-pubescent within;
      cultivated . . . . P. padus
   B-Petals 2.5-4 mm long; hypanthium nearly glabrous within; native.
      C-Leaves ovate to obovate, mostly tending to be widest above the
         middle when fully expanded, usually minutely puberulent on
         the midrib and larger lateral veins above; pubescence along

the midrib beneath, when present, greater at the junctions of
the lateral veins and often extending a short distance along
them; leaf teeth not notably appressed or incurved; calyx lobes
semicircular or broad-oblong to triangular, fringed with 8-20
fine irregular teeth often tipped with red glands . . . . P. virginiana
  C-Leaves narrowly ovate to elliptic, seldom widest above the middle,
glabrous above; pubescence of the midrib beneath, when present,
uniform as far as it goes, not extending out the lateral veins;
leaf teeth appressed or incurved; calyx lobes triangular to oblong,
entire or with up to 7 minute gland-tipped or glandless teeth
. . . . P. serotina
A-Flowers single or in umbel-like clusters or corymbs, appearing before or with the leaves.
  D-Flowers double (i. e. petals 10 or more); cultivated.
    E-Leaves obovate, the apex abruptly acuminate; pedicels 3-6
mm long . . . . P. triloba
    E-Leaves oblong-lanceolate, blunt or acutish at the apex; pedi-
cels 9-16 mm long . . . . P. glandulosa
  D-Flowers single (i. e. petals normally 5); native or cultivated.
    F-Either the leaves red-purple or the pedicels 1-3 mm long;
cultivated.
      G-Leaves red-purple (in age becoming greenish-red), the
young ones not as below; pedicels 5-20 mm long
. . . . the hybrid 'Newport' Plum. See P. cerasifera
      G-Leaves green, the young ones densely white-hairy beneath;
pedicels 1-3 mm long . . . . P. tomentosa
    F-Leaves green, or not yet present; pedicels (of fully opened
flowers) 4-30 mm long; native or cultivated.
    H-Sepals pubescent at least on one surface.
      I-Leaf teeth acuminate to a fine point, normally glandless;
sepals entire or sometimes with a few marginal glands,
green or slightly red-tinged; native . . . . P. american
      I-Leaf teeth each tipped with a tiny differentiated "gland";
sepals from glandless to consistently glandular, green
to red; native or cultivated.
        J-Young leaves acuminate, 2.1-3.1 times as long as wide,
or not yet present; sepals usually red or reddish-green,
consistently with minute gland-tipped teeth; native . . P. nigra
        J-Young leaves present, rounded to acute, 1.5-2.4 times
as long as wide; sepals green, entire or glandular;
cultivated . . . . P. domestica
    H-Sepals glabrous.
      K-Shrub 0.5-1.5 m high; leaves rounded to acute at apex
(rarely at maturity with an acuminate tip to 2 mm long);
petals 4-8 mm long; native . . . . P. pumila
      K-Shrub or tree 2-10 m high; leaves acuminate or long-acute
to acute but if acute or short-acuminate then the petals
10-15 mm long (when acuminate the tip at maturity well
over 2 mm long); petals 3.5-15 mm long; native or
cultivated.
        L-Petals 3.5-7 mm long; sepals entire; native. . . P. pensylvanic
        L-Petals 7-15 mm long; sepals entire or with minute
gland-tipped teeth, if entire then the petals 10-15
mm long; native or cultivated.
          M-Flower clusters without basal green bracts; young
leaves acuminate, 2.1-3.1 times as long as wide, or
not yet present; native . . . . P. nigra

M- Flower clusters with basal green bracts 4-8 mm long
or longer arising from the same bud as the flowers;
young leaves acute or short-acuminate, 1.4-2 times
as long as wide; cultivated . . . . P. cerasus

P. americana Marsh. Wild Plum. Shrub or small tree, forming thickets;
eaves 6-10 cm long, acuminate; sepals pubescent above; petals white, 7.5-
5 mm long. Mesic openings, roadsides, and riverbanks, Houston to Jackson
nd Pipestone counties, n. to Washington, Isanti, Pope, and Kittson counties,
nd in Itasca and St. Louis counties.

P. cerasifera Ehrh., cv. Atropurpurea, a purple-leaved form of the
pecies, is not hardy in Minnesota but has been crossed with various species
o produce more hardy plants. The common ornamental cv. Newport is a
ybrid of this cultivar with the cv. Omaha, itself a hybrid of P. americana
rith P. salicina. The latter species is from China; P. cerasifera is from
sia Minor and the Caucasus.

P. cerasus L. Sour Cherry; cultivated. Leaves 6-9 cm long, abruptly
hort-acuminate, the teeth gland-tipped; pedicels 15-30 mm long; sepals
reen or somewhat reddish, glabrous above, with minute marginal gland-
ipped teeth or entire; petals white to pink, 10-15 mm long. Many horti-
ultural forms are derived from this species. From Eurasia.

P. domestica L. Common, Garden, or European Plum; cultivated.
mall tree; leaves 5-10 cm long, ovate to obovate, rounded to acute at the
pex, pubescent at least below; pedicels 7-15 mm long; sepals green,usually
rith minute marginal gland-tipped teeth; petals 9-12 mm long, white or
ream. With many cultivars. Probably from sw. Asia, but known only as
cultigen.

P. glandulosa Thunb. Dwarf Flowering Cherry, Flowering Almond; culti-
ated. Shrub; leaves 4-9 cm long, tapering to a blunt apex, not acuminate,
he teeth gland-tipped; petals deep to light pink, 7-14 mm long. The double
orm common in cultivation usually produces no fruit. From China.

P. nigra Ait. Canada or Wild Plum. Small tree; leaves 7-12 cm long,
bruptly acuminate, the teeth gland-tipped; sepals glabrous to pubescent
bove, usually red or reddish-green, consistently with minute marginal
land-tipped teeth; petals (7-) 9-14 mm long, white, or pinkish toward the
ase; fruit red to yellow. Mesic to moist openings and thickets, St. Louis
o Kittson Co., s. to Otter Tail, Goodhue, and Houston counties.

P. padus L. European Bird-cherry; cultivated. Tall shrub or small tree;
eaves 5-10 cm long, ovate to obovate; pedicels 6-10 (-20) mm long; petals
hite; base of hypanthium remaining at base of fruit. From Eurasia. Our
ost common form is P. p. var. commutata Dipp., in which the leaves un-
old earlier than in most forms, are nearly green beneath, and have a rounded
broadly wedge-shaped base and relatively coarse teeth.

P. pensylvanica L. Pin or Bird Cherry. Tall shrub or small tree; leaves
-8 cm long, mostly oblong-lanceolate, acuminate or long-acute, the teeth
land-tipped; green bracts sometimes at base of flower cluster, arising from
he same bud as the flowers; pedicels 10-25 mm long; sepals green; petals
hite. Mesic to dry openings and thickets, throughout the state except sw. of
line from Lac Qui Parle to Freeborn Co.

P. pumila L. Sand Cherry. Leaves narrowly elliptic to oblanceolate, 3-
cm long, 8-27 mm wide, glabrous, the teeth mostly gland-tipped; pedicels
-14 mm long; sepals often minutely toothed, the teeth often gland-tipped; pet-
ls white, 4-7 (-8) mm long. Three varieties are sometimes distinguished in
linnesota, all of which intergrade; of these, probably only the small-leaved
ar. besseyi has any validity:

161

A-Leaves usually narrowly oblanceolate, 3-6 times as long as wide at
   maturity, the apex acute; Lake to Kittson Co., s. to Clay, Stearns,
   Rice, and Houston counties, and in Yellow Medicine Co. P. p. var. pumi
A-Leaves elliptic to oblong or narrowly obovate, 1.5-3 times as long
   as wide, rounded to broadly acute at the apex.
   B-Leaves of fertile branchlets mostly 3-6 cm long, blunt or some-
      times acute at the apex, with petioles 5-10 mm long; fruit 10-14
      mm thick; stones 5-6 mm wide; widely scattered from Cook to
      Kittson Co., s. to Polk, Becker, Dakota, and Houston counties,
      and in Pipestone Co. . . . .
      . . . . . . P. p. var. cuneata (Raf.) Bailey (P. susquehanae Willd.).
   B-Leaves of fertile branchlets mostly 2-4 cm long, acute or rarely
      obtuse at the apex, with petioles 5-6 mm long; fruit 15-18 mm
      thick; stones 6-8 mm wide; Pipestone to Kittson Co., e. to
      Otter Tail and Douglas counties, and in Benton Co.. . . . . .
      . . . . P. p. var. besseyi (Bailey) Gl. (P. besseyi Bailey).

Note: hybrid "Cherry Plums", cultivated to some extent in the state,
especially in the north, would key out to this species or near it. One
parent is P. pumila, the other usually the Japanese Plum P. salicina Lindl.
or another hybrid derived partly from P. salicina. These plants become
large bushes or small trees; their leaves are acute to sometimes short-
acuminate at the apex, and both leaf and floral dimensions average somewhat larger than those of P. pumila.

P. serotina Erhr. Black, Rum, or Cabinet Cherry. Tree to 25 m high;
leaves 6-14 cm long, 2-4 times as long as wide; pedicels 2-7 mm long;
petals white; calyx persistent under the fruit. Mesic to dry woods and
openings, from Houston to Faribault Co. and n. and w. to Carlton, Aitkin,
Pennington, and Clay counties.

P. tomentosa Thunb. Nanking Cherry; cultivated. Shrub or small tree;
leaves 3-7 cm long, broadly ovate to obovate, abruptly acuminate, at maturity
densely yellowish-gray hairy beneath; petals white or tinted, 8-12 mm long.
From China, Manchuria, and Japan.

P. triloba Lindl. Flowering Almond; cultivated. Shrub; leaves 3-6 cm
long, often 3-lobed at the apex; petals light pink, 10-18 mm long. The double
form common in cultivation usually produces no fruit. From China.

P. virginiana L. Chokecherry. Tall shrub or small tree; leaves 5.5-10
cm long, 1.4-2.1 times as long as wide; pedicels 3-11 mm long; petals white;
calyx soon deciduous. Moist to dry thickets and edges of woods, throughout
the state.

PYRUS ----- PEAR, APPLE *

Trees or shrubs, sometimes with more or less thorn-like spur
shoots; leaves simple, toothed or lobed; flowers in corymbs or umbel-like
clusters, white or pink, appearing with or before the leaves; hypanthium
bell-shaped to obovoid; sepals and petals 5 each; stamens 15-50; carpels
2-5, their ovaries united and fully inferior, their styles free or united at
the base; ovules 2 per locule; fruit a 2-5-locular pome. (The classical
name for the pear tree.) Here including Malus. Hybridization and selection
have produced many cultivars which cannot be referred to any one original
species or which are not normal for that species. Only the most well defined
of these cultivars are identified here. We have but one native species, P.
ioensis.

A-Styles separate (closely constricted at base by surrounding hypanthium
  tissue); leaf margins inrolled in bud; fruit usually pear-shaped, with
  many grit cells . . . . P. communis
A-Styles fused at base; leaves mostly folded or rolled together lengthwise in bud; fruit apple-shaped, mostly without grit cells.
  B-Lower surface of leaves and outer surface of sepals densely and
    persistently gray- to white-hairy; sepals persistent on the fruit.
    C-Leaves on elongated shoots closely crenate-serrate, abruptly
      short-acuminate; sepals reflexed . . . . P. malus
    C-Leaves on elongated shoots lobed, strongly notched, or irreg-
      ularly toothed, obtuse or short-acute; sepals erect or spreading.
      D-Some of the leaves more or less prominently lobed or strongly
        notched; sepals mostly erect; fruiting pedicels slender,
        usually more than 2.0 cm long; fruit green . . . . . . P. ioensis
      D-Leaves mostly only coarsely toothed; sepals spreading; fruit-
        ing pedicels stout, 2.0 cm or less long; fruit yellow
        . . . . P. X soulardii
  B-Lower surface of leaves glabrous or pubescent when young,
    mostly glabrous with age, hypanthium and outer surface of
    sepals glabrous or somewhat pubescent but not densely and
    persistently hairy; sepals persistent or deciduous in fruit.
    E-Calyx lobes shorter than or as long as the hypanthium above
      the ovary; calyx deciduous in fruit . . . . P. halliana
    E-Calyx lobes distinctly longer than the hypanthium above the
      ovary; calyx deciduous or persistent.
      F-Styles mostly 4; leaves each folded lengthwise face to face in
        bud, sharply serrate or cut . . . . P. pulcherrima
      F-Styles mostly 5; leaves rolled up lengthwise in bud or involute,
        finely crenate-serrate.
        G-Flowers rose-red to purple-red; pedicels and hypanthium
          more or less pubescent; sepals free to the base; young
          foliage, pedicels, and calyx purplish . . . .
          . . . . the hybrid 'Hopa' Crab. See P. baccata
        G-Flowers usually white, sometimes pinkish; pedicels and hypan-
          thium glabrous to pubescent; sepals fused at base; young foli-
          age, pedicels, and calyx green.
          H-Pedicels 25-50 mm long; sepals deciduous; ripe fruit
            8-12 mm thick . . . . P. baccata
          H-Pedicels 15-35 mm long; sepals persistent; ripe fruit
            25-35 mm thick . . . . P. prunifolia

P. baccata L. Siberian Crab; cultivated. Small tree; leaf blades 3-8 cm
long; flowers 25-35 mm wide. From Asia. Extensively used horticulturally.
The cv. Hopa appears to be a hybrid of this species with P. malus.

P. communis L. Pear; cultivated. Tree to 15 m high, sometimes spiny;
leaf blades 3-9 cm long, ovate to broadly elliptic, finely toothed to nearly
entire, becoming glabrous; pedicels 1.5-3 cm long; flowers white or rarely
tinged pink, 25 mm or more wide; calyx lobes persistent. From Eurasia.
Many cultivars exist.

P. halliana Voss. Hall Crab; cultivated. Shrub or small tree; leaf blades
3.5-8 cm long; pedicels purple, ca. 3 cm long; flowers deep rose, 25-35 mm
wide; styles 4-5; fruit ca. 13 mm thick. Probably from China. The double-
flowered form is P. h. cv. Parkmanii.

P. ioensis (Wood) Carruth. Wild, Iowa, or Prairie Crab. Small tree,
often with thorn-like spur shoots; leaf blades ovate to oblong, 3-8 cm long;
pedicels 1-3 cm long; flowers white or rose-tinted, 3-4 cm wide; styles 5;
fruit dull green with persistent calyx, 23-30 mm thick. Thickets and edges

of woods, from Houston to Freeborn Co. and n. to Blue Earth, Hennepin, and Chisago counties. A cultivated double-flowered form with larger flowers and longer pedicels is the cv. Plena, also known as Bechtel's Crab. Other cultivars exist.

P. malus L. Apple; cultivated. Tree; leaf blades 5-10 cm long; pedicels 10-25 mm long; flowers white to pink, 30-55 mm wide; styles 5. From Eurasia. The common apple, from which many cultivars have been developed.

P. prunifolia Willd. Plum-leaf Crab; cultivated. Small tree; leaf blades 4-10 cm long; flowers 25-35 mm wide. Probably from ne. Asia. Perhaps of hybrid origin.

P. pulcherrima Aschers. & Graebn. (Malus floribunda Sieb.). Showy or Flowering Crab; cultivated. Shrub or small tree; leaf blades 3-8 cm long; pedicels 25-45 mm long; flowers red in bud, opening pink to white or fading white, 25-30 mm wide; fruit 8-12 mm thick, the calyx deciduous. Probably from China or Japan. Perhaps of hybrid origin.

P. X soulardii Bailey (hybrid between P. ioensis and P. malus). Soulard's Crab; cultivated. More or less intermediate between the parents.

ROSA ----- ROSE *

Shrubs or woody vines; stems usually prickly, sometimes with a pair of well-developed prickles just below each node (infrastipular prickles) distinctly larger than the others; leaves pinnately compound, the leaflets in ours 3-11, the stipules persistent, large, usually fused to the petiole for most of their length; hypanthium globose to urn-shaped; sepals 5, usually long and narrow or with a somewhat broadened tip, sometimes lobed; petals 5 (numerous in many cultivated forms); stamens many; carpels mostly many, the ovaries separate, borne on the concave inner surface of the hypanthium but concealed from view by the constricted opening, the styles sometimes united; fruit a group of achenes inside the fleshy hypanthium. (The ancient Latin name.) Our wild roses are noted for their variability and intergradation with each other, a situation usually ascribed largely to widespread hybridization.

A-Native shrubs; flowers pink (rarely nearly white) with 5 petals.
  B-Infrastipular prickles (see generic description) distinctly differentiated from the other prickles, or the others none; sepals 1.7-2.3 (-2.6) mm wide . . . . R. woodsii
  B-Infrastipular prickles absent or little differentiated from the others; sepals 2.4-5.0 mm wide.
    C-New shoots from the rhizome often bearing flowers; plants usually less than 5 dm high; stems usually densely prickly to near the top, often dying back to base in winter; leaflets 7-11, typically obovate; flowers usually in clusters of 3-10 or more . . . R. arkans
    C-New shoots from the rhizome without flowers; plants 2-20 dm high; stems prickly or not, seldom dying back to base; leaflets 3-9, typically elliptic; flowers 1-8 in a cluster.
      D-Prickles none or confined to base of stem or sometimes scattered above but usually not extending far into the flowering part; upper stipules usually non-glandular, seldom with minute sessile or stalked globular "glands"; leaflets singly serrate or rarely doubly serrate; flowers 1-8 in a cluster. . . . R. blanda
      D-Prickles dense, extending nearly or fully to the top of the stem; upper stipules glandular; leaflets often doubly serrate; flowers 1-3 in a cluster . . . . R. acicula

Cultivated shrubs or vines, occasionally persisting near old gardens;
flowers of various colors, petals often many.
  E-Flowering branchlets smooth or only with prickles; flowers
    yellow to coppery.
    F-Leaflets, stipules, and sepals with minute globular "glands"
      at least on the edges; odor of flower somewhat unpleasant . . . R. foetida
    F-These parts without glands; odor pleasant . . . . R. hugonis
  E-Flowering branchlets usually with both prickles and smaller bris-
    tles, rarely smooth; flowers rose-purple, pink, white, or yellowish.
    G-Leaflets 17-45 mm long, pubescent beneath . . . . R. rugosa
    G-Leaflets 6-14 mm long, glabrous or glandular (see F) . . . . . R. pimpinellifolia

R. acicularis Lindl. Prickly Wild Rose. Upper year-old stems greenish-
own to dark purplish-red, rather dull; leaflets 3-7; petiole and leaf rachis
ually glandular; ovary 4-7 mm high in flower (10% less dry); fruit globose
elongate. 2n = 42. Moist to mesic openings in the north, from Cook to
kin, Clearwater, and Kittson counties.

R. arkansana Porter. Prairie Wild Rose. Upper year-old stems greenish
rownish or pinkish-brown or sometimes purplish-red, rather dull; stipules
escent to glabrous, usually glandular at least on the edges; petiole and leaf
his pubescent, nonglandular or sometimes with a few stalked glands; petals
n pale and streaked with darker pink; ovary 5-9 mm high in flower (10% less
). 2n = 28. Mesic to dry openings and grasslands, Rock to Houston Co., n.
Washington, Crow Wing, Beltrami, and Kittson counties, and from Carlton
. Lake Co. Forms with the leaflets finely woolly-pubescent beneath, rather
n glabrous or nearly so, have been called R. a. var. suffulta (Greene) Cocke-
l (R. suffulta Greene). Forms with the fruit narrowed to an acute base,
nd in se. Minnesota, have been named R. a. var. bushii (Rydb.) Butters.
ms with stalked globular "glands" on pedicel and hypanthium may pos-
ly derive from hybridization between R. arkansana and R. carolina L.,
elated species approaching the state in Wisconsin and Iowa.

R. blanda Ait. Smooth Wild Rose. Upper year-old stems reddish-brown
dark purplish-red, a bit lustrous; leaflets 5-9; petiole, rachis, and lower
flet surface hairy to seldom glabrous, the petiole and rachis rarely glandu-
; ovary 3.5-6 mm high in flower (10% less dry); fruit globose to slightly
ngate. 2n = 14. Riverbanks, grasslands, and moist to dry openings
oughout the state. See R. woodsii.

R. foetida Herrm. Austrian Brier; cultivated. Shrub 6-12 dm high, some-
es with long semi-climbing shoots; leaves fragrant, with 5-9 leaflets; pet-
golden-yellow or coppery; fruit red. From Asia. R. f. cv. Bicolor has
nge-scarlet or coppery petals rather than yellow. A commonly grown
mi-double hybrid, R. f. X R. pimpinellifolia, is known as R. X harisonii
.; it has the pedicel and hypanthium bristly and the fruit nearly black.

R. hugonis Hemsl. Hugo Rose; cultivated. Shrub with arching stems and
ut prickles; leaflets 5-11, glabrous; flowers single, light yellow; fruit being blackish-red. From China.

R. pimpinellifolia L. (R. spinosissima L.). Scotch or Burnett Rose;
tivated. Shrub to 1 m high, densely prickly; leaflets 5-11; leaflets and
ules usually but not always glandless; petals white, pale pink, or yel-
ish; fruit black or dark brown. From Eurasia. R. p. var. altaica (Willd.)
ory is larger in all ways, is less bristly, and has glabrous pedicels (rather
n glandular) and white flowers.

R. rugosa Thunb. Rugose Rose; cultivated. Shrub to 2 m high; leaflets
, wrinkled above; flowers rose-purple or white; fruit red. From e. Asia.

R. woodsii Lindl. (Incl. R. fendleri Crep. & R. macounii Greene).
Internodal prickles most numerous at base; leaflets 5-9, typically obovate;
flowers 1-8 in a cluster. 2n = 14. A western species, typically with infrastipular prickles 3-8 mm long and narrow sepals (see key). This typical
form is known in Minnesota only from one colony, probably introduced,
along some railroad tracks near Minneapolis. However, extensive hybridization of the western plants with R. blanda has produced numerous intergrading plants with shorter prickles and wider sepals. Such forms are
found from Kittson to Big Stone and Murray counties and e. to s. Lake,
Pine, and Ramsey counties.

RUBUS ----- BRAMBLE, BLACKBERRY, RASPBERRY

Perennial shrubs or less often herbs, usually prickly, most of the
shrubby species producing biennial stems that are vegetative the first year
(primocanes) and which produce flowers the second year (then termed floricanes) on short lateral shoots; leaves simple or usually compound; flowers
bisexual or unisexual, white (to red or purple); hypanthium flat to shallowly
cup-shaped; sepals mostly 5, bractlets none; petals as many as the sepals;
stamens many; carpels usually many, separate, borne on the convex to
conic receptacle, ripening to drupelets and forming an aggregate fruit; ovules
2, 1 maturing. (L. rubus, bramble, akin to ruber, red.)
The groupings of Rubus, especially among the blackberries, are often
unclear, being complicated by hybridization, polyploidy, and apomixis, as
well as normal variation. Our state of knowledge of some of these groups is
so poor, and the disagreement among different authors so great, that it is
not possible at this time to present a satisfactory treatment of them. In col-
lecting material for identification, as many different parts and stages as
possible should be taken, accompanied by careful notes on growth form.

A-Stems herbaceous (or slightly woody only at the base), without
    prickles (rarely with a few weak bristles), at least the non-
    flowering stems trailing on or near the ground or up to 12 cm high;
    flowering shoots basal or from elongate stems of the previous year.
    B-Petals 5-8 mm long, white to occasionally pink; terminal leaflet
        3.5-10 cm long; flower-bearing shoots basal or from trailing
        stems of the previous year . . . . R. pubescens
    B-Petals 9-17 mm long, pink; terminal leaflet 1-4 cm long; flower-
        bearing shoots always basal . . . . R. acaulis
A-Stems somewhat woody, more or less prickly, mostly higher,
    flowering shoots always from elongate stems of the previous year.
    C-Leaflets finely and densely white- to light gray-tomentose beneath
        (first leaves of season sometimes green); fruit readily separating
        from the receptacle. (Raspberries.)
        D-Canes erect or ascending, not rooting at the tip, sparsely to
            densely set with usually straight, usually slender-based
            prickles or smaller bristles or both; pedicels usually with
            small bristles and globular-tipped hairs and sometimes a few
            small prickles; fruit red . . . . R. idaeus
        D-Canes ascending, tending to arch over to the ground, the tips
            then rooting; stems sparsely set with straight or hooked prickles
            with broadened bases, bristles none; pedicels with small prickles
            only; fruit purple-black. . . . . R. occidentalis

C-Leaflets greenish beneath, more or less pubescent but not as above;
  fruit not separating from the receptacle. (Blackberries.)
  E-At least the floricanes prostrate or low-arching, mostly less
    than 1.2 m high; tips of the primocanes or their branches
    trailing on the ground, growing along the surface and often
    rooting at the ends and sometimes at some of the nodes, the
    flowering shoots turning upward from the stems; prickles of
    the primocanes hooked or straight, rarely absent. R. flagellaris complex
  E-Canes normally erect or high-arching, up to 3 m high, not usually
    with trailing tips nor tip-rooting; prickles of the primocane
    straight or slightly curved, spreading or barely reflexed, or
    none.
    F-Leaves glabrous above, glabrous or nearly so beneath; canes
      glabrous or nearly so, without or with a few straight prickles
      . . . . R. canadensis
    F-Leaves sparsely hairy above when young, velvety pubescent
      beneath; canes glabrous to pubescent when young, mostly
      with strong prickles.
      G-Pedicels and often other parts with numerous globular-tipped
        hairs; racemes of the inflorescence usually elongate, 8-25
        cm long. . . . . R. allegheniensis
      G-Pedicels and other parts without globular-tipped hairs, or
        rarely with a very few; racemes relatively short and com-
        pact, 6-13 cm long . . . . R. pensilvanicus

R. acaulis Michx. Arctic Raspberry, Nagoonberry. Stems 3-12 cm high;
leaflets 3. Cool bogs and moist woods, Cook to Lake of the Woods Co., s. to
Clearwater and Cass counties.

R. alegheniensis Porter. Common Blackberry. Primocane leaves with
5 (3-7) palmate leaflets, the terminal one 8-20 cm long; floricane leaves with
3 leaflets; petals 1-2 cm long. Edges of woods and openings, from St. Louis
to Clearwater Co. and s. to Todd, Carver, Fillmore, and Houston counties.

R. canadensis L. Smooth Blackberry. Primocane leaves with 5 (3-7)
palmate leaflets, the terminal one 8-15 cm long; floricane leaves with 3 leaflets; pedicels and other parts without globular-tipped hairs; petals 10-15 mm
long. Edges of woods and clearings, recorded from Lake, St. Louis,
Koochiching, Wadena, Scott, and Goodhue counties.

R. flagellaris Willd. complex. Dewberry. Primocane leaves with 3-5
palmate leaflets. A highly diverse and confusing complex, much subdivided
by some authors. Variation involves characters from stature to inflorescence.
Those wishing to attempt a further narrowing of identification in this group
are referred to L. H. Bailey's keys in Gentes Herbarum (1943), M. L.
Fernald's Gray's Manual of Botany, H. A. Gleason's Britton and Brown's
Illustrated Flora, and C. O. Rosendahl's Trees and Shrubs of the Upper Midwest. Names which have been applied to our early-blooming members are
R. flagellaris Willd., R. folioflorus Bailey, R. minnesotanus Bailey, R.
multifer Bailey, and R. rosendahlii Bailey. The complex as a whole has
been recorded from Lake to Clearwater and Becker counties and s. to
Sherburne, Scott, Mower, and Houston counties.

R. idaeus L. Raspberry. Stems often somewhat waxy-whitened; primocane
leaves with 3-7 pinnate leaflets; floricane leaves with 3 leaflets; petals 4-6.5
mm long, 0.6-1.2 the length of the sepals.

A-Pedicels and hypanthium without globular-tipped hairs or bristles,
   sometimes with small prickles; stamens erect, not incurved; cultivated; European . . . . R. i. var. idaeus.
A-Pedicels and hypanthium nearly always with globular-tipped hairs
   and small bristles in addition to any small prickles; stamens curved
   inward, concealing the hypanthium; native of woods and thickets,
   throughout the state except for the extreme sw. corner
   . . . . . R. i. var. strigosus (Michx.) Maxim. (R. strigosus Michx.).

   R. occidentalis L. Black Raspberry. Plants not glandular; primocanes
strongly waxy-whitened, their leaves with 3-5 palmate leaflets; floricane
leaves with 3 leaflets; petals 2.5-5 mm long, 0.45-0.8 the length of the sepals.
Open woods, fields, and thickets, Houston to Pipestone Co., n. to Washington,
Mille Lacs, Crow Wing, and Norman counties. The hybrid between this
species and R. idaeus var. strigosus resembles R. occidentalis but the primocane leaves are sometimes pinnately compound and the petioles, peduncles,
and pedicels bear globular-tipped hairs; the fruit is dark red. The hybrid
has been named R. X neglectus Peck.

   R. pensilvanicus Poir. Primocane leaves mostly with 5 palmate leaflets,
the terminal one 6-14 cm long; floricane leaves with 3 leaflets; petals 8-11
mm long. Ours often divided as follows:

A-Plants 1-2 m high; terminal primocane leaflets not lobed; Houston
   Co. to Blue Earth, Becker, Clearwater, Itasca, and Lake counties
   . . . . R. pensilvanicus.
A-Plants less than 1 m high; terminal primocane leaflets irregularly
   toothed to lobed; St. Louis, Clearwater, and Ramsey counties
   . . . . R. recurvans Blanchard.

   R. pubescens Raf. Dwarf Red Blackberry, Swamp Blackberry. Flowering
stems upright, 1-4 dm high; leaflets 3 (occasionally 5, then palmate). Bogs,
moist woods, and damp slopes, common in the n., less so to the s., throughout the state except from Mower to Martin to Lac Qui Parle to Rock Co.

SORBUS ----- MOUNTAIN ASH*

   Trees or large shrubs; leaves in ours pinnately compound; flowers in
branched round- or flat-topped clusters, small, white; hypanthium obconic;
sepals and petals 5 each; stamens 15-20; carpels 2-5 (2-4 in ours), united at
least below, the ovary 1/2-3/4 inferior; styles separate; fruit a small red
pome. (The ancient Latin name.) Sometimes combined with Pyrus.

A-Twigs, lower surface of leaflets, branches of the inflorescence,
   and hypanthium all more or less densely white-hairy, less so later
   in the season; winter buds white-hairy, not sticky; cultivated and
   sometimes escaped . . . . S. aucuparia
A-Twigs, leaves, branches of the inflorescence, and hypanthium
   sparsely pubescent to glabrous; outer scales of winter buds
   glabrous or very sparsely pubescent on the outside, the buds
   sticky; native.
   B-Leaflets long-acuminate, 3-5 times as long as wide; petals 2.5-
      3.6 mm long; fruits 4-7 mm thick . . . . S. americana
   B-Leaflets acute to short-acuminate, 2-3.4 times as long as wide;
      petals 3.5-4.5 mm long; fruits 6-10 mm thick . . . . S. decora

   S. americana Marsh. (Pyrus americana (Marsh.) DC.) American Mountain Ash, Roundwood, Dogberry. Shrub to tree to 10 m high; inner bud scales

glabrous or sparsely hairy on the edges; rachises of leaves and under side of leaflets becoming glabrous or nearly so; leaflets 13-17, lanceolate to lance-oblong, 5-9 cm long, pale green to slightly whitened beneath, not papillose. Moist soil, Cook to Itasca and Carlton counties.

S. aucuparia L. (Pyrus aucuparia (L.) Gaertn.). European Mountain Ash, Rowan Tree; cultivated. Tree to 15 m high; leaflets 11-17, oblong to lance-elliptic, 2-5 cm long, 2.3-3.6 times as long as wide; petals 3-5 mm long; fruits ca. 10 mm thick. From Eurasia.

S. decora (Sarg.) Schneid. (Pyrus decora (Sarg.) Hyland). Mountain Ash, Roundwood, Dogberry. Shrub to tree to 12 m high; inner bud scales usually conspicuously brown-hairy at least on the edges; rachises of leaves and under side of leaflets mostly remaining sparsely pubescent; leaflets 11-17, oblong to elliptic-oblong, 3.5-7.5 cm long, usually slightly whitened and minutely papillose beneath (papillae visible at 40X). Moist to mesic woods, rocky slopes and shores, Cook to Clearwater and Becker counties, s. to Anoka and Chisago counties.

SPIRAEA

Shrubs with simple leaves; flowers in panicles, corymbs, or umbel-like racemes, small, white to reddish; hypanthium cup-shaped to top-shaped; sepals 5, petals 5; stamens 15-many, borne from the outer edge of a con-tinuous series of lobed nectar glands; carpels mostly 5, separate but 1/6-1/3 inferior; ovules 2-several per carpel; fruit a group of follicles. (Probably from the Gr. speira, wreath.)

A-Flowers in umbel-like racemes on short leafy shoots of the new
    season; leaves sub-palmately 3-5-veined . . . . S. X van-houttei
A-Flowers in sessile umbels on old wood, with or without some leaves
    at base; leaves pinnately veined.
  B-Leaves pubescent beneath at least when young, elliptic to ovate or
    ovate-oblong . . . . S. prunifolia
  B-Leaves glabrous or nearly so, linear-lanceolate to narrowly
    elliptic to oblanceolate or obovate.
    C-Leaves linear-lanceolate; flowers 6-8 mm wide . . . . . . S. thunbergii
    C-Leaves narrowly elliptic to oblanceolate or obovate;
      flowers 8-13 mm wide . . . . S. X arguta

S. X arguta Zabel (S. thunbergii X the hybrid between S. crenata L. and S. hypericifolia L.). Cultivated. Leaves 1.5-3 cm long, serrate above the middle; petioles 0-1.5 mm long; pedicels 5-15 mm long; flowers white. Ends of twigs usually winter-killed.

S. prunifolia Sieb. & Zucc. Bridal Wreath; cultivated. Leaves 2.5-5 cm long, serrate except at base; petioles 2-3 mm long; pedicels 10-20 mm long; flowers white, 10-12 mm wide. China and Japan. Twigs often partly winter-killed in Minnesota.

S. thunbergii Sieb. Cultivated. Leaves 2-4 cm long, serrate; petioles 1-3 mm long; pedicels 5-11 mm long; flowers white. China and Japan. Ends of twigs usually winter-killed.

S. X van-houttei (Briot) Zabel (S. trilobata L. X S. cantoniensis Lour.) Bridal Wreath; cultivated. Leaves 1.5-4 cm long, rhombic-ovate to somewhat obovate; petioles 3-8 mm long; pedicels 5-12 mm long; flowers white, 5-10 mm wide.

WALDSTEINIA ----- BARREN STRAWBERRY *

Low perennial herbs, resembling Fragaria; leaves basal, palmately 3-5-cleft or (in ours) compound; hypanthium obconic, with a nectar disk at the rim; sepals 5, alternating with 5 often minute and deciduous bractlets, or these none; petals 5, yellow; stamens many; carpels 2-6, free, on a hairy receptacle; styles long, deciduous from a basal joint; ovule 1; fruits achenes. (In honor of the German botanist F. Adam, count of Waldstein-Wartenburg.)

W. fragarioides (Michx.) Tratt. Leaflets 3, obovate, wedge-shaped at base, serrate and often lobed; petals 5-10 mm long. Mostly mesic to dry woods of Pinus banksiana, St. Louis and Lake counties.

FABACEAE (LEGUMINOSAE) ----- PEA, BEAN, or PULSE FAMILY

Herbs, vines, shrubs, or trees; leaves mostly (and in ours) alternate, usually stipulate, mostly compound; flowers hypogynous or perigynous, mostly bisexual, regular or zygomorphic; sepals 3-5, often united; petals (1-) 3-5, free or sometimes some of them fused, the petals in zygomorphic corollas often of 3 types, a large upper one (the standard), 2 lateral ones (wings), and 2 lower ones (together the keel) more or less united to enclose stamens and carpel; stamens many to (in ours) 10 or rarely fewer, 9 of the 10 filaments often fused, the uppermost free ("diadelphy"); carpel 1, 1-many-seeded; fruit typically elongate, dry or leathery, and splitting lengthwise into 2 parts (a "legume"), but often otherwise.

A-Trees or shrubs.
  B-Leaves 40-90 cm long, twice pinnately compound; leaflets ovate
    to elliptic-ovate, acute to acuminate . . . . GYMNOCLADUS
  B-Leaves 1-30 cm long, once or twice pinnately compound or once
    palmately compound or the leaves appearing simple; leaflets
    elliptic to ovate-elliptic, lanceolate, or obovate, their tips
    usually rounded and often mucronate.
    C-Flowers clear yellow, single or in small umbel-like clusters;
      leaflets 4-12 or the leaves appearing simple . . . . . . CARAGANA
    C-Flowers yellowish-green, white, pink, purple, or blue, in
      racemes which are often dense and spike-like; leaflets 9
      to many.
      D-Flowers yellowish-green; trees, the leaflets on stalks
        0.5-1.2 mm long . . . . GLEDITSIA
      D-Flowers white to pink, purple, or blue; trees or shrubs, the
        leaflets on stalks 1.8-5 mm long except for one low prairie
        shrub.
        E-Flowers white, pink, or pale purple, 15-30 mm long; petals
          5 . . . . ROBINIA
        E-Flowers purple to blue, 5-8 mm long; petal 1 . . . . AMORPHA
A-Herbs.
  F-Leaves with 5 or more palmately arranged leaflets.
    G-Lower leaves with 7-11 leaflets . . . . LUPINUS
    G-Leaves with 5 leaflets . . . . PSORALEA
  F-Leaves either pinnately compound or with 3 leaflets.
    H-Leaves with tendrils, even-pinnate, one or more of the terminal
      leaflets represented by tendrils.
      I-Stipules as large as or larger than the leaflets; cultivated . . PISUM
      I-Stipules smaller than the leaflets; native or naturalized.

J-Style bearded at or all around the tip . . . . VICIA
J-Style bearded along the upper side toward the tip (like
    a toothbrush) . . . . LATHYRUS
H-Leaves without tendrils, the terminal leaflet present.
  K-Leaflets more than 3.
    L-Petal 1; plants woody at base . . . . AMORPHA
    L-Petals 5; plants herbaceous throughout.
      M-Keel blunt to acute . . . . ASTRAGALUS
      M-Keel abruptly acuminate into a sharp erect point. . OXYTROPIS
  K-Leaflets 3.
    N-Leaflets entire (or with a single apical tooth) . . . . . BAPTISIA
    N-Leaflets toothed.
      O-Flowers in spike-like racemes 2.5-10 cm long, (3-)
        3.5-9 times as long as wide; flowers yellow, 5-7 mm
        long. . . . . MELILOTUS
      O-Flowers in head-like racemes or spikes or racemes
        often shorter than above, up to 3.5 times as long as
        wide, the flowers of various colors, often longer or
        shorter than above.
        P-Inflorescence head-like; petals more or less adherent
          to the stamen tube, more or less persistent after
          anthesis; flowers yellow or white to magenta; fruit
          straight or slightly curved . . . . TRIFOLIUM
        P-Inflorescence head-like or a dense or spike-like
          raceme up to 3 1/2 times as long as wide; petals
          free from the stamens, deciduous after anthesis;
          flowers yellow, blue, or purple; fruit slightly
          curved to spiralled or coiled . . . . MEDICAGO

AMORPHA

Shrubs, often low and delicate; leaves once odd-pinnate, sometimes dotted with minute internal secretory cavities; flowers in spike-like racemes, blue to purple; calyx 5-toothed; petal 1, the standard, wrapped around the stamens and carpel; stamens 10, monadelphous only at base, free above; fruit oblong, often curved, 1-2-seeded. (Gr. amorphos, deformed, from the absence of 4 petals.)

A-Shrub 10-30 dm high; leaflets 20-50 mm long . . . . A. fruticosa
A-Shrub 2-7 dm high; leaflets 6-10 mm long. . . . . A. nana

A. fruticosa L. False Indigo. Petioles 20-50 mm long; leaflets 13-35, usually sparsely short-hairy beneath; flowers violet. River valleys, stream banks, and lake shores, Houston to Rock Co., n. to Hennepin, Mille Lacs, Otter Tail, and Kittson counties.

A. nana Nutt. Fragrant False Indigo. Petioles 3-5 mm long; leaflets 21-41, glabrous or nearly so, dotted beneath; flowers violet. Mesic prairies, Rock to Kittson Co., e. to Martin, Blue Earth, Stearns, Crow Wing, and Mahnomen counties.

ASTRAGALUS ----- MILK VETCH

Ours perennial herbs; leaves once odd-pinnate with several to many leaflets; flowers zygomorphic, white or yellowish to purple, in axillary racemes; calyx 5-toothed; keel blunt to acute; stamens 10, diadelphous; fruit variable, often nearly spherical, often 2-locular or nearly so through the development of a secondary partition. (The ancient Gr. name of a leguminous plant.)

A-Flowers 8.5-11 mm long; calyx tube 2.5-3.5 mm long.
  B-Hairs of lower surface of leaflets mostly or all laterally attached,
    with both ends free; flowers yellow or cream; leaflets 7-15
    . . . . A. lotiflorus
  B-Hairs of lower surface of leaflets attached at base, one end free;
    flowers whitish or purplish; leaflets 15-23 . . . . A. flexuosus
A-Flowers 13-25 mm long; calyx tube 3-7 mm long.
  C-Ovary (and fruit) glabrous.
    D-Calyx lobes narrowly linear, needle-like; calyx tube 3-5.5 mm
      long; corolla 13-16 mm long; fruit linear, 3-angled. . A. racemosus
    D-Calyx lobes narrowly triangular; calyx tube 5-7 mm long;
      corolla (14-) 17-25 mm long; fruit subglobose . . . . A. crassicarpus
  C-Ovary (and fruit) sparsely to densely pubescent.
    E-Hairs of lower surface of leaflets all basally attached, one
      end free; ovary (and fruit) with spreading hairs . . . . A. agrestis
    E-Hairs of lower surface of leaflets mostly or all laterally
      attached, both ends free; ovary (and fruit) with hairs appres-
      sed to the surface.
      F-Calyx tube 3.5-5 mm long; fruits 7-10 mm long, 2-locular,
        deeply grooved on the lower side; leaflets mostly 10-23
        mm long, linear to narrowly elliptic . . . . A. adsurgens
      F-Calyx tube 5-6.5 mm long; fruits 15-25 mm long, 1-locular,
        not deeply grooved below; leaflets 5-14 mm long, elliptic
        to broadly elliptic or obovate . . . . A. missouriensis

A. adsurgens Pall. (A. striatus Nutt.). Prairie Milk Vetch. Stems 2-4 dm long; flowers white or purple, 13-17 mm long; fruit oblong. Prairies, Rock to Kittson Co., e. to Jackson, Dakota, Renville, Otter Tail, and Roseau counties.

A. agrestis Dougl. (A. goniatus Nutt.). Nickleaf Milk Vetch. Stems 1-3 dm long; leaflets 8-20 mm long; flowers purple, 13-20 mm long; calyx tube 4.5-6.5 mm long, more or less dark-hairy; fruits ovoid to subglobose, 6-9 mm long, 2-locular. Damp prairies and meadows, Rock to Kittson Co., e. to Blue Earth, Stearns, Otter Tail, Pennington, and Lake of the Woods counties.

A. crassicarpus Nutt. (A. caryocarpus Ker). Ground or Prairie Plum, Buffalo Bean. Stems 2-5 dm long; leaflets 8-15 mm long; flowers purple to whitish; fruit 20-25 mm long, ·2-locular. Western prairies, Rock to Kittson Co., e. to Houston, Ramsey, Meeker, Douglas, Clay, and Mahnomen counties.

A. flexuosus Dougl. Flexile Milk Vetch. Stems 3-5 dm long; leaflets 5-15 mm long; ovary and fruit pubescent; fruit lance-linear, 10-22 mm long, 1-locular. Sandy prairies and bluffs, Traverse, Big Stone, and Chippewa counties.

A. lotiflorus Hook. Low Milk Vetch. Stems up to 1 dm long, usually less; leaflets 8-15 mm long; ovary and fruit pubescent; fruit lance-ovoid, 15-25 mm long, 1-locular. Sandy prairies and bluffs, Yellow Medicine, Chippewa, and Big Stone counties to Becker Co.

A. missouriensis Nutt. Missouri Milk Vetch. Stems rarely over 5 dm long; flowers few, purple, 15-20 mm long; fruit lanceolate to oblong. Dry bluffs and prairies, mostly near the Minnesota R. on both sides, w. Renville to Big Stone Co.

A. racemosus Pursh. Racemose Milk Vetch. Stems 4-10 dm long; leaflets 10-30 mm long; flowers white or pinkish; fruit 20-25 mm long, 1-locular. Prairie, Pipestone Co.

BAPTISIA ----- WILD OR FALSE INDIGO *

Perennial herbs; leaves palmately 3-foliolate, the leaflets entire except often for an apical tooth (often blackening in drying); flowers zygomorphic, showy, in terminal racemes; calyx 2-lipped, 4-5-toothed; sides of standard reflexed, keel petals nearly separate, straight; stamens 10, separate or fused at very base; fruit stalked in the persistent calyx, roundish to cylindric or thick lens-shaped, appearing inflated. (Gr. baptizein, to dye; sometimes used as a dye.)

A-Plants pubescent; bracts 1-3 cm long, persistent; stipules to 4 cm
    long . . . . B. leucophaea
A-Plants glabrous; bracts less than 1 cm long, falling before the
    flowers open; stipules to 1 cm long.
    B-Flowers white, 18-30 mm long . . . . B. leucantha
    B-Flowers yellow, 8-16 mm long . . . . B. tinctoria

B. leucantha T. & G. Atlantic or Large White Wild Indigo. Petioles 6-12 mm long; leaflets 3-6 cm long; fruits 25-40 mm long, on stalks twice as long as the calyx. Prairies, Houston and Fillmore to Washington, Ramsey, and Hennepin counties, and in Faribault Co.

B. leucophaea Nutt. Plains Wild Indigo. Petioles 2-5 mm long; leaflets 4-8 cm long; flowers white or cream, 20-28 mm long; fruits 3-5 cm long, on short stalks. Prairies, Houston to Wabasha Co. and in Steele Co.

B. tinctoria (L.) R. Br. Yellow Wild Indigo, Rattleweed, Horsefly Weed. Petioles 1-3 mm long; leaflets 6-18 (-40) mm long; fruits 8-15 mm long, on stalks 5-10 mm long. Dry open places, Wabasha Co., perhaps introduced.

CARAGANA ----- PEA TREE

Shrubs or small trees, sometimes spiny; leaves once even-pinnate, sometimes appearing palmately compound or simple; flowers zygomorphic, mostly yellow, single or in few-flowered, umbel-like clusters; calyx 5-toothed; stamens 10, diadelphous; fruit linear, the seeds several to many. (Tartar name of the original species.)

A-Leaflets 8-12 . . . . C. arborescens
A-Leaflets 4, close together, appearing palmate, or the leaves
    appearing simple.
    B-Leaves petioled, appearing palmately compound . . . . . . C. frutex
    B-Leaves sessile, each leaflet seeming a simple leaf . . . . C. pygmaea

C. arborescens Lam. Siberian Pea Tree; cultivated. Shrub or small tree to 6 m high; stipules usually spine-tipped; leaflets elliptic to obovate; pedicels 2-5 cm long. Siberia and Manchuria.

C. frutex (L.) Koch. Shrubby Pea Tree; cultivated. Shrub 2-3 m high; stipules not spiny; leaflets obovate; pedicels 15-25 mm long. S. Russia to Japan.

C. pygmaea (L.) DC. Dwarf Russian Pea Tree; cultivated. Shrub to 1.3 m high; leaflets oblanceolate to linear, each group of 4 usually subtended by 3 spines; pedicels 5-10 mm long. Central Asia.

GLEDITSIA *

Monoecious or polygamous trees (ours) or tall shrubs, usually thorny; leaves evenly pinnate or bipinnate; flowers in spike-like racemes, small, yellowish-green, unisexual or rarely bisexual, radially symmetrical or nearly so; hypanthium present, obconic; sepals and petals each 3-5, nearly alike, the 2 lower petals sometimes united; stamens 3-10, free; fruit large, flat, elliptic to linear and elongate, dehiscent or indehiscent. (Named for J. G. Gleditsch, German botanist.)

G. triacanthos L. Honey Locust. Tree to 20 m high or sometimes higher, thorns usually large, simple or branched; leaves once or twice pinnately compound, the leaflets oblong-lanceolate, somewhat crenulate, 1-4 cm long; inflorescences 4-10 cm long; male flowers 3.5-6 mm long, female flowers 7-8 mm long; fruits 15-45 cm long, indehiscent, their pulp sweetish, edible. Low woods in the Mississippi Valley, Houston Co., perhaps no longer occurring naturally; often planted. The thornless form is known as G. t. forma inermis (L.) Zabel.

GYMNOCLADUS *

Polygamous, monoecious, or dioecious trees; leaves large, bipinnately compound; flowers in terminal racemes or panicles, whitish or greenish-white, radially symmetrical or nearly so; hypanthium tubular; sepals and petals each 5, similar; stamens 10, free, shorter than the sepals and petals; fruit flat, oblong. (Gr. gymnos, naked, and clados, branch.)

G. dioica (L.) K. Koch. Kentucky Coffee-tree. Tree to 30 m high; bark gray, scaly; leaves 40-90 cm long, the leaflets ovate or elliptic-ovate, entire, 2-10 cm long; inflorescences 8-18 cm long; flowers 13-26 mm long; fruits 11-25 cm long, 3-5 cm wide. Rich soil, mostly on river bottoms, Houston to Blue Earth Co., n. to Brown and s. Ramsey counties.

LATHYRUS ----- VETCHLING, WILD PEAVINE *

Annual or perennial herbs, often vine-like; leaves once pinnate, in most (including ours) with 1 or more of the terminal leaflets modified into tendrils; stipules prolonged basally; flowers zygomorphic, variously colored, in racemes; calyx 5-toothed; wings lightly coherent with the keel; stamens diadelphous; style bearded along the upper side toward the tip; fruit flat to cylindric, oblong to linear, seeds 2-many. (Gr. lathyros, a kind of legume.)

A-Larger stipules 1-7 mm wide, 3-9 times as long as wide.
  B-Leaflets of larger leaves 8-12, elliptic to ovate, 12-30 mm wide; racemes with (5-) 10-20 flowers; stems wingless; mesic to dry woods. . . . . L. venosus var. intonsus
  B-Leaflets of larger leaves 4-6 (-8), linear to narrowly elliptic, 3-15 mm wide; racemes with 2-6 (-9) flowers; stems often winged; moist places . . . . L. palustris
A-Larger stipules 7-28 mm wide, 1.5-2.5 times as long as wide.
  C-Flowers yellowish white; stipules each with 1 basal lobe . . L. ochroleucus

C-Flowers purple to bluish; stipules each with 2 basal lobes . L. japonicus

L. japonicus Willd. (L. maritimus (L.) Bigel.). Beach Peavine. Leaflets 6-12, oblong to obovate, 1-1.8 times as long as the stipules; stipules 7-28 mm wide; racemes usually with 5-10 flowers. Shores and moist dunes, Cook to Lake of the Woods Co.

L. ochroleucus Hook. Cream Peavine. Leaflets 4-8, lance-ovate to obovate, 1.6-3 times as long as the stipules; stipules 7-18 mm wide; racemes shorter than the subtending leaves, with 5-10 flowers. Mesic to dry open woods or clearings, Cook to Kittson Co., s. to Clay, Kandiyohi, Blue Earth, Olmsted, and Houston counties.

L. palustris L. Marsh Peavine. Leaflets 1.8-3 times as long as the stipules; racemes nearly equalling to overtopping the subtending leaves. Moist open places throughout the state except for Cook and Lake counties.

L. venosus var. intonsus Butters & St. John. Veiny Peavine. Leaflets 2-6 times as long as the stipules; racemes much exceeded by the subtending leaves. Mesic to dry open woods and clearings, throughout the state.

LUPINUS ----- LUPINE*

Herbs with palmately compound leaves, usually with several to many leaflets; flowers zygomorphic, in terminal racemes or spikes; calyx deeply 2-lipped; sides of standard reflexed; stamens 10, monadelphous; fruit oblong, somewhat flattened, often constricted between the seeds. (The ancient Latin name.)

L. perennis var. occidentalis S. Wats. Wild Lupine. Perennial to 6 dm high; leaflets 7-11 on the lower leaves; racemes erect; flowers blue, varying to pink or white; fruit pubescent. Sandy soil, open or wooded, from Houston and Fillmore counties to Pine, Crow Wing, and Morrison counties.

MEDICAGO ----- MEDICK*

Herbs; leaflets 3, pinnately arranged (see figs. 10 and 11), serrulate; flowers zygomorphic, small, yellow, blue, or purple, in axillary head-like racemes or spike-like racemes up to 3 1/2 times as long as wide; calyx 5-lobed; petals free from the stamens, deciduous after anthesis; stamens 10, diadelphous; fruit slightly curved, spiralled, or coiled, usually indehiscent, 1-several-seeded. (Gr. medice, alfalfa.)

A-Flowers yellow, 2-4 mm long . . . . M. lupulina
A-Flowers blue to purple, 7-12 mm long . . . . M. sativa

M. lupulina L. Black Medick, Nonesuch. Annual; leaflets broadly elliptic to obovate; fruit kidney-shaped, 1.5-3 mm long. Eurasia; in disturbed ground, Houston to Rock Co., n. to Isanti, Clearwater, and Kittson counties, and in St. Louis and s. Lake counties.

M. sativa L. Alfalfa, Lucerne; cultivated. Perennial; leaflets oblanceolate to narrowly obovate; fruit coiled into a loose spiral of 1-3 complete turns. From Asia, escaping from cultivation in disturbed ground throughout most of the state, not recorded from Cook or Lake Co., several southeastern counties, and others.

MELILOTUS ----- SWEET CLOVER

Annual or biennial herbs; foliage fragrant when dried; leaves pinnate with 3 leaflets (see figs. 10 and 11), serrulate; flowers zygomorphic, white or yellow, in elongate narrow racemes; calyx lobes 5; wings and keel coherent, the corolla free from the stamen tube, deciduous; stamens 10, diadelphous; fruit ovate to roundish in outline, slightly flattened or not, 1-4-seeded, usually indehiscent. (Gr. meli, honey, and lotos, some leguminous plant.)

M. officinalis (L.) Desr. Yellow Sweet Clover; cultivated. Racemes 2.5-10 cm long, (3-) 3.5-9 times as long as wide; flowers yellow, 5-7 mm long; pedicels 1.5-2 mm long. From Eurasia, common as a weed in disturbed ground, probably throughout the state, unrecorded from Roseau to Koochiching and Beltrami counties.

OXYTROPIS

Similar to Astragalus. Perennial herbs, ours stemless or nearly so; leaves once odd-pinnate; flowers zygomorphic, purple to yellowish white, in dense spikes or heads on long peduncles; calyx 5-toothed; keel abruptly acuminate into a sharp erect point; stamens 10, diadelphous; fruit sessile, ovoid to cylindric, grooved on the upper side, partly or completely 2-locular through the development of a secondary partition. (Gr. oxys, sharp, and tropis, keel.)

O. lambertii Pursh. Locoweed. Plants more or less silky-pubescent; leaflets 9-19, linear to linear-lanceolate; spikes 3-15 cm long in flower, sometimes elongating further; flowers rose-purple, fading blue-purple, 1.5-2 cm long; fruits erect, 2-3 cm long, incompletely 2-locular. Dry prairies, Rock to Clay and Mahnomen counties, e. to Jackson, Pope, and w. Otter Tail counties, and in Hennepin, Ramsey, and Crow Wing counties.

PISUM ----- PEA

Annual and perennial herbs; leaves once even-pinnate, one or more of the terminal leaflets usually represented by tendrils; stipules large and leaf-like; flowers zygomorphic, white or colored, axillary, single or in few-flowered racemes; calyx 5-toothed; wings somewhat adherent to the keel; stamens diadelphous; style bearded down one side; fruit flattened, elongate, dehiscent, few- to many-seeded. (The ancient Latin name.)

P. sativum L. Garden Pea; cultivated. Glabrous annual climber; leaflets ovate to oblong, entire; stipules mostly larger than the leaflets; flowers 1-3, white or colored with pinkish standard, purple wings, and greenish keel; seeds 2-19. Eurasia.

PSORALEA ----- SCURF PEA

Perennial herbs, more or less dotted with minute internal secretory cavities; leaflets 3 or 5, palmately arranged or sometimes pinnate, rarely only 1; flowers zygomorphic, mostly blue, in spikes or racemes; calyx 5-lobed; stamens 10 (-9), diadelphous or sometimes monadelphous; ovule usually 1; fruit short, flattened or not, indehiscent or irregularly dehiscent. (Gr. psoraleos, scurfy, from the conspicuous internal cavities.)

<u>P</u>. esculenta Pursh. Breadroot, Prairie Turnip. Producing a thick edible root 5-10 cm long; stems with dense long spreading hairs; leaflets 5, palmate; petioles mostly 4-8 cm long; flowers blue, 15-20 mm long; calyx tube 4.5-6.5 mm long. Mesic to dry prairies, western, e. to Fillmore, Scott, Stearns, Otter Tail, and Kittson counties.

ROBINIA ----- LOCUST*

Trees or shrubs; leaves once odd-pinnate; stipules often modified into spines; flowers zygomorphic, showy, in racemes; calyx 2-lipped, 5-toothed; stamens 10, monadelphous but the upper filament partly free; fruit oblong to linear, flat, several- to many-seeded. (Named for the French botanists J. and V. Robin.)

A-Tree 6-20 m high; twigs, petioles, and fruits glabrous or nearly so;
    flowers white or rarely light rose . . . . R. pseudoacacia
A-Shrub to 2.5 m high; twigs, petioles, and fruits bristly; flowers
    rose to pale purple . . . . R. hispida

<u>R</u>. hispida L. Rose Acacia, Bristly Locust; cultivated. Flowers 2-3 cm long, not fragrant. From Virginia to e. Tennessee, Georgia, and Alabama.

<u>R</u>. pseudoacacia L. Black Locust, False Acacia; cultivated. Flowers 15-23 mm long, very fragrant. Se. United States, n. to s. Indiana and Iowa, often escaping cultivation.

TRIFOLIUM ----- CLOVER, TREFOIL

Annual, biennial, or perennial herbs; leaflets 3, mostly serrulate, usually palmately but sometimes pinnately arranged (see leaf illustrations); flowers zygomorphic, small, in heads or head-like spikes, racemes, or umbels, or rarely in more elongate dense spikes; calyx 5-toothed, sometimes 2-lipped; petals free or more or less fused to the stamen tube or to each other or both, usually persistent after anthesis; standard often folded around the wings; stamens 10, diadelphous, the tenth partly separate; fruit short, straight, 1-6-seeded, dehiscent or indehiscent. (L. <u>tri</u>-, three, and <u>folium</u>, leaf.)

A-Flowers yellow; heads 8-12 mm thick . . . . T. campestre
A-Flowers white to pink or magenta; heads 15-35 mm thick.
  B-Flowers sessile in the heads . . . . T. pratense
  B-Flowers obviously pedicelled in the "heads".
    C-Stems creeping, rooting at the nodes; peduncles 6-30 cm
      long . . . . T. repens
    C-Stems erect or ascending; peduncles 2-9 cm long . . . . T. hybridum

<u>T</u>. campestre Schreb. (<u>T</u>. procumbens L.). Low Hop Clover. Annual with pubescent stems; leaves pinnate; flowers on short pedicels; calyx strongly 2-lipped. Eurasia and n. Africa, established as a weed in disturbed ground or old fields over most of the state. The 2-lipped calyx aids in distinguishing this species from <u>Medicago</u>.

<u>T</u>. hybridum L. Alsike Clover; cultivated. Glabrous perennial; leaves palmate; calyx teeth slightly longer than the tube; corolla pink and white or all pink. From Eurasia, commonly escaped throughout the state.

T. pratense L. Red Clover; cultivated. Biennial or short-lived perennial; stems glabrous to hairy; leaves palmate; peduncles 0-2 cm long; corolla pink-magenta or seldom white. From Europe, commonly escaped in fields and roadsides, throughout the state.

T. repens L. White Clover; cultivated. Glabrous perennial; leaves palmate calyx teeth shorter than to just equalling the tube; corolla white or pink-tinged. Eurasia, often escaped into lawns and fields, throughout the state.

VICIA ----- VETCH

Annual or perennial herbs, mostly vine-like; leaves once pinnate, one or more of the terminal leaflets usually represented by a tendril; flowers zygomorphic, axillary in few-flowered clusters or racemes; calyx 5-toothed; wings adherent to the keel; stamens 10, more or less diadelphous; style pubescent at or all around the tip; fruit flattened or not, oblong to linear, 2-many seeded. (The ancient Latin name.)

A-Leaflets with 10 or more pairs of lateral veins; inflorescences 2-9-
    flowered; flowers 16-22 mm long. . . . . V. americana
A-Leaflets with 6 or fewer pairs of lateral veins; inflorescences 9-
    30-flowered; flowers 9-18 mm long.
    B-Flowers 13-18 mm long; stems and axes of leaves and inflor-
        escences spreading-hairy . . . . V. villosa
    B-Flowers 9-13 mm long; stems and axes of leaves and inflores-
        cences appressed pubescent. . . . . V. cracca

V. americana Muhl. American Vetch. Perennial; stems glabrous or nearly so; stipules all or mostly several-toothed; inflorescences shorter than to about equalling or rarely exceeding the subtending leaves; flowers blue-purple; calyx not or only slightly pouch-like at base on upper side.

A-Leaflets elliptic to oblong-ovate, 6-14 mm wide, the lateral veins often
    branching; mesic to moist more or less open places throughout the
    state. . . . . V. a. var. americana.
A-Leaflets linear to linear-oblong, 1-4 mm wide, the lateral veins
    essentially unbranched; dry to moist open places from Pipestone
    and Lyon to Stevens and Traverse counties and in Lake of the Woods
    Co. . . . . V. a. var. angustifolia Nees (V. sparsifolia Nutt.).

V. cracca L. Bird or Tufted Vetch, Canada Pea; cultivated. Perennial; stipules with 1 basal tooth or lobe; inflorescences about equalling to exceeding the subtending leaves; calyx not or only slightly pouch-like at base on upper side; flowers blue, becoming blue-violet (rarely white). From Eurasia and possibly ne. N. America, escaped in fields and roadsides, recorded from Cook, St. Louis, Kittson, and Polk counties.

V. villosa Roth. Hairy or Winter Vetch; cultivated. Annual or biennial; stipules with 1 basal tooth or lobe; inflorescences about equalling to exceeding the subtending leaves; upper side of calyx pouch-like at base, the pedicel appearing attached laterally near the base of the flower; flowers violet and white (rarely all white). From Europe, escaped widely into fields and roadsides, recorded from Houston to Blue Earth Co., n. to St. Louis and Itasca counties.

OXALIDACEAE ----- WOOD SORREL FAMILY

Herbaceous (ours) or woody plants; leaves compound (ours) or seldom simple, alternate or all basal; flowers single or in cymes or umbel-like clusters or racemes, bisexual, regular, hypogynous; sepals 5, free or fused; petals 5, free or sometimes united at base, convolute; stamens 10 (in ours) or 15, the filaments usually fused at base, sometimes 5 without anthers; ovary 5-locular; styles 5; ovules 1-many per locule, axile; fruit a loculicidal capsule or rarely a berry.

OXALIS ----- WOOD SORREL *

A nnual or in ours perennial herbs with acid juice, often with bulbs; leaflets 3, palmate, obcordate; flowers white, yellow, pink, or violet; petals sometimes united at base; stamens 10, alternately long and short; fruit a capsule. (Gr. name for sorrel, from oxys, sour.)

A-Flowers white, pink, or purple; leaves all basal.
 B-Flowers 3-12 in an umbel-like cluster . . . . O. violacea
 B-Flowers single on each stem . . . . O. acetosella
A-Flowers yellow; stem leaves present.
 C-Fruits 8-15 mm long, the body glabrous or with wide-spreading
  hairs, the pedicels ascending or spreading in fruit but not below
  horizontal; plants usually with long slender rhizomes; stipules
  none or vestigial . . . . O. stricta
 C-Fruits 11-25 mm long, pubescent with appressed hairs (these
  diverging to 30° from the surface), sometimes also with some
  spreading hairs, the pedicels ascending or spreading, often
  deflexed below horizontal; plants without rhizomes, initially
  from a taproot but the base of the stem often prostrate and
  rooting; stipules to 3 mm long . . . . O. dillenii

O. acetosella L. (O. montana Raf.). American Wood Sorrel. Plants from a scaly rhizome; petals mostly white veined with pink or violet. Moist often mossy places in the woods, Carlton to Cook counties.

O. dillenii Jacq. (O. stricta L., misapplied). Yellow Oxalis. Gray-green; hairs of the stem and petioles pointed, nonseptate. Probably native to America; common in disturbed ground and in natural habitats, Houston to Pipestone Co., n. to Washington, Morrison, Clay, and Kittson counties, and in s. St. Louis Co.

O. stricta L. (O. europaea Jord.). Yellow Oxalis. Leaflets greenish to purple; hairs of the stem and petioles (or many of them) septate (multicellular) and blunt. Probably native to N. America; common in disturbed ground and in natural habitats, throughout most of the state, not recorded from Cook, Koochiching, Itasca, and a few other counties.

O. violacea L. Violet Wood Sorrel. Plants from a scaly bulbous base; petals rose-violet to rarely white. Mesic to dry woods and prairies, Houston to Rock Co., n. to Chisago, Morrison, Otter Tail, and Red Lake counties.

GERANIACEAE ----- GERANIUM FAMILY

Annual or perennial herbs or sometimes shrubs; leaves opposite or sometimes alternate, simple or compound, often palmately veined and cleft; inflorescence cymose or umbel-like; flowers bisexual, hypogynous, regular or slightly zygomorphic; sepals mostly 5; petals mostly 5, free, usually with alternating nectar glands on the receptacle; stamens typically 5-15, often some sterile, the filaments often fused at base; ovary of mostly 5 fused carpels with as many styles, often deeply 5-lobed, in fruit usually separating

179

into as many divisions as carpels, each division splitting away from an elongate central axis; ovules axile, usually 2 per locule, 1 abortive.

A-Leaves palmately cleft to compound; anther-bearing stamens
   usually 10 . . . . GERANIU[
A-Leaves pinnately cleft to compound; anther-bearing stems 5 . . . ERODIUℕ

ERODIUM ----- STORK'S BILL*

Herbs; leaves mostly opposite (members of the pair often of unequal size) or all basal, serrate to usually pinnately compound; flowers small, pink to purple, in umbel-like clusters; nectar glands present; anther-bearing stamens 5, alternating with an outer series of staminodia; divisions of the fruit 5, elongate, splitting away from the central axis, becoming spirally twisted when dry. (Gr. erodios, heron, from the beak-like fruit.)

E. cicutarium (L.) L'Her. Filaree. Winter annual or biennial; larger leaves compound; flowers ca. 1 cm wide. From the Mediterranean region, established as a weed, recorded only from Hennepin and Kittson counties.

GERANIUM ----- CRANE'S BILL*

Annual or perennial herbs; leaves mostly opposite, palmately lobed to compound, the lobes or divisions tipped with minute concave "glands"; flowers pink to purple, usually in pairs; nectar glands present; stamens 10, all normally fertile; ovary deeply 5-lobed; fruit consisting of 5 divisions that split away from the elongate central axis, the enlarged seed-containing basal portion of each division separating first and coiling up and away from the axis. (From Gr. geranos, crane.)

A-Petals 12-23 mm long, much exceeding the sepals . . . . . G. maculatum
A-Petals 6-10 mm long, about as long as the sepals.
   B-Narrowed apex of pistil just below the style branches, the "beak",
      0.7-1.4 mm long in flower, 4-5 mm long in fruit; longer hairs
      on ovary 1-1.4 mm long; pedicels at maturity 1-3 times as long
      as the calyx . . . . G. bicknellii
   B-Beak 0.5-0.7 mm long in flower, 1-2 mm long in fruit; longer
      hairs on ovary 1.2-2 mm long; pedicels at maturity 1/2-2
      times as long as the calyx . . . . G. carolinianum

G. bicknellii Britt. Bicknell's Geranium. Annual or biennial; pedicels with globular-tipped hairs mixed with plain hairs. Open woods and disturbed ground, Cook to Kittson Co., s. to Otter Tail, Stearns, Scott, and Goodhue counties.

G. carolinianum L. Carolina Geranium. Annual; pedicels with both plain and globular-tipped hairs. Dry rocky or sandy soil and disturbed ground, Rock to Kittson Co., e. to Renville and Brown counties and in St. Louis Co.

G. maculatum L. Wild or Spotted Geranium. Perennial; pedicels pubescent but without globular-tipped hairs. Mesic to moist woods and thickets, from s. Lake and St. Louis Co. to s. Beltrami, Clay, Stearns, Blue Earth, Mower, and Houston counties.

RUTACEAE ----- RUE FAMILY

Trees, shrubs, or sometimes herbs, dotted with minute internal oil-illed cavities ("glands"); leaves alternate or opposite, pinnately compound, rifoliolate, or sometimes simple; flowers bisexual or unisexual, hypogynous or slightly perigynous, regular or sometimes somewhat zygomorphic; peri-anth usually differentiated; sepals 3-5 (rarely none); petals 3-5, mostly ree, rarely none; stamens usually as many or twice as many as the petals; nectar gland more or less continuous between stamens and ovary; carpels ypically 4-5, fused or rarely free; ovary usually deeply lobed; ovules 1-several per locule; placentation axile; fruit highly variable.

A-Herbs (more or less woody at base); cultivated . . . . DICTAMNUS
A-Shrubs or small trees; native or cultivated.
  B-Leaflets 5-11; branches thorny; native . . . . ZANTHOXYLUM
  B-Leaflets 3; branches thornless; cultivated . . . . PTELEA

DICTAMNUS ----- DITTANY, FRAXINELLA

Perennial, more or less woody at base; leaves alternate, odd-pinnate; lowers in terminal racemes, white, pink, or rose-violet, slightly zygomor-hic; sepals 5; petals 5; stamens 10; ovary deeply 5-lobed; fruit a hard 5-ocular capsule. (The old Gr. name.)

D. albus L. Cultivated. Strong-smelling plant to 1 m high; leaflets 9-11; lowers 20-30 mm long. S. Europe to n. China. D. a. cv. Ruber has rosy-purple flowers. Sometimes called Gas Plant or Burning Bush because its oils volatilize to produce a flammable gas in hot weather.

PTELEA ----- HOP TREE

Thornless shrubs or small trees; leaves alternate (rarely opposite), ours with 3 leaflets; flowers in compound terminal cymes, greenish-white or ellowish-white, polygamous; sepals and petals 4 or 5 each; stamens as many as the petals and alternate with them; ovary usually of 2 fused carpels, com-pressed, the ovules 2 per locule, 1 abortive; fruit thin, flat, round, and dry, a broad wing surrounding the central body. (Gr. name of the elm.)

P. trifoliata L. Cultivated. To 6 m high; leaflets ovate or ovate-oblong o obovate, 5-15 cm long; fruit 2-3 cm wide. E. N. America, reaching Iowa, sometimes escaping.

ZANTHOXYLUM ----- PRICKLY ASH*

Thorny dioecious shrubs or trees; leaves alternate, odd-pinnate; flowers small, greenish to whitish; sepals 4-5 or none; petals 4-5; stamens 4-5, alter-ate with the petals; carpels (1-) 2-5, separate but their styles connivent or lightly united; ovules 2 per carpel; carpels becoming somewhat fleshy fol-icles with 1-2 seeds. (Gr. xanthos, yellow, and xylon, wood.)

Z. americanum Mill. Shrub to 4 m high or rarely higher, aromatic; leaf-ets 5-11; flowers in umbel-like axillary clusters; sepals none; petals fringed t the tip; carpels 3-5; fruits 5 mm long, pungent. Mesic to moist woods and thickets, throughout the lower 3/4 of the state, n. to Polk, s. Beltrami, . Itasca, Kanabec, and Chisago counties.

POLYGALACEAE ----- MILKWORT FAMILY

Herbs (ours), shrubs, woody vines, or trees; leaves simple; flowers in spikes, racemes, or panicles, or single, bisexual, hypogynous, zygomorphic; sepals typically 5, the 2 inner often much larger than the 3 outer; petals 5 or fewer, more or less fused to each other and to the stamen tube; stamens mostly 8, their filaments usually fused; anthers usually opening by an apical pore; ovary usually 2-locular with axile placentation and 1-2 ovules per locule; fruit usually a loculicidal capsule.

POLYGALA ----- MILKWORT

Ours herbs with alternate or whorled leaves; flowers in racemes; the 3 outer sepals small, the 2 inner larger and often colored like the petals; petals 3, more or less fused with each other and the stamen tube, the lowermost one folded lengthwise and (in ours) bearing a fringe-like outgrowth of 4 or more linear structures near its tip; stamens, ovary, and fruit typical for the family. (Gr. polys, much, gala, milk, from some plant thought to increase lactation.)

A-Flowers white, numerous in a spike-like raceme, the 2 inner sepals
    3-3.3 mm long . . . . P. senega
A-Flowers rose-purple to white, 1-4 on conspicuous pedicels, the
    inner sepals 13-19 mm long . . . . P. paucifolia

P. paucifolia Willd. Flowering Wintergreen, Fringed Polygala. Perennial; leaves alternate; stamens 6; fruit ca. 6 mm long. Light usually sandy soil in mesic to moist woods, northern, Cook to Koochiching Co., s. to Hubbard and Anoka counties.

P. senega L. Seneca Snakeroot. Perennial; leaves alternate; stamens 8; fruit 2.5-3.5 mm long. Mesic to moist woods and thickets and open ground, Houston to Faribault Co. and n. to Anoka, Cass, and Lake of the Woods counties on the e., and Kandiyohi, Clay, and Kittson counties on the w.

EUPHORBIACEAE ----- SPURGE FAMILY

Herbs, shrubs, or trees, often with milky juice; leaves alternate to whorled, simple to compound, or none; flowers regular, hypogynous, unisexual or very rarely bisexual; perianth usually 5-merous when present, the calyx present or absent; petals usually none; stamens 1-many, the filaments sometimes branched; carpels usually 3, fused; styles wholly or partly free, often 2-parted; ovules 1 or 2 per locule, axile; fruit usually a capsule.

EUPHORBIA ----- SPURGE

Monoecious herbs (ours), shrubs, or trees with milky, often acrid, juice; leaves variable; flowers extremely reduced, the flower cluster (cyathium, fig. 69) simulating an ordinary flower; staminate flowers each consisting of a single stamen without perianth; pistillate flower consisting of a 3-locular ovary with 3 2-cleft styles, the perianth none or rudimentary, the ovary becoming exserted on a stalk, the capsule 3-lobed, 3-seeded; cyathium containing 1 pistillate flower and several to many staminate ones in a cup-shaped involucre of 4-5 fused bractlets, usually with nectar-producing outgrowths ("glands") of various forms between some or all of the bractlets, the outgrowths sometimes further expanded into petal-like structures. (Named for Euphorbus, Greek physician.)

A-Leaves finely toothed at least toward the tip; glands straight or
    convex on the outer edge . . . . E. spathulata
A-Leaves entire; glands concave on the outer edge.
    B-Leaves narrowly linear, 1-2 cm long, 0.5-3 mm wide; glands
        crescent-shaped . . . . E. cyparissias
    B-Leaves linear or broader, 3-8 cm long, 3-10 mm wide; glands with
        their tips prolonged into short horns . . . . E. esula

E. cyparissias L. Cypress Spurge. Perennials from deep roots, often tufted; stem commonly branching above the middle, the branches eventually overtopping the original terminal inflorescence; stamens 5-10. From Eurasia, established as a weed in fields and disturbed ground, recorded from Houston to Freeborn Co., n. to Brown, Anoka, and Washington counties. and in Douglas, Clay, Lake of the Woods, and St. Louis counties.

E. esula L. (E. virgata Waldst. & Kit.). Leafy Spurge. Perennial from deep roots; not tufted; branches not overtopping the original terminal inflorescence; stamens 12-13. From Eurasia, established as a weed in fields and disturbed ground, recorded from Pipestone to Martin, Ramsey, St. Louis, and Clay counties.

E. spathulata Lam. (E. dictyosperma F. & M.). Glabrous annual; leaves linear- to oblong-oblanceolate, 1-4 cm long. Grasslands, Rock and Pipestone to Chippewa, Dakota, and Jackson counties.

LIMNANTHACEAE ----- FALSE MERMAID FAMILY

Annual herbs; leaves alternate, pinnately divided; flowers single in the leaf axils, bisexual, regular, hypogynous or slightly perigynous, 3- or 5-merous; sepals free or nearly so; petals free; stamens twice the petals, in 2 whorls; ovary of 2-5 carpels, the ovaries free or nearly so but the styles united; ovule 1 per locule; carpels separating in fruit, becoming achenes.

FLOERKEA ----- FALSE MERMAID*

Delicate annuals; sepals 3; petals 3, shorter than the calyx; stamens 6; carpels 2 or 3. (Named for the German botanist H. G. Floerke.)

F. proserpinacoides Willd. Leaflets 3-7, linear or lanceolate to oblanceolate; sepals ca. 3 mm long in flower, 7 mm in fruit; petals ca. 2 mm long. Moist woods, Winona Co.

ANACARDIACEAE ----- CASHEW FAMILY

Trees, shrubs, or woody vines with resinous bark; leaves alternate (rarely opposite), estipulate, mostly compound; flowers bisexual or unisexual, regular; sepals 3-7; petals 3-7 or 0, free (rarely fused, not in ours); stamens usually twice as many as the petals (5 in ours), arising from or under the rim of a nectar gland circling the ovary; ovary superior, usually of 3 fused carpels, 1-locular; stigmas usually as many as the carpels; ovule 1, basal; fruit usually a drupe.

RHUS ----- SUMAC; POISON IVY

Polygamo-dioecious trees, shrubs, or woody vines; leaves alternate, compound; flowers in terminal or lateral branched inflorescences; sepals 5; petals 5, greenish-white or yellowish; stamens 5, alternating with the petals; nectar gland lobed; fruit small, rather dry. (The ancient classical name.)

A-Leaflets 3; shrub to 6 dm high or trailing or climbing . . . . . . R. radicans
A-Leaflets 7-13; shrub or small tree to 8 m high . . . . R. vernix

R. radicans L. Poison Ivy. Leaflets ovate to nearly round, acute to acuminate, rounded to wedge-shaped at base, entire to irregularly serrate or crenate, dark green and usually shining and glabrous above, paler and pubescent mainly along the veins beneath or rarely glabrous; terminal leaflet on a longer stalk than the lateral ones, 4-14 cm long; flowers yellowish-green, in small axillary panicles 3-10 cm long; fruit grayish- to yellowish-white, 5-6 mm thick. Thickets and open woods, sometimes in clearings or disturbed ground.

A-Stems erect or nearly so, 1-6 dm high, seldom branched, without aerial roots, spreading by rhizomes; terminal leaflet broadly ovate-rhombic or broadly ovate to nearly round, usually abruptly acute or acuminate; throughout the state except in Cook Co. ..
. . . . R. r. var. rydbergii (Small) Rehder.
A-Stems long, trailing or climbing by aerial rootlets; terminal leaflet narrowly to broadly ovate, gradually tapered to the acute or short-acuminate apex; Houston to Faribault and Brown counties, scattered infrequently n. to Morrison and Mille Lacs counties
. . . . R. r. var. radicans.

R. vernix L. Poison Sumac. Bark gray; leaflets obovate to elliptic, acute to acuminate, tapered or rounded at base, entire, green on both sides, glabrous or slightly puberulent, 4-14 cm long; flowers green, in numerous axillary panicles 10-17 cm long; fruit yellowish-green, smooth and shining, ca. 4 mm thick. Swamps and tamarack bogs, recorded from Chisago, Anoka, Ramsey, Hennepin, and Rice counties.

AQUIFOLIACEAE ----- HOLLY FAMILY

Shrubs or trees; leaves alternate, simple; flowers single or cymose in the axils, bisexual or unisexual, regular, hypogynous; sepals 3-6; petals 4-5, free or sometimes slightly united at base; stamens 4-5, alternating with the petals, free or sometimes adhering basally to the petals; ovary of 3-many fused carpels, with as many locules; style 1, short; placentation axile, ovules 1-2 per locule; fruit a berry with usually as many stones as carpels.

NEMOPANTHUS ----- MOUNTAIN HOLLY*

Polygamo-dioecious glabrous shrub; leaves entire or minutely toothed; flowers 4-5 merous; sepals none or minute and deciduous; petals linear-oblong, free; stamens free; ovary 4-5-locular. (Gr. nema, a thread, pous, foot, and anthos, flower.)

N. mucronata (L.) Trel. To 3 m high; leaves elliptic, 2-5 cm long; flowers greenish-white to greenish-yellow, the pistillate single in the axils, the staminate 1-4; petals ca. 2 mm long; fruits red to yellow, ca. 6 mm thick. Swamps and damp thickets and woods, Wabasha to Ramsey to Carlton counties.

CELASTRACEAE ----- STAFF-TREE FAMILY

Trees or shrubs, often climbing or twining; leaves simple, alternate or opposite; flowers bisexual or unisexual, regular, somewhat perigynous or partly epigynous; sepals 4-5; petals 4-5, free (rarely 0); stamens in ours 4-5, alternate with the petals, arising from or below the rim of a fleshy nectar gland circling the ovary; ovary superior or partly inferior by adnation to the gland, of 2-5 fused carpels with as many locules; style 1; ovules usually 2 per locule, axile; fruit in ours a loculicidal capsule, the seeds wholly or partly covered by a bright-colored fleshy or membranous layer, the "aril".

A-Leaves alternate; stems trailing or twining. . . . . CELASTRUS
A-Leaves opposite; erect shrubs or small trees . . . . EUONYMUS

CELASTRUS ----- STAFF-TREE; BITTERSWEET*

Dioecious or polygamo-dioecious woody trailers or twiners with alternate serrulate leaves; flowers small, greenish to whitish, in raceme-like cymes or panicles, 5-merous; vestigial stamens and pistil present in the respective unisexual flowers; carpels 3; aril scarlet-orange. (Gr. celastros, name for some evergreen tree.)

C. scandens L. Climbing Bittersweet. Vine climbing to 10 m high, or sprawling on the ground; leaves 5-10 cm long, glabrous; flowers yellowish-green, the petals 3-4 mm long; capsule nearly round, ca. 1 cm thick. Thickets, woods, and clearings, probably throughout the state, unrecorded from Cook and a few other counties.

EUONYMUS ----- SPINDLE TREE*

Shrubs or small trees, occasionally climbers; leaves opposite, finely serrate; flowers single or in axillary cymes, bisexual, 4-5-merous; style none, the stigma sessile; carpels 3-5; ovules 1-4 per locule; aril scarlet to orange. (Gr. eu, good, and onoma, name, used ironically, the plant believed poisonous.)

A-Twigs mostly with 2-4 conspicuous corky wings; leaves (including
    petioles) 3-6 (-8) cm long; cultivated . . . . E. alatus
A-Twigs without corky wings; leaves (including petioles) 4.5-15 cm
    long; native or cultivated.
  B-Petals purplish-brown; leaves pubescent beneath; aril scarlet;
    native . . . . E. atropurpureus
  B-Petals yellowish-green; leaves glabrous; aril orange; cultivated
    . . . . E. europaeus

E. alatus (Thunb.) Sieb. Cultivated. Branches stiff and spreading; leaves elliptic to obovate, tapering at both ends, crimson in fall; flowers greenish-yellow, 1-3 in a cyme; anthers with distinct filaments; capsule purplish; aril orange-red. China, Japan.

E. atropurpureus Jacq. Burning Bush, Wahoo. Leaves (incl. petioles) 6-15 cm long, elliptic to lance-ovate, acute at base; flowers 5-15 in a cyme; anthers sessile; capsule pink to purplish. Mesic to moist soil in woods in the s. 1/3 of the state, n. as far as Washington, Meeker, and Big Stone counties.

E. europaeus L. Cultivated. Leaves (incl. petioles) 4.5-9.5 cm long, ovate or oblong-lanceolate; flowers 2-7 in a cyme; anthers with distinct filaments; capsule red or pink. Eurasia.

STAPHYLEACEAE ----- BLADDERNUT FAMILY

Trees or shrubs; leaves mostly opposite, pinnately compound or the leaflets 3; flowers usually bisexual, regular, slightly perigynous, in drooping racemes of panicles; sepals 5; petals 5, free; stamens 5, alternate with the petals, rising near the outside of a large encircling nectar gland; ovary superior, of 2-3 fused carpels and with as many locules; styles as many as the carpels, free or adherent to each other; placentation axile; ovules several to many per locule; fruit usually a capsule, appearing inflated.

STAPHYLEA ----- BLADDERNUT*

Shrubs or small trees; leaves opposite; flowers white or greenish-white; carpels 3; styles free below, coherent above; seeds 1-4 per locule. (Gr. staphyle, a bunch of grapes.)

S. trifolia L. Branches greenish, striped; leaflets 3, 5-10 cm long, serrate; flowers whitish, 8-10 mm long, in racemes; fruits ca. 5 cm long. Thickets and edges of woods on rich soil, Houston and Fillmore counties w. and n. to Blue Earth, Hennepin, and Washington counties.

ACERACEAE ----- MAPLE FAMILY

Polygamo-dioecious, dioecious, or monoecious trees or large shrubs; leaves opposite, simple or compound; flowers regular, slightly perigynous; sepals 4-5; petals 4-5, free, or none; encircling nectar gland usually present; stamens 4-10 (-12), mostly 8, placed within or without the gland; ovary of 2 fused carpels, 2-locular, usually flattened at right angles to the partition, 2-lobed; placentation axile; ovules 2 per locule; styles 2, free or fused below; fruit a pair of dry 1-winged 1-seeded indehiscent units.

ACER ----- MAPLE*

Characters of the family. (The ancient Latin name.) "Depth of cutting" as used in the descriptions is measured against the lateral leaf lobes, not the terminal one.

A-Leaves compound, appearing with the flowers; plants strictly
    dioecious . . . . A. negundo
A-Leaves simple, appearing with, before, or after the flowers;
    flowers bisexual and staminate, on the same or different plants.
    B-Flowers in stalked racemes or panicles, the stalks (1.5-) 2-6.5
        cm long; petals present, 2-3.2 mm long.

C-Branches of inflorescence, pedicels, and outer surface of calyx
puberulent, without globules; sepals 0.8-1.4 mm long; native
. . . . A. spicatum
C-Branches of inflorescence, pedicels, and outer surface of calyx
glabrous or with minute sessile or nearly sessile globules;
sepals 1.8-3 mm long; cultivated.
  D-Leaves lustrous dark green, usually with a lobe on each side
    near the base; flowers yellowish-white . . . . A. ginnala
  D-Leaves medium green, dull or not particularly lustrous,
    unlobed; flowers greenish-white . . . . A. tataricum
B-Flower clusters either sessile (head-like, umbel-like, racemose,
or paniculate), or on stalks up to 1 or rarely 1.5 cm long, the
petals then none or 5-6 mm long.
  E-Pedicels (especially toward apex) and edges of calyx lobes
    hairy; pedicels mostly 15-35 mm long or longer . . . . . A. saccharum
  E-Pedicels (when present) and calyx lobes glabrous; pedicels
    0-25 mm long.
    F-Flowers in a short rounded panicle on a stalk 5-15 mm long;
      petals 5-6 mm long; flowers appearing with the leaves;
      cultivated . . . . A. platanoides
    F-Flowers in sessile head-like or umbel-like clusters; petals
      1.5-2.5 mm long or none; flowers appearing many days
      before the leaves; native (often cultivated).
      G-Sepals fused for 1/3 to all of their length, sometimes 1
        or 2 sepals free; petals none; ovary and young fruit white-
        hairy . . . . A. saccharinum
      G-Sepals all free; petals usually present; ovary and young
        fruit glabrous . . . . A. rubrum

A. ginnala Maxim. Amur Maple; cultivated. Flowers appearing after the
leaves; petioles 2-4 cm long; blades 4-8 cm long, cut (0-) 0.2-0.8 of the way
to the base; petals 0.6-1.2 mm wide; sepals pubescent on the edges. Ne.
Asia and Japan.

A. negundo L. Box Elder. Leaves pinnately compound, the leaflets 3-5
(-9); flowers greenish except for the anthers; staminate flowers on pendulous
pedicels in sessile umbel-like clusters, the pistillate in drooping racemes;
petals none. River banks and shores and mesic thickets and disturbed ground.
A-Twigs glabrous; leaflets elliptic to obovate; throughout the state
  except for Cook and Lake counties . . . .
    . . . . A. n. var. negundo (incl. A. n. var. violaceum (Kirsch.) Jager.
A-Twigs puberulent; leaflets ovate to oblong; Otter Tail Co. . . . .
  . . . . A. n. var. interius (Britt.) Sarg.

A. platanoides L. Norway Maple; cultivated. Juice milky; leaves very
similar to those of A. saccharum, the blades cut 0.2-0.45 of the way to the
base; flowers yellowish-green; pedicels 4-25 mm long. Europe and w. Asia.
several cultivars are grown, some with reddish leaves.

A. rubrum L. Red or Swamp Maple. Leaves somewhat silvery-whitened
and glabrous to rarely pubescent below at maturity, 3-5-lobed, cut 0.2-0.47
of the way to the base, the lobes with at least 2 or 3 teeth per cm; flowers
crimson to yellowish, in small clusters subtended by colored bracts, the
clusters themselves flower-like when the pedicels are very short; pedicels
1-15 mm long in flower, rapidly elongating in fruit. Swamps and moist
woods, mostly northern, from Cook to Koochiching Co., w. and s. to se.
Polk, Otter Tail, Pope, and Rice counties, and reported in Winona and
Fillmore counties.

A. saccharinum L. Soft or Silver Maple. Leaves usually silvery-whitened (and downy when young) below, 5-lobed, cleft 0.5-0.8 of the way to the base, the lobes with at least 2 or 3 teeth per cm; flowers pale greenish-yellow to yellowish-red, in small clusters subtended by colored bracts, the clusters themselves flower-like when the pedicels are very short; pedicels 0-8 mm long in flower, rapidly elongating in fruit. Riverbanks and bottomlands, widely scattered throughout most of the state, more common southward, not recorded from Cook Co. and most of the western counties. Often cultivated.

A. saccharum Marsh. Sugar or Hard Maple. Leaves light green to somewhat whitened below, 3-5-lobed, cut 0.25-0.55 of the way to the base, the lobes entire except for occasional large round-tipped teeth, these seldom more than 1 tooth per cm; flowers appearing with the leaves, in umbel-like clusters or sessile or short-peduncled racemes or panicles; flowers yellowish or greenish-yellow; sepals 2-5 mm long, fused for 1/2-3/4 of their length or sometimes a sepal free; petals none; ovary white-hairy. Mesic to moist upland. Intermediates between the two varieties are frequent in our area.

A-Lower surface of leaf green to somewhat whitened, usually glabrous, when pubescent the hairs appressed to the surface; angle of the notches between lobes averaging 30-80°; leaf margins not drooping; edges of notch at leaf base not touching; stipules none; new twigs usually reddish-brown; Houston to Freeborn Co., w. and n. to Murray, Pope, Clay, Polk, Beltrami, Koochiching, and Cook counties, local and infrequent in the n. and e. . . . . A. s. var. saccharum.
A-Lower surface of leaf yellowish-green, usually very pubescent, the hairs erect from the surface; angle of the notches between lobes averaging 80-115°; leaf margins, especially of the lower lobes, tending to droop; edges of basal notch sometimes touching or overlapping; stipules often present; new twigs usually gray-brown; Houston to Washington Co. and in Freeborn, Blue Earth, and Brown counties . . . . A. s. var. nigrum (Michx. f.) Britt. (A. nigrum Michx. f.). Black Maple.

A. spicatum Lam. Mountain Maple. Shrub to small tree; petioles 3-10 cm long; blades 6-12 cm long, pubescent beneath, not whitened, 3- (-5-) lobed, cleft (0-) 0.15-0.4 of the way to the base, more or less heart-shaped at base; flowers appearing after the leaves in narrow ascending or erect racemes or panicles, greenish-yellow; petals 0.2-0.5 mm wide. Cool moist woods, Cook to Lake of the Woods Co. and s. to Clearwater, Morrison, and Chisago counties, and from Goodhue to Houston counties.

A. tataricum L. Tartarian Maple; cultivated. Flowers appearing after the leaves; petioles 1.5-4 cm long, blades 5-8 cm long, unlobed or rarely cut to 0.2 of the way to the base; petals 0.9-1.4 mm wide; sepals pubescent on the edges. Se. Europe and w. Asia.

HIPPOCASTANACEAE ----- HORSE-CHESTNUT FAMILY

Trees or shrubs with opposite, palmately compound leaves; flowers in terminal panicles, bisexual (or sometimes the upper ones staminate), zygomorphic, hypogynous; sepals 4-5; petals 4-5, free; nectar gland present outside the stamens; stamens 5-8, free; ovary of 3 fused carpels, 3-locular, the placentation axile; ovules 2 per locule; style 1; fruit a leathery 1-3-locular capsule with 1-3 large seeds.

AESCULUS ----- HORSE-CHESTNUT, BUCKEYE

Sepals united in a tube. Other characters those of the family. (The ancient name of some tree with a similar fruit.)

A-Petals usually 5, white marked with red or yellow toward the base
. . . . A. hippocastanum
A-Petals 4, greenish yellow . . . . A. glabra

A. glabra Willd. Ohio Buckeye; cultivated. Tree to 15 m high; leaflets 5-7, 6-16 cm long, acuminate; fruit prickly or becoming nearly smooth. Pennsylvania to Michigan, Iowa, Texas, and Alabama.

A. hippocastanum L. Horse-chestnut; cultivated. Tree to 25 m high; leaflets 5-7, 8-25 cm long, abruptly short-acuminate; fruit spiny. Se. Europe and adjacent Asia.

RHAMNACEAE ----- BUCKTHORN FAMILY

Mostly shrubs, trees, or woody vines; leaves simple, opposite or alternate; flowers bisexual or unisexual, regular, slightly perigynous or partly epigynous; sepals 4-5; petals 4-5 or none; stamens as many as and opposite the petals (alternate with the sepals); ovary encircled by a nectar gland that lines or rims the hypanthium, the ovary superior or partly inferior by adnation to the gland, of 2-4 fused carpels with as many locules; ovules 1 (-2) per locule on basal placentas; styles 1-4, united at least below; fruit usually a capsule or berry-like drupe.

RHAMNUS ----- BUCKTHORN *

Shrubs or trees; leaves alternate or opposite; flowers single or in umbel-like clusters in the leaf axils, greenish or greenish-white, bisexual or unisexual, 4-5-merous; petals present or absent, often with the sides folded around the stamen; ovary 2-4-locular; fruit a drupe with 2-4 1-seeded stones. (The ancient Gr. name.)
A-Sepals, and petals and stamens when present, 4 each; leaves usually
mostly opposite or subopposite (rarely mostly alternate). . R. cathartica
A-Sepals, and petals and stamens when present, 5 each; leaves all or
mostly alternate.
B-Leaves crenate-serrate; petals none; flowers bisexual and unisexual . . . . R. alnifolia
B-Leaves entire or sometimes faintly crenulate; petals present;
flowers bisexual . . . . R. frangula

R. alnifolia L'Her. Dwarf Alder. Shrub to 6 dm high, thornless; leaves all alternate, the blades 4-10 cm long, with 5-7 pairs of lateral veins; petioles 4-13 mm long. Mostly in swamps and low wet woods and meadows, Cook to Kittson Co. and s. to Norman, Morrison, Hennepin, and Fillmore counties; mostly northern.

R. cathartica L. Common Buckthorn; cultivated. Dioecious or polygamo-dioecious shrub or tree to 6 m high, some of the branches usually thorn-tipped; leaf blades 3-6 cm long, with 3-4 pairs of lateral veins, finely serrate; petioles 1-2 cm long; petals present but often vestigial. From Eurasia; widely escaping cultivation throughout most of the state, mostly in damp places, unrecorded from Cook, Lake, and other counties.

R. frangula L. Alder Buckthorn; cultivated. Shrub to 7 m high; leaves all or mostly alternate, the blades 3.5-6.5 cm long, with 5-8 pairs of lateral veins; petioles 1-2 cm long. From Eurasia, escaping mostly into bogs, swamps, and creeksides; recorded as naturalized in St. Louis, Hennepin, and Rice counties.

VITACEAE ----- GRAPE FAMILY

Mostly woody vines, climbing by tendrils; leaves alternate or the lower opposite, simple or compound; tendrils and inflorescences opposite the leaves; flowers bisexual or unisexual, regular, slightly perigynous or partly epigynous; sepals mostly 4-5; petals mostly 4-5, falling early; stamens as many as the petals and opposite them; ovary encircled by a series of nectar glands or a continuous one, superior or partly or fully inferior by adnation to the gland, mostly of 2 fused carpels and 2-locular; ovules 2 per locule, axile; style 1; fruit a berry.

VITIS ----- GRAPE *

Plants dioecious or polygamo-dioecious; leaves simple, more or less palmately lobed; flowers small, fragrant, in compound panicles, mostly actually or functionally unisexual but with sterile organs of the opposite sex present, 5-merous; calyx very short with small teeth or a mere vestigial rim or none; petals free below, fused above, falling as the flower opens; berry juicy; seeds 4 or fewer. (The classical Latin name.)

A-Leaves pubescent beneath with a continuous tomentum, the surface itself not exposed till old age or not then; tendrils or panicles produced at 3-7 or more successive nodes; berries 14-18 mm thick; cultivated . . . . V. labrusca
A-Leaves with a scattered tomentum or only short unmatted hairs beneath, the surface exposed when half expanded or sooner, or the leaves glabrous; tendrils or panicles produced only at 2 successive nodes (except rarely in V. riparia); berries 8-12 mm thick; native.
  B-Leaves pubescent beneath with short grayish hairs, mostly along the main veins and in their axils, or glabrous; blades green on both sides; margins sharply and coarsely toothed . . . . . V. riparia
  B-Leaves with a reddish or rusty cobwebby tomentum beneath, scattered along and between the smaller veins as well as along the main ones and in their axils; lower surface of blade usually whitened; margins crenate-dentate . . . V. aestivalis var. argentifolia

V. aestivalis var. argentifolia (Munson) Fern. Summer, Pigeon, Silverleaf, or Blue Grape. Mesic wooded hillsides, thickets, and roadsides, Winona and Wabasha counties.

V. labrusca L. Fox Grape; cultivated. Margins shallowly serrate or dentate. Eastern N. America, w. to s. Michigan. Ancestor of the Concord and many other cultivated grapes. Our present cultivated forms are mostly hybrids.

V. riparia L. Riverbank or Frost Grape. Riverbanks and mesic to moist open woods and thickets, throughout most of the state, not recorded from Cook and a few other counties.

MALVACEAE ----- MALLOW FAMILY

Herbs (ours), shrubs, or trees; leaves alternate, simple or compound, usually palmately veined;flowers usually bisexual, regular, hypogynous; sepals (3-) 5, free or more or less fused, often subtended by a few sepal-like bractlets; petals 5, free from each other but often fused to the filament tube; stamens many, their filaments fused; anthers 2-sporangiate; carpels (1-) 5-many, weakly or strongly united; styles as many as the carpels, usually fused below, rarely fully separate; ovules 1-several per carpel, axile; fruit usuallyeither a loculicidal capsule or of separate dry dehiscent or indehiscent carpels.

MALVA ----- MALLOW

Annual to perennial herbs; leaves simple to compound, broad; flowers single or clustered in the axils; bractlets subtending the calyx 3; petals in ours obcordate; anthers borne only at the top of the stamen column; carpels 10-20, 1-ovuled, separating at maturity. (The ancient Latin name.)

M. neglecta Wallr. Common Mallow, Cheeses. Prostrate to ascending annual to biennial; leaf blades roundish to kidney-shaped, 3-6 cm wide, shallowly 5-9-lobed, crenate, the base cordate; petals 6-12 mm long, white or tinged with pink or purple; carpels usually 12-15. From Eurasia, now a weed of disturbed ground, recorded n. to s. St. Louis, Hubbard, and Clay counties.

CISTACEAE ----- ROCK ROSE FAMILY

Herbs or shrubs, often with branched hairs; leaves simple, mostly opposite (alternate to whorled), entire; flowers single or in cymes or cymose racemes, bisexual, regular except for the calyx, hypogynous; sepals typically 5, the outer 2 usually smaller than the inner 3; petals mostly 5, free, convolute, falling or withering early, or none in some flowers; stamens many, free; ovary 1-locular with 3 or 5-10 parietal placentas; ovules 2-many per placenta; style 1; fruit a loculicidal capsule.

A-Larger leaves 15-40 mm long . . . . HELIANTHEMUM
A-Larger leaves 1-4 mm long . . . . HUDSONIA

HELIANTHEMUM ----- SUN-ROSE, FROSTWEED

Perennial herbs or near-shrubs from rhizomes; pubescence all or partly of branched star-like hairs; leaves opposite, alternate, or opposite below and alternate above; sepals 3 or 5, when 5 the outer 2 much narrower than the inner 3; petals 5, yellow in ours, present in the first flowers of the season, the later ones mostly without petals and with only 3-10 stamens. (Gr. helios, sun, and anthemon, flower.)

H. canadense (L.) Michx. Frostweed. Plants mostly 2-4 dm high; leaves all or mostly alternate, those of the primary branches 1.5-4 cm long, smaller on smaller branches; petal-bearing flower 1 (-2) at the end of each stem, soon overtopped by lateral branches. Dry usually sandy soil; bluffs, clearings, or open woods, Houston, Fillmore, Winona, and Washington counties.

HUDSONIA ----- FALSE HEATHER *

Low prostrate or bushy somewhat woody heath-like plants; stems covered with alternate awl-shaped or scale-like persistent pubescent leaves; flowers yellow, numerous, each solitary at the end of a short leafy lateral branch; sepals apparently 3 (the outer 2 fused to 2 of the inner); petals 5; stamens 10-30; placentas 3; fruit a 3-parted capsule; seeds few. (Named for W. Hudson, English botanist.)

H. tomentosa Nutt. Leaves lance-ovate, 1-4 mm long, closely appressed to the stem, overlapping, densely pubescent; flowers 6-10 mm wide; ovary and fruit glabrous. Open sandy places and shores, Wabasha to Dakota Co. and in Anoka, Sherburne, Meeker, Morrison, Crow Wing, s. St. Louis, and Polk counties.

VIOLACEAE ----- VIOLET FAMILY

Herbs (ours) or shrubs; leaves simple or rarely compound, alternate, basal, or rarely opposite; flowers solitary to paniculate, bisexual, hypogynous or slightly perigynous, regular or (in ours) zygomorphic; sepals 5; petals 5, free, or none; stamens 5; ovary 1-locular with 3-5 parietal placentas; ovules many or 1-2 per placenta; style 1; fruit in ours a many-seeded loculicidal capsule.

VIOLA ----- VIOLET *

Herbs; leaves simple or rarely compound, alternate or all basal; flowers borne singly; sepals usually with short backward extensions at base; petals somewhat unequal in size and shape, the 2 lateral ones often bearded at base, the lower one usually with a basal spur or pouch; stamens closely surrounding the ovary, often slightly cohering with each other, the 2 lowest ones with nectar-producing outgrowths that extend into the spur of the lower petal; placentas 3. (The classical name.) Most species produce showy petal-bearing open-pollinated flowers in spring and closed petalless self-pollinated flowers in summer. All species with blue to violet flowers produce occasional white-flowered forms. Hybridization is common between some species. The following treatment draws largely from publications of Dr. N. H. Russell in the Proc. Minn. Acad. Sci. vols. 25, 26, 1957-58, and in Sida 2: 1-113, 1965.

A-Flowers and some of the leaves borne on an above-ground stem.
  B-Stipules 1/2 as wide to wider than the leaf blade, prominently
    toothed to lobed, 4-22 mm wide; spur of corolla 3-13 mm long,
    if less than 8 mm long then the leaf blades of the middle and
    upper stem broadly to narrowly acute at base; sepals 4-17 mm
    long; cultivated or weedy introduced plants.
    C-Spur 8-13 mm long; stipules coarsely toothed . . . . . . V. cornuta
    C-Spur 3-6 mm long; stipules deeply pinnately cleft at least
      toward the base.
      D-Petals pale yellow, shorter than to 2 mm longer than the
        sepals, 5-9 mm long . . . . V. arvensis
      D-Petals variously colored, 3 mm or more longer than the
        sepals, 9-30 mm long.
        E-Petals slightly shorter than to longer than wide, not
          overlapping laterally, 9-20 mm long . . . . V. tricolor

E-Petals wider than long, overlapping laterally, 15-30 mm
     long . . . . V. X wittrockiana
B-Stipules less than 1/2 as wide as the leaf blade, entire to toothed,
    1-8 mm wide; spur 0.5-6 mm long; leaves truncate to heart-
    shaped at base; sepals 4-10 mm long; natives.
    F-Petals white or yellow on the face, often purple-veined, often
      purple-tinged on the back; spur 0.5-2.5 mm long.
      G-Petals white; spur 1-2.5 mm long . . . V. canadensis var. rugulosa
      G-Petals yellow; spur 0.5-1 mm long. . . . . V. pubescens
    F-Petals blue to violet; spur 3-6 mm long.
      H-Plants usually puberulent throughout; leaf blades round-
        ovate to triangular, the bases truncate to slightly heart-
        shaped, the apexes tending to be rounded to blunt even
        on the triangular leaves but sometimes some of them acute
        . . . . V. adunca
      H-Plants glabrous or with scattered hairs only on the upper
        leaf surface; leaf blades roundish, heart-shaped at base,
        tending to be acute at the apex.
        I-Leaf blades 1-5 cm long; stipules usually all toothed;
          widespread . . . . V. conspersa
        I-Leaf blades 1-2.5 cm long; stipules often entire; Cook Co.
          . . . . V. labradorica
A-Flowers and leaves all basal.
  J-Petals white, often veined with purple; flowers 7-14 mm long.
    K-Leaves lanceolate to narrowly elliptic, wedge-shaped at
      base . . . . V. lanceolata
    K-Leaves ovate to kidney-shaped, cordate at base.
      L-Lateral petals glabrous; plants not developing stolons;
        leaves roundish to broader than long . . . . V. renifolia
      L-Lower lateral petals slightly to heavily bearded on the
        inner face; plants developing stolons (sometimes leafy)
        in the late spring; leaves ovate to roundish.
        M-Leaf blades completely glabrous on both sides; petiole
          usually pubescent; lower lateral petals with slight beard
          . . . . V. mackloskeyi subsp. pallens
        M-Leaf blades pubescent to some degree, either above or on
          both sides; petioles variously pubescent; lower lateral
          petals with heavy beard . . . . V. incognita
  J-Petals normally some shade of blue or violet; flowers often larger.
    N-Leaf blades compound or deeply cleft into linear to lanceolate
      divisions.
      O-All petals glabrous, wide-spreading . . . . V. pedata
      O-Lower 3 petals bearded on the inner face; petals directed
        forward . . . . V. pedatifida
    N-Leaf blades entire to prominently toothed, not deeply cleft as above.
      P-Leaf blades prominently toothed or lobed at base at least
        when over 3 cm long, very shallowly toothed above the base,
        oblong-ovate to lanceolate to rarely ovate-triangular, 1.5-3
        times as long as wide . . . . V. sagittata
      P-Leaf blades regularly toothed to entire, not lobed, tri-
        angular to roundish, 0.7-1.5 (-2) times as long as wide.
        Q-Spur 5-7 mm long. V. selkirkii
        Q-Spur 2-3.5 mm long.
          R-Leaf blades pubescent on both surfaces.
            S-Blades 1-2 times as long as wide; sepals glabrous
            or very slightly fringed with hairs . . . . . . V. novae-angliae

S-Blades 0.7-1.2 times as long as wide; sepal edges
    fringed with hairs at least below . . . . **V.** sororia
R-Leaf blades glabrous on the lower surface, and either glabrous
    or sparsely pubescent with short stiff hairs on the upper surface.
T-Leaf blades completely glabrous on both surfaces; peduncles
    shorter than to slightly exceeding the petioles.
    U-Leaves somewhat triangular in overall shape, the apexes
        definitely so and with fewer teeth than the rest of the
        margin or none; petals pale violet . . . . . **V.** missouriensis
    U-Leaves roundish to sometimes triangular, toothed uni-
        formly or nearly so to the acute apex; petals blue-
        violet or purple . . . . **V.** pratincola
T-Leaf blades pubescent with a few short stiff hairs on the
    upper surface of the basal lobes; peduncles exceeding
    the petioles at flowering time except in the rare **V.** affinis.
V-Spur petal glabrous; lateral petals bearded with club-
    shaped or knobbed hairs on the inner face. . **V.** cucullata
V-Spur petal bearded; lateral petals bearded with cylin-
    drical hairs or sometimes the hairs slightly club-
    shaped in the rare **V.** affinis of the extreme se.
    W-Peduncles exceeding the petioles at flowering time;
        hairs of leaf blades tiny and inconspicuous without
        magnification; widespread plants of open fields
        and bogs . . . . **V.** nephrophylla
    W-Peduncles about equalling the petioles; hairs
        relatively large, sometimes visible without
        magnification; plants of deciduous woods, known
        only from Fillmore Co. . . . . **V.** affinis

V. adunca Sm. Plants sometimes glabrous; stipules entire to toothed;
spur 4-6 mm long. Mostly open rocky to sandy places, Cook to e. Roseau
Co., s. to Polk, ne. Todd, Anoka, and Goodhue counties.

V. affinis LeConte. Fruits from self-pollinated flowers borne on prostrate
peduncles. Deciduous woods; reported from Fillmore Co. by Dr. Russell.

V. arvensis Murr. European Field-pansy. Pubescent to glabrous annual;
leaves crenate to entire, the lowest roundish, the upper ovate to narrowly
elliptic; style much enlarged upward. From Europe, occasional in disturbed
ground, recorded from Cass Co., reported from Ramsey Co.

V. canadensis var. rugulosa (Greene) Hitchc. (**V.** rugulosa Greene).
Cheyenne Violet. Plants with long stolons or shallow rhizomes, densely
pubescent; leaves cordate-ovate or broader; stipules entire or nearly so.
Mesic to moist well-drained usually shady places, throughout most of the
state, unrecorded from Cook to Aitkin and Koochiching counties except near
Lake Superior in Lake and St. Louis counties, unrecorded also from several
other counties.

V. conspersa Reichenb. American Dog-violet. Spur 3-6 mm long. River
forests, bog forests, and other shady moist places, Lake to Kittson Co., s.
to Clay, Douglas, McLeod, Hennepin, and Winona counties.

V. cornuta L. Horned Violet, Tufted or Bedding Pansy; cultivated. Leaves
ovate, slightly cordate, usually acuminate, crenately serrate, pubescent
beneath on nerves and margins; style much enlarged upward. Spain and the
Pyrenees.

V. cucullata Ait. Bogbice Violet. Bogs, swamps, and wet places, Cook
to St. Louis Co., s. to Mille Lacs, Hennepin, and Chisago counties. Often
hybridizes with other species.

V. incognita Brainerd. Bigleaf White Violet. Mesic to moist woods, mostly northeastern, Cook to Lake of the Woods Co., s. to Becker, Douglas, Le Sueur, and Houston counties.

V. labradorica Schrank (**V. adunca**. var. **minor** (Hook.) Fern.). Labrador Violet. Similar to **V. conspersa** according to Dr. Russell, probably representing a variety or subspecies of that species. Bogs; Cook Co.

V. lanceolata L. Lance-leaved Violet. Glabrous; lateral petals usually beardless. Damp sandy places mostly near lakes, Chisago, Anoka, Hennepin, Ramsey, and Winona counties. Occasionally hybridizes with **V. mackloskeyi** ssp. **pallens**; plants resembling the eastern **V. primulifolia** L. are of this origin, according to Dr. Russell.

V. mackloskeyi subsp. **pallens** (Banks) Baker (**V. pallens** (Banks) Brain.). Pallid Violet. Leaves rather thick, clear green, shallowly scalloped, the young ones tending to remain folded till nearly full size; petioles with a double fringe of long white hairs, especially on plants in the sun. Open or shaded swamps or bogs, mostly northeastern, Cook to e. Roseau Co., s. to Pennington, Clearwater, ne. Todd, Hennepin, Rice, and Goodhue counties.

V. missouriensis Greene. Missouri Violet. Sepals often narrowly white-edged; spur petal glabrous. Low woods and river flood-plain forests, Houston to Anoka counties and in Watonwan and Cottonwood counties.

V. nephrophylla Greene. Wanderer or Northern Bog Violet. Differs from other blue violets in spring in that the young leaves are purple on the under surface. Bogs, sloughs, damp slopes and fields, Houston to Pipestone Co., n. to Anoka, Wadena, Lake of the Woods, and Kittson counties, and in s. Pine and s. Lake counties.

V. novae-angliae House. New England Violet. The pubescence of this species is usually of shorter hairs, and the petioles tend to be more heavily pubescent at their bases, than in the similar **V. sororia**. At least the lower 3 petals bearded on the inner face. Typically on rocky lake shores and rocky places near streams in the spruce-fir region, Lake to Pine and n. Koochiching counties and in Clearwater Co.

V. pedata L.. Bird-foot or Pansy Violet. Rhizome erect, not horizontal or branching; stolons none; plants glabrous or nearly so; flowers all open and petal-bearing, spring and summer; the 2 upper petals sometimes darker than the 3 lower. Open dry sandy soil, Houston to Mower counties and n. to Anoka and Carlton counties.

V. pedatifida G. Don. Prairie or Bearded Bird-foot Violet. Rhizome short, vertical; plants glabrous to pubescent; closed petalless flowers produced in summer; petals all colored about the same. Prairies and grassy openings, Houston to Rock Co., n. to Chisago, Crow Wing, and Kittson counties. Hybridizes with several other species.

V. pratincola Greene (**V. papilionacea** Pursh, in part). Spur petal glabrous or nearly so. Open mesic to dry mostly disturbed ground, Houston to Rock Co., n. to Washington, Scott, McLeod, Grant, and Kittson counties, and in Lake of the Woods and Koochiching counties.

V. pubescens Ait. Common Yellow Violet. Leaves broadly cordate-ovate or broader; stipules entire to slightly and irregularly toothed.

A-Plants glabrous to finely pubescent; flowering stems 2 or more; basal leaves 3 or more; stem leaves with 25-30 teeth (including both sides); moist open woods and meadows, throughout most of the state, unrecorded from several extreme nw. counties and a few others
. . . . **V. pubescens** var. **eriocarpa** (Schwein.) Russ. (**V. eriocarpa** Schwein.; **V. pensylvanica** Michx.).

A-Plants more or less hairy; flowering stem 1; basal leaves 0-2;
   stem leaves with 30-45 teeth; rich to poor often sandy soil in
   mesic to dry woods, Lake to Red Lake Co., s. to Swift, Freeborn,
   and Houston counties . . . . V. pubescens var. pubescens.

V. renifolia Gray. Kidney-leaf Violet. Plants pubescent to sometimes
glabrous. Usually beneath evergreens, especially Picea, Abies, and Thuja;
mostly northeastern, Cook to Lake of the Woods Co., s. to Clearwater and
Hennepin counties.

V. sagittata Ait. Arrow-leaved Violet. Plants moderately to heavily
pubescent. Mostly moist to mesic sandy places, Houston to Mower Co. and
n. to Hennepin, Crow Wing, and Carlton counties.

V. selkirkii Pursh. Great-spurred or Wilderness Violet. Stolons usually
none; pubescence of leaves mostly concentrated on the upper surfaces of the
basal lobes, the lobes tending to overlap each other; petals beardless. Under
coniferous trees, Cook to St. Louis and Carlton counties and in Lake of the
Woods and Clearwater counties.

V. sororia Willd. Common Blue or Sister Violet. Pubescence varying
from uniformly dense to present only on the petiole and major veins; lateral
petals bearded on the inner face, the spur petal glabrous or sparsely hairy.
Meadows, rich soil in woods, and moist slopes, throughout the state except
for Cook Co.

V. tricolor L. Wild or Field Pansy, Johnny-jump-up, Heartsease. Glabrous
or pubescent annual or short-lived perennial; leaves crenate, the lowest
roundish or cordate, the upper ovate-oblong to elliptic; style much enlarged
upward. From Europe, occasional in disturbed ground, perhaps sometimes
cultivated; recorded from Blue Earth, Stearns, Cook and Kittson counties.

V. X wittrockiana Gams. Garden Pansy; cultivated. The common garden
plant, thought to have been derived from crosses involving V. tricolor and
probably two other wild species. Annual or short-lived perennial, in form
much like V. tricolor.

BEGONIACEAE ----- BEGONIA FAMILY

Mostly monoecious herbs or low shrubs; leaves alternate, mostly simple,
mostly palmately veined and often lobed; flowers unisexual, regular or zygomorphic, epigynous; perianth of the male flowers of 2 free sepals and 2 free petals,
of the female flowers of 2-many tepals; stamens many, free to basally fused;
ovary inferior or rarely half inferior, often with 1-3 (-6) vertical angles or
wings, mostly 3-locular with axile placentation; ovules many; styles 2-5, free
or basally fused, the stigmas often twisted; fruit usually a loculicidal capsule.

BEGONIA

Characters of the family. (Named for M. Begon, French promoter of
botany.)

B. semperflorens Link & Otto. Roots fibrous; plants glabrous except for
the leaf margins, somewhat succulent; leaves glossy, 5-10 cm long, ovate to
elliptic or broadly so, more or less asymmetric at base, rounded or blunt at
apex, finely serrulate, the margin fringed with hairs; flowers rose-red to
whitish, the female with 5 tepals; fruit green with red-tinged wings. Brazil.
The source of many cultivars. Often planted outside in spring.

THYMELAEACEAE ----- MEZEREUM FAMILY

Mostly trees or shrubs; leaves simple, alternate (in ours) or rarely opposite, entire; flowers bisexual (in ours) or unisexual, regular, perigynous; hypanthium bell-shaped to tubular; sepals 4-5, usually fused, often colored, sometimes minute; petals 4-12, scale-like, or none; stamens mostly as many or (in ours) twice as many as the sepals; ovary 1-2-locular; ovules 1 per locule, pendulous; style 1 or none; fruit usually a drupe or nut.

DIRCA ----- LEATHERWOOD*

Shrubs with tough fibrous bark; flowers pale yellow, nearly sessile, appearing before the leaves in lateral clusters of 2-4; hypanthium and calyx tube together corolla-like, narrowly funnel-shaped, tubular below, the calyx tube shallowly 4-lobed or wavy-edged; petals none; stamens 8; ovary 1-locular; fruit a drupe. (From Dirce, a character in Greek mythology.)

D. palustris L. Shrub 1-2 m high; leaves ovate to obovate, entire, 5-8 cm long; flowers 6-11 mm long. Mostly in moist woods, St. Louis to Clearwater and Becker counties, s. to Todd, Wright, Hennepin, Nicollet, Blue Earth, Fillmore, and Houston counties.

ELAEAGNACEAE ----- OLEASTER FAMILY

Shrubs or seldom trees; surfaces of leaves and other parts more or less covered with closely appressed scales or branched hairs, these silvery, brownish-red, or golden, in ours the scales often splitting in age along many fine radiating lines to form star-like branched hairs; leaves simple, entire, alternate, opposite, or whorled; flowers small, solitary or clustered, bisexual or unisexual, regular, perigynous; hypanthium in bisexual and pistillate flowers closely enclosing but free from the ovary, extending beyond it, the ovary often appearing inferior; perianth undifferentiated, the tepals usually 4; stamens as many or twice as many as the tepals; ovary 1-locular with 1 basal ovule; style and stigma 1; fruit drupe-like, consisting of an achene enclosed by the persistent fleshy or mealy base of the hypanthium.

A-Leaves alternate; stamens 4; flowers bisexual or unisexual . ELAEAGNUS
A-Leaves opposite; stamens 8; plants dioecious . . . . SHEPHERDIA

ELAEAGNUS ----- OLEASTER*

Shrubs or trees more or less covered with silvery to brownish-red scales, or these in age becoming star-like branched hairs; leaves alternate; flowers bisexual or polygamous, in small axillary clusters; hypanthium tubular, constricted above the ovary; stamens 4. (Gr. elaia, olive, and agnos, name of another plant.)

A-Young twigs covered with brownish scales; leaves 2-3 times as long
      as wide; native shrub. . . . . E. commutata
A-Young twigs covered with silvery scales; leaves 3-8 times as long
      as wide; small tree, cultivated . . . . E. angustifolia

E. angustifolia L. Russian Olive, Oleaster; cultivated. Sometimes spiny; leaves lanceolate to oblong-lanceolate, 3-10 cm long, gray-green above, silvery below; tepals yellow within; fruit yellowish. Europe and w. Asia.

E. commutata Bernh. Silverberry. Shrub to 5 m high, thornless; leaves ovate-oblong to obovate-oblong, 2-6 cm long, silvery on both sides; tepals yellow within; fruit silvery. Calcareous dry to moist prairies or open woods, northwestern, Kittson and Roseau counties s. to Mahnomen and Traverse counties.

SHEPHERDIA*

Dioecious shrubs or small trees; leaves opposite, covered with silvery to brownish-red scales at least beneath, sometimes also with branched hairs, the scales splitting radially or not; flowers single or clustered, in the leaf axils or at the nodes of the preceding year; tepals greenish-yellow within; stamens 8. (Named for J. Shepherd, an English botanist.)

A-Young twigs and leaf buds silvery, rarely faintly tinged with orange-
    red; shrubs or small trees, often thorny . . . . S. argentea
A-Young twigs and leaf buds rusty-red; thornless shrub . . . . . S. canadensis

S. argentea Nutt. Buffalo-berry. Leaves oblong to oblanceolate, the scales of the lower surface tightly appressed and inconspicuously frayed; fruit scarlet, edible. Banks of streams, damp woods, prairie slopes, and rocky places, Polk to Pipestone counties and in Brown Co.

S. canadensis (L.) Nutt. Soapberry. Leaves ovate to narrowly elliptic or lanceolate, the scales of the lower surface loose, conspicuously frayed, forming a woolly pubescence; fruit yellowish-red or yellow, nauseous. Rocky outcrops often near water and in open woods, Cook to St. Louis Co. and in n. Koochiching Co.

ONAGRACEAE ----- EVENING PRIMROSE FAMILY

Herbs (ours), rarely shrubs or trees; leaves alternate or opposite, simple; flowers bisexual, regular or rarely zygomorphic, epigynous with the hypanthium usually prolonged above the ovary; sepals usually 4 (2-6); petals usually present, usually as many as the sepals, usually convolute in bud; stamens usually as many or twice as many as the sepals; ovary locules typically 4 (1-several); placentation axile; ovules 1-many per locule; style 1; fruit usually a loculicidal capsule.

A-Petals yellow . . . . OENOTHERA
A-Petals pink to white, fading reddish . . . . GAURA

GAURA

Annual or perennial herbs; leaves alternate; flowers in terminal spikes or racemes; sepals 4; petals 4, pink to white, fading reddish; stamens 8; ovary 4-locular or 1-locular by abortion of the partitions; ovule 1 per locule; fruit indehiscent, 1-4-seeded. (Gr. gauros, superb.)

G. coccinea Pursh. Perennial, pubescent to nearly glabrous; leaves lanceolate to linear, entire or few-toothed; flowers in spikes; petals 3-6 mm long; fruit 4-sided above. Dry western prairies, Nobles and Pipestone counties to Polk and Pennington counties.

OENOTHERA ----- EVENING PRIMROSE

Annual to perennial herbs; leaves alternate or rarely all basal; flowers single in the axils or in a terminal raceme; sepals 4; petals 4, yellow or sometimes white or pink; stamens 8; ovary 4-locular; fruit a many-seeded capsule. (Gr. name for a species of Epilobium.)

O. serrulata Nutt. Perennial; leaves linear to linear-oblanceolate, nearly entire to sharply toothed; flowers sessile in the upper axils; petals yellow, 8-14 mm long. Dry prairies, Houston to Jackson and Pipestone counties, n. to Dakota, Morrison, Becker, and Kittson counties, and in s. St. Louis Co.

ARALIACEAE ----- GINSENG FAMILY

Trees, shrubs, vines, or seldom herbs; leaves alternate or rarely opposite, compound or less often simple; flowers in heads or umbels, small, bisexual or unisexual, regular, epigynous; sepals minute, usually 5, or the calyx a vestigial rim; petals mostly 5-10, falling early; stamens usually as many as the petals and alternate with them; nectar gland covering the top of the ovary; ovary usually 2-15-locular with 1 pendulous ovule per locule; styles as many as the locules (and carpels), free or fused, or the stigmas sessile; fruit a berry or rarely a drupe.

A-Leaves alternate or basal, 2-3 times compound; umbels 2 or more
. . . . ARALIA
A-Leaves in a single whorl, once palmately compound; umbel 1 . . PANAX

ARALIA

Polygamous or polygamo-dioecious perennial herbs, shrubs, or trees, prickly or not; leaves alternate or basal, compound once or more times; flowers white or greenish, in 2 or more umbels per inflorescence; petals and stamens each 5; carpels (and locules) mostly 5; styles free or somewhat fused at base; fruit a berry, tipped by the styles, usually with as many seeds as carpels. (A French-Canadian name, according to M. L. Fernald.)

A. nudicaulis L. Wild Sarsaparilla. Polygamo-dioecious herb, perhaps always functionally dioecious; stem none or very short, the usually single leaf basal or nearly so with 3 major divisions, each division pinnately compound; umbels 3 (2-7) on a stalk usually shorter than the leaf. Moist to mesic woods, Cook to Kittson Co., s. to Polk, Otter Tail, Pope, Blue Earth, Fillmore, and Houston counties, and in Chippewa and Jackson counties.

PANAX ----- GINSENG*

Polygamo-dioecious perennial herbs, the stem with a single whorl of usually 3 once palmately compound leaves and a single terminal umbel; flowers greenish, white, or tinged with pink; petals and stamens each 5; carpels (and locules) 2-3; styles free; fruit a 2-3-seeded berry. (Gr. pas, all, and akos, cure; a panacea.)

A-Leaflets long-stalked, acuminate . . . . P. quinquefolius
A-Leaflets sessile or nearly so, blunt or somewhat acute. . P. trifolius

P. quinquefolius L. Ginseng, Sang. Root large and spindle-shaped, often forked; leaflets 3-7, 6-15 cm long; flowers greenish-white; styles usually 2; fruit bright red. Rich soil in mesic to moist woods, Houston to Jackson to Mille Lacs to Washington Co., now exterminated or nearly so by herb-hunters, its commercial value arising from supposed therapeutic properties.

P. trifolius L. Dwarf Ginseng. Root globular; leaflets 3-5, 4-8 cm long; flowers white or tinged with pink; styles usually 3; fruit yellowish. Rich soil in moist woods or in springy or swampy depressions, Pine to s. St. Louis Co.

APIACEAE (UMBELLIFERAE) ----- PARSLEY or CARROT FAMILY

Herbs (ours) or rarely shrubs; leaves mostly alternate or basal, usually compound, sometimes simple; petiole usually broadened at its base to sheath the stem; flowers mostly in compound umbels (the terminal clusters called umbellets), less often in simple umbels or heads or racemes or solitary; umbellets sometimes with both stalked and sessile flowers, sometimes their flowers all staminate; flowers small, usually regular, bisexual or unisexual, epigynous; sepals 5, minute, or none; petals 5; stamens 5, alternate with the petals, arising from a circular nectar gland on top the ovary; ovary 2-locular with 1 pendulous ovule per locule; styles 2; fruit dry, separating into 2 indehiscent divisions (mericarps) each usually suspended at its apex from a slender erect stalk, the fruits varying greatly in shape and ornament; usually containing minute oil tubes around the edges.

A-Leaves all once palmately compound or parted with 3-7 sessile divisions (rarely these on stalks to 9 mm long); ovary covered with hooked prickles (the flowers bisexual or staminate). . . . . .SANICULA
A-At least the basal leaves other than above; ovary without prickles.
  B-Petals yellow or pale yellow.
    C-Leaflets entire or sometimes wavy-edged . . . . TAENIDIA
    C-Leaflets prominently toothed.
      D-Teeth of leaflets 4-10 per cm; central flower of each umbellet, if bisexual, sessile or nearly so (if staminate then with a short to long pedicel); widespread. . . . . ZIZIA
      D-Teeth at least on the larger leaflets 2-3 per cm; all flowers pedicelled; southern . . . . THASPIUM
  B-Petals greenish-white to white or tinged with pink or purple.
    E-Leaflets 3, the larger 10-40 cm wide, palmately lobed and coarsely toothed . . . . HERACLEUM
    E-Leaflets 9 or more, 1-7 cm wide, or the leaves finely dissected into linear or lanceolate divisions.
      F-Leaflets toothed to cleft but distinct as leaflets, the widest ones 6-30 mm wide measured at the notches (excluding the teeth or lobes), the smallest divisions nearly always more than 1.5 mm wide.
        G-Flowers white; ovary pubescent, the fruit with stiff appressed hairs at least on the angles; widespread . . . . OSMORHIZA
        G-Flowers cream; ovary and fruit glabrous; southern. THASPIUM
      F-Leaflets finely dissected into many linear or lanceolate divisions, often not apparent as leaflets, the maximum width of any part 3.5 mm or less, the smallest divisions 1.5 mm wide or less.
        H-Stem leaves present; bractlets subtending the umbellets none or vestigial. . . . . CARUM

H-Leaves all basal; bractlets subtending the umbellets well
developed, equalling the flowers, mostly on one side of
the umbellet......................... LOMATIUM

CARUM*

Biennials or perennials from taproots; leaves pinnately dissected into
lanceolate to linear or thread-like divisions; umbels compound; bracts subtending the umbel few, awl-shaped, or none; bractlets subtending the umbellets
few and minute or none; pedicels very unequal; sepals none; petals white or
rarely pink; fruit glabrous, oblong to elliptic, somewhat flattened at right
angles to the partition; oil tubes 1 in each interval between the ribs, 2 on the
contact face of each mericarp. (Modification of the old Latin name Careum.)

C. carvi L. Caraway; cultivated. Glabrous biennial; leaf divisions linear
or thread-like. From Eurasia; often escaped to disturbed ground and old
fields, throughout the state.

HERACLEUM ----- COW PARSNIP*

Tall stout biennials or perennials; leaves large, once compound; umbels
compound, their bracts lanceolate; bractlets of the umbellets linear; sepals
minute or none; petals white, obcordate, those near the outer edge of the
inflorescence usually larger than the others and 2-cleft; fruits usually pubescent, elliptic to obovate, strongly flattened parallel with the partition, the
edges winged; oil tubes 1 in each interval between the ribs, 2-4 on the contact
face of each mericarp and extending only part way to the base, visible externally. (Dedicated to Hercules.)

H. lanatum Michx. (H. maximum, Bartr.). Biennial 1-3 m high, more
or less pubescent; leaflets 3, the larger 10-40 cm wide, palmately lobed and
coarsely toothed. Rich damp soil, throughout the state.

LOMATIUM*

Perennials, stemless or nearly so; leaves deeply dissected into lanceolate to linear divisions; umbels compound, their bracts minute or none; bractlets of the umbellets (in ours) well developed, mostly on one side of the umbellet; sepals minute or none; petals yellow or white; fruits oblong to nearly round,
strongly flattened parallel with the partition, the ribs on the edges winged;
oil tubes usually many. (Gr. lomation, little border, in reference to the winged
fruit.)

L. orientale Coult. & Rose. Puberulent to glabrous; leaves twice pinnately
cut into divisions 1.5 mm wide or less; flowers white or pinkish; fruit glabrous.
Dry prairies, Rock to Blue Earth counties, n. to Swift, Traverse, Clay, and
Red Lake counties.

OSMORHIZA ----- SWEET CICELY*

Perennials from aromatic roots; leaves twice ternately compound, the
leaflets ovate to lanceolate, toothed to cleft; umbels compound, with or without bracts; umbellets few-flowered; sepals none or vestigial; petals white or

greenish-white; fruits linear to narrowly club-shaped, very slightly flattened at right angles to the partition, with stiff appressed hairs on the angles; oil tubes obscure or none. (Gr. osme, odor, and rhiza, root.)

A-Bractlets of the umbellets mostly none; styles (including the swollen base) in flower 0.25-0.3 mm long, in fruit ca. 0.5 mm long. . O. obtusa
A-Bractlets subtending the umbellets regularly present; styles in flower 0.5-2.3 mm long, in fruit 1.2-4 mm long.
  B-Styles in flower 0.5-1 mm long, in fruit 1.2-1.5 mm long; stem (at least above) and leaves mostly hairy; crushed leaves not anise-scented . . . . O. claytoni
  B-Styles in flower 1.5-2.3 mm long, in fruit 2.5-4 mm long; stems mostly glabrous except at the nodes, leaves slightly hairy to nearly glabrous; crushed leaves usually anise-scented . . . . O. longistylis

O. claytoni (Michx.) Clarke. Bractlets 3-8 mm long; crushed flowers slightly anise-scented; styles in flower shorter than the petals, in fruit nearly straight and parallel. Mesic to moist woods throughout the state except for the extreme nw. corner and most of the western tier of counties.

O. longistylis (Torr.) DC. Bractlets 5-10 mm long; crushed flowers strongly anise-scented; styles in flower equalling or exceeding the petals, in fruit nearly straight and parallel. Rich often alluvial soil in moist woods and thickets throughout most of the state, unrecorded from Cook and many other counties.

O. obtusa (C. & R.) Fern. (O. depauperata Phil.). Stems glabrous or slightly pubescent; leaves more or less pubescent; styles in fruit bent sharply outwards. Moist woods in Cook Co.

SANICULA ----- BLACK SNAKEROOT, SANICLE*

Glabrous biennials or perennials; leaves once palmately divided into 3-5 (-7) divisions; flowers greenish-white to greenish-yellow, bisexual or staminate; umbel compound, somewhat irregular; umbellets often head-like, the bisexual flowers sessile or short-stalked, the staminate all or mostly on longer stalks, the umbellets commonly with 3 bisexual and several staminate flowers; sepals narrow, fused at base, persistent; ovary of bisexual flowers and the fruits densely covered with hooked bristles; vestigial ovary of staminate flowers smooth; fruits ovoid or oblong to nearly round, slightly flattened at right angles to the partition, the halves seldom separating. (Name said to derive from L. sanare, to heal.)

A-Styles much exceeding the calyx and the bristles of the ovary and fruit, 2-4 mm long; staminate flowers 12-25 per umbellet.
  B-Calyx lobes of the staminate flowers narrowly triangular, stiff, sharp, 1.2-1.8 mm long; staminate flowers about equalling to exceeding the fruits, on pedicels 1.6-4 mm long . . . . . S. marilandica
  B-Calyx lobes of the staminate flowers ovate, not stiff and sharp, 0.5-1 mm long; staminate flowers shorter than to about equalling the fruits, on pedicels 1.5-2.5 mm long . . . . S. gregaria
A-Styles usually shorter than the calyx and the bristles, rarely about equalling or slightly exceeding them, 0.7-2 mm long; staminate flowers 1-7 per umbellet.
  C-Sepals of bisexual flowers 0.7-1.4 mm long, shorter than to about equalling the nearest bristles; pedicels of staminate flowers 1-2.2 mm long; fruits 3-5.5 mm long . . . . S. canadensis

C-Sepals of bisexual flowers 1.5-2.2 mm long, equalling to exceeding the nearest bristles; pedicels of staminate flowers 2.5-5.5 mm long; fruits 5.5-8 mm long . . . . S. trifoliata

S. canadensis L. Staminate flowers mostly 2-3 per umbellet; petals white with a brownish midvein; fruits on pedicels 1-2 mm long. Mesic to moist woods, recorded only from Houston, Blue Earth, and Wright counties.

S. gregaria Bickn. Petals yellowish-green; fruits 3-5 mm long, on pedicels 0.4-0.6 mm long. Rich soil in mesic to moist woods and thickets, Houston to Martin Co., n. to McLeod, Mille Lacs, and Washington counties, and in Big Stone and s. St. Louis counties.

S. marilandica L. Petals greenish-white; fruits 4-6 mm long, sessile. Dry to moist woods and thickets or moist open places, throughout the state, less frequent in the drier parts.

S. trifoliata Bickn. Staminate flowers mostly 4-5 per umbellet; petals white; fruits sessile. Rich soil in moist woods, Houston and Fillmore counties.

TAENIDIA ----- YELLOW PIMPERNEL*

Glabrous perennials; leaves 1-3 times pinnately or ternately compound; umbels compound, without subtending bracts; umbellets many-flowered, without subtending bractlets, the inner flowers staminate and short-pedicelled, the outer bisexual and long-pedicelled; petals yellow; fruits elliptic to broadly ovate-oblong, flattened at right angles to the partition, the ribs low; oil tubes mostly 3 between the ribs, 4 on the contact face of each mericarp. (Gr. tainidion, little band, in reference to the low ribs.)

T. integerrima (L.) Drude. Stems somewhat whitened; leaflets entire or sometimes wavy-edged; fruit 3-4 mm long. Mesic to moist woods and meadows, Houston to Mower to Rice and Goodhue counties.

THASPIUM ----- MEADOW PARSNIP*

Perennials; leaves compound (or sometimes the lowest simple); umbels compound, mostly without subtending bracts; flowers of the umbellet all pedicelled, bisexual and staminate; sepals ovate or obovate; petals yellow (in ours) or purple; fruits ovoid to ellipsoid, unflattened or slightly flattened parallel with the partition, 3 or 4 or all of the ribs winged; oil tubes 1 in each interval between the ribs, 2 on the contact face of the mericarp. (Anagram of Thapsia, a related plant.)

T. barbinode (Michx.) Nutt. Larger leaves twice pinnate or ternate with each primary division pinnate; leaflets ovate to lanceolate, the teeth at least on the larger ones 2-3 per cm; peripheral flowers of the umbellet bisexual and thus fruiting, the inner all staminate; petals yellow to pale yellow or cream; fruit glabrous, 4-6 mm long. Woods and bluffs, Winona Co. and near the Minnesota River Valley in Nicollet, Blue Earth, and Brown counties.

ZIZIA ----- ALEXANDERS*

Perennials, glabrous or nearly so; leaves some or all 1-3 times ternately compound; umbels compound, without subtending bracts; flowers bisexual and staminate, the central flower of each umbellet sessile or nearly so if bisexual, if staminate then with a short to long pedicel; sepals short, triangular; petals yellow; fruits glabrous, ovate to oblong in outline, flattened at right angles to the partition; ribs thread-like; oil-tubes 1 in each interval between the ribs, 1 in each rib, and 2 on the contact face of each mericarp. (Named for the Rhenish botanist J. B. Ziz.)

A-Basal leaves once or twice ternately compound . . . . Z. aurea
A-Basal leaves simple, cordate at base . . . . Z. aptera

Z. aptera (Gray) Fern. Heart-leaved Alexanders. Basal leaves and sometimes the lower stem leaves simple, the others compound, teeth of leaves and leaflets 4-10 per cm. Mesic to moist prairies, meadows, and open woods, throughout the state, infrequent in the extreme n.

Z. aurea (L.) Koch. Golden Alexanders. Leaves all compound; teeth of leaflets 4-10 per cm. Moist to wet meadows and thickets throughout the state.

CORNACEAE ----- DOGWOOD FAMILY

Trees, shrubs, or rarely herbs; leaves simple, opposite or sometimes whorled or alternate; flowers in cymes, these sometimes panicle- or raceme-like, or in heads; bisexual or unisexual, regular, epigynous; calyx 4-5-parted or toothed; petals 4-5, free; stamens as many as the petals and alternate with them, or twice as many, attached with the petals at the outer edge of a circular nectar gland; ovary 1-4-locular, with 1 pendulous ovule per locule; styles 1-several; fruit typically a drupe, sometimes a berry.

CORNUS ----- DOGWOOD*

Trees, shrubs, or rarely herbs; leaves opposite or whorled, alternate in 1 species, mostly entire, rarely crenulate; flowers in simple or compound cymes or in heads surrounded in our species by a series of petal-like bracts; calyx lobes, petals, and stamens each 4; ovary 2-locular; style 1; fruit a drupe with a 2-locular and 1-2-seeded stone. (L. name from cornu, horn, in reference to the hard wood.) Our two late-blooming species are included here because they have conspicuous flower buds early in June.

A-Low herb with leaves whorled or nearly so, the flowers in a head-
   like cluster surrounded by usually 4 petal-like bracts . . . C. canadensis
A-Shrubs; leaves opposite or alternate; flowers white to cream in
   open cymes without petal-like bracts.
  B-Leaves alternate, often closely crowded . . . . C. alternifolia
  B-Leaves opposite.
   C-Lateral veins 5-9 to a side; pith white; branchlets of the pre-
    ceding year greenish to yellowish to red or red-purple; spring-
    blooming.
    D-Branchlets not flecked with purple, green to red or red-
     purple on all sides, sometimes with darker red pinpoints; leaves
     ovate to obovate to ovate-lanceolate, with 5-7 lateral veins to a
     side . . . . C. alba
    D-At least the youngest branchlets with purple flecks, other-
     wise greenish or yellowish-green or sometimes reddish
     above; leaves broadly ovate to roundish, with 6-9 lateral
     veins to a side . . . . C. rugosa
   C-Lateral veins 3-4 to a side; pith usually brown, if sometimes
    white then the branchlets of the preceding year gray; not
    blooming till mid-June.
    E-Branchlets of the preceding year gray; inflorescences usually
     about as high as wide; pubescence not red-brown
     . . . . C. foemina ssp. racemosa

E-Branchlets of the preceding year red- to purple-brown; inflorescences flatter; pubescence of young fast-growing twig-tips,
petioles, and sometimes blades usually red-brown
.... C. amomum ssp. obliqua

C. alba L. Shrub to 4 m high, often broadening by means of spreading rooting lower branches (then loosely termed "stoloniferous"); branches turning red
in late summer, fading starting at the base in spring (April in the Twin Cities),
those of most plants all greenish by mid-July or sooner, some remaining dull
reddish; pubescence of the lower leaf surface appressed or spreading; fruit
white or lead-colored, sometimes bluish. Our native representatives of this
complex are customarily treated as separate from the Asiatic ones; however,
W. Wangerin (Pflanzenreich 4, 229: 53-56) in 1910 in the last study of these
plants on a world-wide basis concluded that the American ones were part of
a single complex, and there seems to be no convincing reason not to follow
him.
A-Stones of fruits 1.6-2.4 mm thick; sepals 0-0.4 mm long; cultivated
only .... C. a. subsp. alba. Siberian Dogwood.
Stones of fruits 4-5.6 mm long, 3.1-4.8 mm wide, 1-1.7 times as
long as wide, the highest shoulder 0.11-0.38 of the way to the base;
w. Asia to Kamchatka and Korea.
A-Stones 2.4-3.6 mm thick; sepals 0.2-0.8 mm long; native, often cultivated .... C. a. subsp. stolonifera (Michx.) Wang.
(C. stolonifera Michx.). Red-osier Dogwood. Stones of fruits
3.5-6 mm long, 3.2-6 mm wide, 0.67-1.6 times as long as wide,
the highest shoulder 0.05-0.25 of the way to the base; North America.
Two forms are usually recognized in our area:
B-Pubescence typically appressed throughout; stone of fruit typically
longer than wide; throughout the state ....
.... C. a. subsp. stolonifera forma stolonifera.
B-Pubescence of lower leaf surface of spreading hairs, at least on
the leaves formed early in the season; stone usually wider than
long; Cook to Kittson Co., s. to Otter Tail, Scott, and Houston
counties, and in Lincoln Co. . C. a. subsp. stolonifera forma baileyi
(C. & E.) Morley (C. baileyi Coulter & Evans).

C. alternifolia L. Alternate-leaved or Pagoda Dogwood. Shrub or small
tree to 8 m high; pith white; branchlets of recent years yellowish-green;
leaves elliptic-ovate to elliptic-oblong to obovate with 4-5 lateral veins on
a side; fruit blue. Mesic to moist woods and thickets, Houston and Fillmore
counties to Brown, Clay, Polk, Lake of the Woods, and Lake counties.

C. amomum subsp. obliqua (Raf.) Wilson (C. obliqua Raf.). Shrub to 3
m high; pith brown; new twigs pubescent; leaves elliptic-ovate to elliptic-
lanceolate, appressed-pubescent with more or less spreading hairs along
the veins and sometimes over the whole surface beneath; sepals 1-2.3 mm
long; fruit blue sometimes marked with cream. Swamps, damp thickets,
and river bottoms, Houston to Martin Co., n. to Blue Earth, Hennepin, and
Washington counties, and from Washington to Morrison Co.

C. canadensis L. Bunchberry; Dwarf Cornel. Plants 1-2 dm high; leaves
4-6 with 2-3 pairs of lateral veins; bracts white to purplish; individual flowers
greenish-white to cream, sometimes pink-tipped; fruits red. Moist often
acid woods and bogs, mostly northern, Cook to Kittson Co., s. to Mahnomen,
Pope, Hennepin, Fillmore, and Houston counties.

C. foemina subsp. racemosa (Lam.) Wilson (C. racemosa Lam.). Gray-
barked or Panicled Dogwood. Shrub to 2 m high; pith tan or white; leaves
lanceolate to narrowly ovate, appressed-pubescent on both sides; fruit white

to rarely light blue. Mostly in dry to mesic open woods and edges of woods, Houston to Jackson and Pipestone counties, n. to Chisago, Kanabec, Cass, Clearwater, and Kittson counties, and in Carlton and St. Louis counties.

C. rugosa Lam. Round-leaved Dogwood. Shrub to 3 m high; branchlets often turning reddish above in late summer; leaves soft-pubescent beneath; fruit light blue to whitish. Mesic to moist woods and thickets throughout most of the forested area, Cook to Lake of the Woods Co., s. to Polk, Pope, Brown, and Houston counties.

ERICACEAE ----- HEATH FAMILY (including Pyrola and relatives)

Trees, shrubs or perennial herbs, often evergreen, sometimes without chlorophyll; leaves simple, alternate or sometimes opposite or whorled; flowers mostly bisexual, regular or nearly so, hypogynous or sometimes epigynous; sepals 4-5 (-7); petals 4-5 (-7), free or more often fused; stamens as many or more often twice as many as the petals, rarely intermediate in number, separate, free from the corolla; anthers opening by lengthwise slits or more often recurved on and fused to the filament and opening by apparently terminal but morphologically basal pores; ovary usually with as many locules as the petals, or twice as many through the development of secondary partitions; placentation typically axile, the ovules usually many per locule; style and stigma usually 1; fruit a capsule, berry, or drupe.

A-Leaves all basal or a few of them on the base of the flowering
    stem. . . . . PYROLA
A-Leaves all or mostly on the stem.
  B-Stems prostrate and trailing.
    C-Leaf blades 16-42 mm wide, cordate at base (rarely only
      truncate) . . . . EPIGAEA
    C-Leaf blades 2-12 mm wide, either tapering at base or if rounded
      then 2-7 mm wide.
      D-Stems and lower surface and margin of leaves with short
        stout appressed bristles . . . . GAULTHERIA
      D-Stem and leaves glabrous or soft-pubescent or puberulent.
        E-Corolla cleft nearly or entirely to the base; bog plants
         . . . . VACCINIUM
        E-Corolla cleft 1/8 of the way to the base or less; plants
         of dry to mesic open places . . . . ARCTOSTAPHYLOS
  B-Stems erect, or prostrate at the base with erect or ascending branches.
    F-Ovary inferior.
      G-Leaves without resinous dots, in 1 species with scattered
        dark points below; blades entire or toothed; ovules more
        than 10 . . . . VACCINIUM
      G-Leaves dotted on both sides with tiny resinous golden-
        brown globules, entire; ovules 10 per ovary . . . . . GAYLUSSACIA
    F-Ovary superior.
      H-Petals free; leaves densely woolly beneath . . . . LEDUM
      H-Petals united at least below; leaves glabrous to densely
        pubescent beneath, not woolly.
        I-Corolla 10-65 mm wide, saucer-shaped to bell-shaped,
          if less than 30 mm wide then the leaves opposite or whorled.
          J-Leaves opposite or rarely whorled; corolla 10-18 mm
            wide, saucer-shaped; native . . . . KALMIA
          J-Leaves alternate; corolla 30-65 mm wide, bell-shaped;
            cultivated . . . . RHODODENDRON
        I-Corolla 2-4 mm wide, cylindric to urn-shaped; leaves alternate.

K-Lower leaf surface covered with tiny round scales,
   these often elsewhere, leaves otherwise glabrous;
   calyx subtended by 2 bractlets . . . . CASSANDRA
K-Leaves glabrous to pubescent, without scales; bractlets
   if present at base of pedicel.
   L-Leaf margins inrolled below, the lower surface white
      with a dense pubescence; bog plants . . . . . . ANDROMEDA
   L-Leaf margins not inrolled, the lower surface glabrous
      to puberulent but not white; plants of dry to mesic
      open places . . . . ARCTOSTAPHYLOS

ANDROMEDA*

Low shrubs; leaves alternate, evergreen, narrow, the edges inrolled
below; flowers in terminal umbel-like racemes, white or pink; sepals 5, fused
below; corolla jug-shaped with 5 short lobes; stamens 10, anthers opening by
terminal pores and tipped with slender appendages; ovary superior, 5-locular;
style 1; fruit a loculicidal many-seeded capsule. (A name from Gr. mythology.)

A. glaucophylla Link. Bog Rosemary. Leaves 2-5 cm long, linear to
narrowly elliptic, entire, whitened below with a dense pubescence; corolla
5-6 mm long. Boggy places, more or less acid, Cook to Lake of the Woods
Co., s. to Clearwater, Morrison, Dakota and Chisago counties.

ARCTOSTAPHYLOS*

Shrubs or small trees (ours low and prostrate); leaves alternate, evergreen; flowers white to pink in few-flowered terminal racemes; sepals (4-)
5: corolla bell-shaped to jug-shaped, shortly (4-) 5-lobed; stamens twice the
sepals; anthers opening by terminal pores, with 2 reflexed bristles; ovary
superior, (4-) 5 or (8-) 10-locular with 1 ovule per locule; style 1; fruit a
berry-like drupe with several stones. (Gr. arctos, bear, and staphyle, bunch
of grapes.)

A. uva-ursi (L.) Spreng. Bearberry. Stems prostrate, branchlets often
ascending; leaf blades 10-27 mm long, oblanceolate to oblong-obovate, glabrous to pubescent; corolla white to pale pink, urn-shaped, 4-6 mm long;
fruit red, 6-10 mm long. Dry to mesic sandy soil and rocks, Cook to Kittson
Co., s. to Polk, Clearwater, ne. Todd, Sherburne, Rice, and Wabasha
counties and in Houston Co. Often subdivided into 3 varieties:
A-Twigs and petioles minutely puberulent and sticky, the puberulence
   soon disappearing; leaves glabrous except sometimes at the margins;
   distribution as given . . . . A. u. var. uva-ursi.
A-Twigs and petioles permanently pubescent, not sticky, or with sticky
   globular-tipped hairs mixed with the pubescence; leaves incompletely to fully pubescent below.
   B-Twigs and petioles without swollen-tipped hairs; leaves slightly
      pubescent at the base and along the midrib; distribution as
      given . . . . A. u. var. coactilis Fern. & Macbr.
   B-Twigs and petioles with sticky swollen-tipped hairs mixed with
      the pubescence; leaves persistently puberulent below; Cook to
      Cass, Polk, and Kittson counties . . A. u. var. adenotricha Fern. & Macbr.

CASSANDRA ----- LEATHER-LEAF*

Shrubs, many parts bearing tiny round scales; leaves alternate, ever-green, covered with scales below; flowers in leafy racemes, each flower with 2 small bractlets just below the calyx; sepals 5, free; corolla cylindric or nearly so, 5-lobed; stamens 10; anthers without bristles, drawn into long tubes with terminal pores; ovary superior, 5-locular; style 1; fruit a loculicidal many-seeded capsule. (A character in Homer's Iliad.)

C. calyculata (L.) D. Don (Chamaedaphne calyculata (L.) Moench). To 1.5 m high; leaves elliptic or oblong to rarely obovate, 1.5-5 cm long; corolla white, 6-7 mm long. Bogs and similar wet places, Cook to Lake of the Woods Co., s. to Clearwater, Morrison, Hennepin, and Washington counties, and in Rice Co.

EPIGAEA*

Prostrate creeping nearly herbaceous plants, often dioecious; leaves evergreen, alternate, sometimes crowded; flowers in axillary and terminal clusters, bisexual or unisexual, fragrant, pink to white; sepals 5, free, closely subtended by 2 bractlets; corolla tubular below, wide-spreading above; stamens 10; anthers opening longitudinally, without bristles; ovary superior, 5-locular; style 1; fruit a somewhat fleshy many-seeded loculicidal capsule. (Gr. epi, on, and gaea, the earth.)

E. repens L. Trailing Arbutus, Ground-laurel, Mayflower. Leaf blades ovate to oblong, cordate at base (rarely only truncate), 20-65 mm long; corolla tube 8-15 mm long, the lobes 6-8 mm long. Sandy or gravelly acid soils, Cook to e. Roseau Co., s. to Becker and Pine counties.

GAULTHERIA

Erect shrubby to creeping nearly herbaceous plants with odor of wintergreen; leaves alternate, evergreen; flowers in ours single in or just above the axils; calyx deeply 4-5-lobed, closely subtended by 2 bractlets; corolla tubular to bell-shaped, shallowly lobed; stamens twice the sepals; anthers with or without bristles, opening by terminal pores or slits; ovary superior to 1/2 inferior, 4-5-locular; style 1; fruit a many-seeded berry or capsule, the capsule surrounded by the thick and fleshy calyx and thus berry-like. (Named for J. F. Gaultier, a Quebec naturalist and physician.)

G. hispidula (L.) Muhl. Creeping Snowberry, Moxieplum. Creeping nearly herbaceous plants; stems and lower surfaces and margins of leaves with short stout appressed bristles; leaves broadly elliptic to nearly round, 4-10 mm long; flowers 4- merous; corolla ca. 2.5 mm long; fruit white, 5-10 mm long. Bogs and usually coniferous moist woods, often with mosses and on decaying logs, Cook to Lake of the Woods, Clearwater, and Chisago counties.

GAYLUSSACIA ----- HUCKLEBERRY*

Shrubs; leaves alternate, deciduous (ours) or evergreen; flowers white or pink- or purple-tinged, in racemes; sepals 5, fused below; corolla urn-shaped to bell-shaped with 5 short lobes; stamens 10; anthers without bristles, opening by apical pores in terminal tubules; ovary inferior, of 5 united carpels but 10-locular through the development of secondary partitions, each locule with 1 ovule; style 1; fruit a berry-like drupe with 10 stones more or less grown together. (Named for the French chemist L. J. Gay-Lussac.)

G. baccata (Wang.) Koch. To 1 m high; leaves elliptic to broadly oblanceolate, entire, 2-4 cm long, dotted on both sides with tiny resinous globules; corolla cylindric, 3-5 mm long; fruit black, 6-8 mm long. Dry to moist sandy or rocky soil and edges of bogs, recorded from Houston, Winona, Washington, and Anoka counties.

KALMIA ----- LAUREL (of America)*

Shrubs; leaves alternate, opposite, or whorled, entire, evergreen; buds naked; sepals 5, united below; corolla saucer-shaped, shallowly 5-lobed, with 10 small hollows where the anthers are located until anthesis; stamens 10; anthers without bristles, opening by terminal pores; ovary superior, 5-locular; style 1, thread-like; fruit a many-seeded septicidal capsule. (Named for P. Kalm, a pupil of Linnaeus.)

K. polifolia Wang. Swamp Laurel. To 6 dm high; leaves opposite (rarely in 3's), sessile or nearly so, ovate to linear, 1-3.5 cm long, white-pubescent beneath, the margins inrolled below; corolla pink-purple, 10-18 mm wide; fruit nearly round, 5-7 mm long. Bogs, Cook to Lake of the Woods Co., s. to Clearwater, Cass, Crow Wing, Kanabec, and Pine counties.

LEDUM*

Shrubs; herbage fragrant when crushed; leaves alternate, entire, evergreen; flowers white, in terminal umbel-like racemes; sepals 5, small, fused below; petals 5, free; stamens 5-10; anthers without bristles, opening by terminal pores; ovary superior, 5-locular; style 1; fruit a many-seeded septicidal capsule. (The ancient Gr. name of a plant with a similar fragrance.)

L. groenlandicum Oeder. Labrador Tea. To 1 m high; leaves lanceolate to narrowly elliptic, 2-5 cm long, densely white- to rusty-woolly beneath, the edges inrolled below; petals ca. 5 mm long; stamens 5-7; fruit 5-7 mm long. Bogs and peaty and wet soils, Cook to Roseau Co., s. to Pennington, Becker, Morrison, and Washington counties.

PYROLA ----- SHINLEAF, WINTERGREEN

Low glabrous perennial herbs; leaves evergreen, all basal or a few of them alternate on the base of the flowering stem; flowers in an erect raceme, white to pink or pink-purple; sepals 5, fused below; petals 5, free; stamens 10; anthers without bristles, opening by terminal pores; ovary superior, 5-locular; style 1; fruit a loculicidal capsule with very many minute seeds. (Diminutive of Pyrus, pear, referring to the leaves.)

A-Petals pink or pink-purple . . . . P. asarifolia
A-Petals white or greenish.
  B-Raceme strongly 1-sided; flowers pendent; style straight or
      nearly so . . . . P. secunda
  B-Raceme spiral; flowers more or less horizontal; style strongly
      curved . . . . P. virens

<u>P</u>. <u>asarifolia</u> Michx. Pink Pyrola. Leaf blades roundish, obscurely cren-
ate, mostly 3-6 cm long; sepals 2-3 mm long; petals 5-8 mm long. Moist
woods and bogs, Cook to Kittson Co., s. to Becker, Pope, and Rice counties.

<u>P</u>. <u>secunda</u> L. One-sided Pyrola. Leaf blades elliptic to ovate or some-
times nearly round, crenate-serrate or sometimes entire, 1.5-5 cm long;
sepals 0.5-1 mm long; petals 3.5-5.5 mm long. Mesic to moist woods and
mossy bogs, Cook to Roseau Co., s. to Clay, Morrison, Hennepin, Rice,
Fillmore, and Houston counties.

<u>P</u>. <u>virens</u> Schweigg. Leaf blades ovate to obovate or roundish, obscurely
crenate, 1-3 cm long; calyx lobes 0.8-1.7 mm long; petals 4-9 mm long.
Dry to mesic woods, Cook to Lake of the Woods, Clearwater, and Cass
counties.

RHODODENDRON ----- ROSE BAY; AZALEA

Shrubs or small trees; leaves alternate, deciduous or evergreen;
flowers large, in terminal racemes or umbel-like clusters; calyx 5- (rarely
6-10-) lobed; corolla lobes usually as many as the calyx lobes, the corolla
often somewhat zygomorphic; stamens mostly 5 or 10; anthers without bristles,
opening by terminal pores; ovary superior, 5- (-10-) locular; style 1; fruit
a many-seeded septicidal capsule. (Gr. <u>rhodo</u>, red or rose, and <u>dendron</u>,
tree.)

A-Leaves evergreen, present at flowering . . . . <u>R</u>. <u>catawbiense</u>
A-Leaves deciduous, absent at flowering . . . . <u>R</u>. <u>mucronulatum</u>

<u>R</u>. <u>catawbiense</u> Michx. Mountain Rose Bay, Purple Laurel; cultivated.
Shrub or small tree to 6 m high; leaf blades 6-15 cm long, glabrous, whitish
below; corolla rose- or lilac-purple spotted with olive-green. Mountain
woods of se. United States. Used in the production of many different garden hybrids.

<u>R</u>. <u>mucronulatum</u> Turcz. Shrub to 2 m high; leaf blades 3-8 cm long,
somewhat scaly on both sides, pale green below; corolla rose-purple.
China, Manchuria, Korea. Japan.

VACCINIUM *

Shrubs or small trees or trailing nearly herbaceous plants; leaves
alternate, deciduous or evergreen; flowers single in the axils or in terminal
or lateral racemes or seldom panicles; calyx and corolla each 4-5-lobed, or
the petals rarely separate; stamens twice as many as the corolla lobes;
anthers with or without bristles, opening by apical pores in terminal tubules;
ovary inferior, of 4-5 fused carpels, 4-5-locular or sometimes 8- or 10-locular
through the development of secondary partitions, each locule with several
ovules; style 1; fruit a many-seeded berry. (The classical Latin name.)

A-Corolla cleft nearly or entirely to the base, the petals turned back-
      ward from the base; anthers exserted; leaves evergreen, not
      dotted; creeping plants, the flowering branches sometimes erect;
      flowers 4-merous.
  B-Pedicel bearing a pair of reddish bractlets 0.2-0.7 mm wide; leaves
        ovate to ovate-elliptic or ovate-lanceolate, the apex usually acute
      . . . . <u>V</u>. <u>oxycoccos</u>
  B-Pedicel bearing a pair of green or greenish bractlets 1-2 mm wide;
        leaves oblong-elliptic, the apex usually rounded . . . . . <u>V</u>. <u>macrocarpon</u>

A-Corolla cleft less than 1/2 way to the base; anthers not exserted;
   leaves mostly deciduous, if evergreen then dark-dotted below;
   stems erect, or creeping with erect branches; flowers 4-5 merous.
   C-Leaves sparsely dotted below with blackish to sometimes brown
      raised points, otherwise glabrous or nearly so, evergreen, 5-
      20 mm long; plants dwarf, the stems often creeping with erect
      branches. . . . . V. vitis-idaea var. minus
   C-Leaves without dark dots, glabrous or pubescent, deciduous, 9-35
      mm long; stems erect.
      D-Leaves finely serrate.
         E-Leaves lanceolate to narrowly elliptic with sharp teeth; flowers
            in terminal or lateral racemes or panicles; anthers without
            bristles . . . . V. angustifolium
         E-Leaves obovate to oblanceolate, their teeth blunt with incurved
            points; flowers single in the lower leaf axils of the new growth;
            anthers with a pair of conspicuous bristles in addition to the
            terminal tubules . . . . V. caespitosum
      D-Leaves entire.
         F-Leaves puberulent at least along the midrib above; flowers
            5-merous; anthers without bristles . . . . V. myrtilloides
         F-Leaves glabrous above; flowers mostly 4-merous; anthers with
            a pair of conspicuous bristles in addition to the terminal
            tubules . . . . V. uliginosum

V. angustifolium Ait. Blueberry. Twigs glabrous except for 2 pubescent
lines; leaves 15-35 mm long, glabrous except sometimes for the midrib; berry
10-locular, usually blue, sweet. Dry to mesic sandy to rocky open woods and
clearings, Cook to Kittson Co., s. to Clearwater, Todd, Hennepin, Rice,
Fillmore, and Houston counties.

V. caespitosum Michx. Dwarf Bilberry. Twigs puberulent; leaves 10-35
mm long, glabrous; berry 5-locular, blue-black, sweet. Sandy and gravelly
soils, especially under Pinus banksiana, Cook to Kittson, Clearwater, Cass,
and Carlton counties.

V. macrocarpon Ait. Large Cranberry. Leaf blades entire, 5-14 mm
long, glabrous; bractlets 1/2-7/8 of the way to the apex of the pedicel; fruit
red, 1-2 cm long. Open bogs and wet places, Lake to Clearwater, Otter
Tail, Ramsey, and Washington counties, and in Dakota, Scott, and Blue
Earth counties.

V. myrtilloides Michx. Velvet-leaf Blueberry. Twigs densely woolly-
pubescent; leaves oblong-lanceolate to elliptic, 15-35 mm long, hairy below,
puberulent at least along the midrib above; berry 10-locular, blue, rather
sour. Mesic to moist woods and clearings and in bogs, Cook to Lake of the
Woods Co., s. to Clearwater, ne. Todd, Sherburne, and Dakota counties.

V. oxycoccos L. Small Cranberry. Leaf blades entire or with a few
small teeth, 4-10 mm long, glabrous; bractlets 1/3-2/3 of the way to the
apex of the pedicel; fruit pink to red, 7-13 mm long. Bogs and boggy places,
Cook to Lake of the Woods Co., s. to Polk, Clearwater, Morrison, Hennepin,
and Washington counties, and in Rice Co.

V. uliginosum L. Bilberry. Twigs glabrous to puberulent; leaves elliptic
to obovate to nearly round, 9-30 mm long, glabrous to puberulent above and
below; berry mostly 4-locular, bluish-black, sweet. Edges of low woods and
rocks, e. tip of Cook Co. near Lake Superior.

V. vitis-idaea var. minus Lodd. Mountain Cranberry, Cowberry, Lingen
Berry. Twigs puberulent; leaves elliptic to obovate, 5-18 mm long, entire or
finely crenate, glabrous, or puberulent at base, margins, and midrib, sometimes very finely so elsewhere; flowers 4-merous; berry 4-locular, dark red,
most edible the following spring. Mostly in bogs and swamps, sometimes on
drier ground or rocks, Cook to Lake of the Woods and Clearwater counties.

PRIMULACEAE ----- PRIMROSE FAMILY

Annual or perennial herbs; leaves usually simple, mostly opposite or whorled, sometimes all basal, rarely alternate; flowers bisexual, mostly regular, mostly hypogynous; sepals typically 5 (4-9), fused below; petals fused, as many as the sepals (rarely absent); stamens as many as the petals and opposite them, epipetalous (rarely free); 5 staminodes sometimes alternating with the petals; ovary 1-locular but typically of 5 fused carpels; ovules few to many on a free-central placenta; style 1; fruit a capsule.

A-Leaves all or mostly on the stem.
  B-Foliage leaves opposite at several to many nodes . . . . LYSIMACHIA
  B-Foliage leaves in a single terminal whorl . . . . TRIENTALIS
A-Leaves all basal, in a compact radiating tuft.
  C-Flowers nodding, the corolla lobes turned backward at the base
  . . . . DODECATHEON
  C-Flowers erect, the corolla lobes spreading horizontally or
    ascending.
    D-Leaves 5-25 mm long; corolla 2-4 mm wide . . . . . . ANDROSACE
    D-Leaves usually longer; corolla 8 mm wide or wider . . PRIMULA

ANDROSACE*

Annual (ours) to perennial herbs; leaves all in a compact basal radiating tuft; flowers 5-merous, solitary or (ours) in umbels on a leafless stalk; corolla narrowly tubular below and flaring above, or funnel-shaped, the tube usually shorter than the calyx; stamens not exserted; style very short; capsule 2-many seeded, splitting into 5 segments. (The name used by Pliny for some unidentified plant, of doubtful origin.)

A-Bracts subtending the umbel broadly to narrowly ovate to obovate,
    2-5 mm long; corolla 1.5-2.5 mm wide . . . . A. occidentalis
A-Bracts narrowly lanceolate to needle-like, 1.5-2.5 mm long;
    corolla 3-4 mm wide . . . . A. septentrionalis var. puberulenta

A. occidentalis Pursh. Leaves 5-15 mm long; plants 2-8 cm high; flowers 5-9 in an umbel; corolla white. Dry, usually sandy or rocky open soil, Kittson to Pipestone counties and along the Minnesota R. Valley from Swift to Scott counties, and in Cottonwood, Goodhue, and Stearns counties.

A. septentrionalis var. puberulenta (Rydb.) Knuth. Leaves 6-25 mm long; plants 5-12 cm high; flowers 6-12 per umbel; corolla white. Open sandy soil, Kittson and Roseau counties.

DODECATHEON ----- SHOOTING STAR*

Glabrous perennial herbs; leaves all basal, in a compact radiating tuft; flowers in a terminal umbel, nodding; calyx deeply 5-lobed; corolla 5-cleft nearly to the base, the lobes turned backward at the base; filaments very short, more or less fused at base; capsule opening by 5 short terminal divisions. (Gr. dodeca, twelve, and theos, god, a name for the primrose, believed to be under the care of the 12 superior gods.)

A-Native; leaf bases usually unmarked with red; calyx 3.5-6.5 mm
    long in flower; wall of fruit thin, papery, flexible . . . . . . D. radicatum
A-Cultivated; leaf bases usually tinged or marked with red; calyx
    5.5-10 mm long in flower; wall of fruit thick and firm, not
    flexible . . . . D. meadia

D. **meadia** L. Cultivated. Plants blooming May 18-June 22, 2-6 dm high; flowers mostly 6-30 per umbel, lilac to pale pink or sometimes white; calyx lobes in flower mostly 4-5 (3-7) mm long; anthers 6.5-9.5 mm long; fruit thickest near the base, its wall 0.13-0.32 mm thick. E. N. America, w. to Wisconsin and Iowa.

D. **radicatum** Greene (D. **amethystinum** Fassett). Plants blooming May 1-June 10, 1.5-3.5 dm high; flowers mostly 2-11 per umbel, mostly deep red-purple, rarely white; calyx lobes in flower mostly 3 (2-4) mm long; anthers 4.5-8.5 mm long; fruit thickest near the middle, its wall 0.03-0.12 mm thick. Mesic to moist hillsides and ledges, Houston, Fillmore, Winona, and Wabasha counties.

LYSIMACHIA ----- LOOSESTRIFE

Perennial herbs; leaves entire, whorled, opposite (ours) or rarely alternate; flowers yellow to yellow-orange (rarely white), often marked with dots or lines, axillary or terminal, solitary or in spike-like racemes or panicles; sepals 5 (-6), fused at base or not; corolla 5- (-6-) lobed, the tube often very short; filaments free, or fused at base; capsule few-many-seeded, with 5-6 segments. (Gr. lysis, release from, and mache, strife.)

A-Erect plant; flowers axillary in dense short racemes . . . . L. thyrsiflora
A-Creeping plant; flowers single in the axils . . . . L. nummularia

L. **nummularia** L. Moneywort. Leaves roundish. From Europe; naturalized in moist places, recorded from Houston, Olmsted, and Ramsey counties.

L. **thyrsiflora** L. Tufted Loosestrife. Leaves moderately to narrowly lanceolate to elliptic. Swamps and marshes, probably throughout the state, unrecorded from the southern tier of counties and several other counties interspersed.

PRIMULA ----- PRIMROSE, COWSLIP*

Perennial herbs; leaves all basal, in a compact radiating basal tuft; flowers in an umbel, head, or successive whorls; calyx 5-lobed; corolla narrowly tubular below, flaring above, or funnel-shaped, the 5 lobes usually notched at the ends; filaments very short; capsule many-seeded, splitting at the top into 5 or 10 divisions. (L. diminutive of primus, first, from the early blooming time of some species.)

A-Corolla tube 5-7 mm long; leaves 1.5-6.5 cm long; native . . P. mistassinica
A-Corolla tube 10-16 mm long; leaves 5-18 cm long; cultivated.
 B-Calyx 12-16 mm long . . . . P. X polyantha
 B-Calyx 4-8 mm long.
  C-Corolla 14-28 mm wide; pedicels 3-25 mm long . . . . . . P. auricula
  C-Corolla 9-12 mm wide; pedicels 1-4 mm long . . . . P. denticulata

P. **auricula** L. Cultivated. Leaves 5-18 cm long; bracts of umbel 3-4 mm long or longer; calyx 4-5 (-8) mm long; corolla of many colors, its tube 9-13 mm long. European alps.

P. **denticulata** Smith. Cultivated. Leaves 5-13 cm long; bracts of umbel 2-5 mm long; calyx 5-8 mm long; corolla lilac, purple, or white, its tube 11-13 mm long. Himalayas. The form with rich purple corollas with yellow centers, blooming when the leaves are nearly full size, and with a more mealy surface than usual on the herbage, is P. d. cv. Cachemiriana.

P. mistassinica Michx. (incl. P. intercedens Fern.). Mistassini Primrose. Plants 3-25 cm high; bracts 2-6 mm long; calyx 3-6 mm long; corolla
lilac, pale pink, bluish-purple, or white, 1-2 cm wide. Moist rocky places
near Lake Superior, Cook to St. Louis counties, along the Kettle and St. Croix
Rivers in Pine and Washington counties respectively, and in a Carex meadow
in Norman Co.

P. X polyantha Mill. Cultivated; apparently a hybrid between P. veris and
P. vulgaris (European species), modified in some cases by further crossing
to form a garden group of mixed origin. Leaves 7-15 cm long; bracts ca. 8-
10 mm long; pedicels 10-35 mm long; corolla of many colors, 20-25 mm wide,
its tube 15-16 mm long.

TRIENTALIS ----- STARFLOWER, CHICKWEED-WINTERGREEN *

Low perennial herbs; leaves all or mostly in a single terminal whorl,
the stem below with a few scale-like leaves; flowers 1 or a few at the top,
white to pale pink, mostly 7-merous; corolla saucer-shaped, its tube very
short; filaments connected by a membranous ring; capsule many-seeded,
splitting into 5 divisions. (L. for 1/3 of a foot, referring to the plant's
height.)

T. borealis Raf. Plants 5-20 cm high, spreading by stolons; corolla 8-14
mm wide. Mesic to moist woods and edges of bogs, Cook to Kittson Co., s.
to Mahnomen, Otter Tail, Wright, Hennepin, and Goodhue counties.

PLUMBAGINACEAE ----- LEADWORT FAMILY

Perennial herbs (ours) or shrubs, sometimes climbing; leaves alternate or all basal; flowers bisexual, regular, hypogynous or perigynous; calyx
5-lobed (sometimes with smaller secondary lobes), often 5-10-ribbed or
-winged; petals 5, fused or sometimes free; stamens 5, opposite the petals;
ovary 1-locular but of 5 carpels, with a single basal ovule on a long stalk;
styles 5, free or fused at the base; fruit dry, dehiscent or indehiscent.

ARMERIA ----- THRIFT, SEA-PINK

Perennial herbs or subshrubs; leaves in dense basal tufts, narrow,
often linear; flowers in roundish head-like inflorescences, mixed with bracts,
the outer bracts surrounding the head, the 2 lowest bracts turned downward,
their margins fused to surround the stem; calyx dry, not green; petals barely
united at base, usually pink; styles pubescent at base. (Name of doubtful
origin.)

A. maritima Willd. Cultivated. To 30 cm high or more; leaves linear, 1-
5 mm wide; heads 12-25 mm wide; corolla pink, purple, or white. Europe
and n. N. America.

OLEACEAE ----- OLIVE FAMILY

Trees or shrubs; leaves opposite (rarely alternate, not in ours),
simple or pinnately compound; flowers bisexual or unisexual, regular,
hypogynous; sepals typically 4, fused, rarely absent; petals typically 4,
usually fused, sometimes free or none; stamens typically 2, epipetalous
when the petals are fused; ovary 2-locular, of 2 fused carpels; placentation
axile, the ovules 2 (1-10) per locule; style 1 or none; fruit various.

A-Trees; leaves pinnately compound; petals none . . . . FRAXINUS
A-Shrubs; leaves simple or rarely with 3 leaflets; petals conspicuous.
   B-Flowers yellow . . . . FORSYTHIA
   B-Flowers white to purple.
      C-Corolla lobes shorter than the tube . . . . SYRINGA
      C-Corolla cleft nearly to the base . . . . CHIONANTHUS

CHIONANTHUS ----- FRINGE TREE

Shrubs or small trees; leaves simple, entire; flowers in open panicles from lateral buds, 4-merous; petals united only at the base; stamens 2; ovules 2 per locule; fruit a drupe, usually 1-seeded. (Gr. chion, snow, and anthos, flower, from the snow-white flowers.)

C. virginica L. Cultivated. Shrub or small tree to 10 m high, functionally dioecious although the flowers appear bisexual; leaves mostly lance-elliptic, 6-17 cm long; petals linear, white, 13-30 mm long; drupe dark blue to purple, 10-18 mm long. E. N. America, w. to Missouri.

FORSYTHIA ----- GOLDEN BELLS

Shrub; leaves simple or with 3 leaflets; flowers yellow, appearing before the leaves from lateral buds, 1-5 together, 4-merous; calyx deeply lobed; petals fused for ca. 1/3 their length; stamens 2; fruit a many-seeded septicidal capsule, the seeds winged. (Named for W. Forsyth, an English horticulturist.)

A-Branches hollow between the nodes . . . . F. suspensa
A-Branches with separated cross-wise layers of pith.
   B-Leaves ovate to broadly ovate, simple, 5-7 cm long; flowers 1
      (-2) per node on a side; corolla 12-20 mm long . . . . . . F. ovata
   B-Leaves usually ovate-oblong to oblong lanceolate, 8-12 cm long,
      sometimes 3-parted; flowers usually 2-3 or more per node on
      a side; corolla more than 20 mm long . . . . F. X intermedia

F. X intermedia Zab. (F. suspensa (Thunb.) Vahl X F. viridissima Lindl.). Pith solid at the nodes, layered or partly so between (rarely hollow); leaves on vigorous shoots sometimes 3-parted; calyx shorter than the corolla tube. Several cultivars are grown.

F. ovata Nakai. Pith layered throughout, sometimes absent at base of vigorous shoots; calyx 1/2 as long as the corolla tube. Korea.

F. suspensa (Thunb.) Vahl. Leaves ovate to oblong-ovate, 6-10 cm long, some of them usually compound; flowers 1-3 (-6) per node on a side; calyx about as long as the corolla tube; corolla ca. 18-25 mm long. China. Forms with spreading or arching branches and with pendulous branches are grown.

FRAXINUS ----- ASH*

Trees, ours dioecious or sometimes polygamous; leaves in ours odd-pinnately compound; flowers in ours in dense clusters, racemes, or panicles, appearing before or with the leaves, the female inflorescence greatly expanding after flowering; calyx minute, 4-lobed or irregularly toothed or none; petals in ours none; stamens 2 (rarely 3 or 4); ovules 2 per locule; fruit elongate, winged, dry, indehiscent, 1- (-2-) seeded. (The classical Latin name.)

A-Pistillate (or bisexual) flowers without calyx; young new twigs flecked
    with black; herbage usually with a strong rank odor when crushed;
    bark gray, irregularly scaly or with small scaly ridges; seed-con-
    taining body of fruit flattened, not sharply demarcated, the wing
    extending to the base . . . . F. nigra
A-Pistillate flowers with a calyx, persistent in fruit; new twigs not
    flecked with black; herbage odor mild and inoffensive; bark gray-
    brown to blackish, prominently furrowed; seed-containing body
    of fruit sharply differentiated, roundish in section, the wing
    abruptly narrowed and tapering into the body short of the base.
    B-Stalks of the middle and lower mature leaflets winged nearly to
        the base with blade tissue, 1-5 (-9) mm long; leaflets pale
        green beneath, not papillose; wing of fruit extending 1/3-3/4
        of the way to the base of the body, the body 1-2.2 mm wide
        . . . . F. pennsylvanica
    B-Stalks of the middle and lower mature leaflets wingless for most
        of their length, 3-11 (-15) mm long; leaflets whitened and papil-
        lose beneath (papillae visible at 40X); wing of fruit extending
        1/6-1/2 of the way to the base of the body, the body 1.8-3.4 mm
        wide. . . . . F. americana

    F. americana L. White Ash. Dioecious trees to 40 m high; leaflets 5-9,
the lateral ones ovate to obovate, often asymmetric at base; body of fruit 2-8
times as long as wide. Mesic to moist upland woods, mostly on n. and e.
slopes, Houston and Fillmore counties to Goodhue Co. and in Chisago and
Pine counties.

    F. nigra Marsh. Black Ash. Polygamous or dioecious trees to 25 m
high; leaflets 7-11, the lateral ones sessile, oblong to lanceolate; pistillate
flowers with staminodia. Damp ground and swampy places, Cook to Lake of
the Woods Co., s. to Clearwater, Clay, Douglas, Morrison, Hennepin,
Blue Earth, Fillmore, and Houston counties.

    F. pennsylvanica Marsh. Dioecious trees to 25 m high; leaflets 5-9, the
lateral ones lanceolate to elliptic, seldom asymmetric at base; body of fruit
6.5-18 times as long as wide. Mesic to moist woods throughout the state.
Forms with the twigs, petioles, and usually other parts hairy are often
called Red Ash, F. p. var. pennsylvanica. Glabrous plants or those with
only the rachises hairy are often known as Green Ash, F. p. var. subinteger-
rima (Vahl) Fern.

<h2 style="text-align:center">SYRINGA ----- LILAC</h2>

        Shrubs or small trees; leaves entire or rarely pinnately lobed to com-
pound but otherwise entire; flowers in panicles, often fragrant, white to purple,
4-merous; calyx truncate to toothed; corolla narrowly tubular below, abruptly
wide-spreading above; stamens 2; fruit a 2-locular loculicidal capsule; seeds
2 per locule, narrowly winged. (Gr. syrinx, pipe, referring to the hollow
internodes of a different plant (Philadelphus) to which the name was once applied.

A-Tube of corolla equalling to twice as long as the calyx; stamens
    long-exserted . . . . S. amurensis
A-Tube of corolla 4 or more times as long as the calyx; stamens
    equalling the tube or included within it.
    B-Mature shoots usually ending in 2 lateral buds, the terminal one
        suppressed, the 2 laterals producing panicles directly with few
        or no leaves.
        C-Bases of leaves rounded to acute . . . . S. X chinensis
        C-Bases of leaves truncate to cordate.

D-Calyx lobes 0.3-1 mm long; anther apexes 0.5-1 mm below
    the mouth of the corolla tube . . . . S. vulgaris
D-Calyx lobes 1-1.5 mm long; anther apexes ca. 3 mm below
    the mouth of the corolla tube . . . . S. oblata
  B-Mature shoots with a true terminal bud; panicles borne terminally
    on leafy shoots of the current year.
    E-Inflorescence nodding or pendulous . . . . S. X prestoniae
    E-Inflorescence upright.
      F-Corolla tube narrowly funnel-shaped, gradually widened
        above the middle, the corolla lobes more or less ascend-
        ing or upright; anther apexes 0.8-2 mm below the mouth
        of the tube. . . . . S. josikaea
      F-Corolla tube cylindric, the lobes wide-spreading; anther
        apexes 0-1 mm below the mouth of the tube . . . . . . S. villosa

S. amurensis Rupr. Cultivated. Leaves moderately to broadly ovate, rounded to subcordate at base, glabrous to pubescent beneath; flowers creamy white; fruit 15-20 mm long. Ne. Asia. Most commonly grown here is the Japanese Tree Lilac, S. a. var. japonica (Maxim.) Fr. & Sav., a tree to 10 m high, its leaves to 14 cm long, often subcordate at base, and pubescent beneath at least when young, its fruit to 20 mm long. Japan.

S. X chinensis Willd. (S. persica X S. vulgaris). Cultivated. Leaves ovate-lanceolate, 4-8 cm long; flowers of various colors; corolla tube 7-8 mm long.

S. josikaea Jacq. Hungarian Lilac; cultivated. Leaves 6-12 cm long, acute to rounded at base, sparingly hairy or nearly glabrous beneath; flowers deep lilac to pink, the corolla tube 8-13 mm long. Hungary and Galicia.

S. oblata Lindl. Cultivated. Leaves kidney-shaped or roundish to ovate, often wider than long, abruptly acuminate, glabrous, turning orange, red, or purple in fall; flowers purple to white, the corolla tube 10-15 mm long. N. China and Korea. Most commonly grown is S. o. var. dilatata (Nakai) Rehd., from Korea, with ovate long-acuminate leaves to 12 cm long and a corolla tube 12-15 mm long.

S. X prestoniae McKel. (S. reflexa X S. villosa). Cultivated. Growth form and foliage like that of S. villosa.

S. villosa Vahl. Cultivated. Leaves 5-18 cm long, elliptic to elliptic-ovate to oblong, acute at the base, usually pubescent on the veins and often elsewhere beneath; flowers lilac to pink to whitish, the corolla tube 9-16 mm long. N. China.

S. vulgaris L. Common Lilac; cultivated. Leaves ovate, acute to acuminate, glabrous; flowers white to lilac to reddish-purple, the corolla tube 8-11 mm long. Se. Europe. Many cultivars exist.

GENTIANACEAE ----- GENTIAN FAMILY

Ours herbs, glabrous or nearly so; leaves simple or rarely compound, entire, opposite, whorled, or sometimes alternate; flowers regular, mostly bisexual, hypogynous; sepals usually 4-5, fused; petals usually 4-5, fused; stamens as many as the corolla lobes and alternate with them, epipetalous; ovary usually 1-locular with 2 parietal placentas, the ovules usually many; style 1, entire or 2-cleft; fruit usually a septicidal capsule.

MENYANTHES ----- BUCKBEAN, BOGBEAN*

Perennial herbs, glabrous or with a few hairs; leaves alternate, compound with 3 leaflets, crowded toward the base of the stem; flowers white to pinkish, in a terminal raceme, 5-merous; corolla funnel-shaped, the inner surface of the lobes bearded; stigma 2-lobed; fruit many-seeded, breaking open somewhat irregularly. (Gr. menyein, disclosing, and anthos, flower, the flowers progressively expanding in the raceme.)

M. trifoliata var. minor Raf. To 3 dm high; leaflets sessile or nearly so, elliptic to obovate, entire to very shallowly toothed; corolla 10-14 mm long. Bogs, marshes, and pond margins, Cook to Lake of the Woods Co., s. to Clearwater, Otter Tail, McLeod, Blue Earth, and Goodhue counties.

ASCLEPIADACEAE ----- MILKWEED FAMILY

Herbs (ours), shrubs, vines, or rarely small trees, usually with milky juice; leaves simple, mostly opposite or whorled, rarely alternate; flowers bisexual, regular; sepals typically 5, free or fused below; petals as many as the sepals, fused below, the corolla tube often terminated by a series of appendages; stamens as many as the corolla lobes and alternate with them, often bearing conspicuous outgrowths, the anthers usually fused to the stigma, the pollen grains of each of the 2 anther sacs usually stuck together in a waxy mass, the right-hand pollen mass of one stamen joined to the left-hand pollen mass of its neighbor on the right by a small link, the "translator arm"; carpels 2, typically free except for their fused stigmas, superior or becoming slightly inferior; fruit a pair of follicles (or 1 by abortion); seeds mostly silky-hairy.

ASCLEPIAS ----- MILKWEED

Perennial herbs; juice milky in most species; leaves mostly opposite (sometimes whorled or alternate); flowers (fig. 70) in umbels; filaments fused into a tube, the tube bearing 5 prominent semi-cylindrical structures (hoods), diverse in form, each at the base of an anther, often with an additional narrow structure, the horn, produced within each hood near the base. (From the Gr. Aesculapius, to whom the genus is dedicated.)

A-Leaves elliptic to broadly lanceolate; horns present . . . . . A. ovalifolia
A-Leaves lance-ovate to linear-oblong; horns absent . . . . . A. lanuginosa

A. lanuginosa Nutt. Leaves opposite, alternate, or both; umbel 1; corolla lobes 4-5 mm long; hoods 2-3.5 mm long, purplish. Prairies, Houston to Rock Co., n. to Hennepin, Todd, Polk, and Kittson counties.

A. ovalifolia Decne. Leaves all or mostly opposite; umbel 1 (-3); corolla lobes 5-6.5 mm long; hoods 4-5 mm long, yellowish. Prairies and openings in dry woods, Houston to Rock Co., n. to Washington, Crow Wing, s. Beltrami, Roseau, and Kittson counties and in St. Louis Co.

POLEMONIACEAE ----- PHLOX FAMILY

Annual to perennial herbs (ours), rarely woody; leaves alternate or opposite, simple or compound; flowers bisexual, regular or slightly zygomorphic, hypogynous; sepals 5, fused; petals 5, fused; stamens 5, epipetalous, alternate with the corolla lobes; ovary 3-locular (rarely 2-5-), of as many carpels, the placentation axile with 1-many ovules per placenta; style 1, 3-cleft or with 3 stigmas; fruit usually a loculicidal capsule.

A-Leaves pinnately compound .... POLEMONIUM
A-Leaves simple, entire.
    B-Leaves all or most of them opposite .... PHLOX
    B-Leaves all or mostly alternate .... COLLOMIA

COLLOMIA *

Mostly annuals; leaves mostly alternate, entire (ours) to pinnately cleft; flowers mostly in head-like conspicuously-bracted cymes; calyx obconic; stamens often unequal or unequally inserted; fruit a capsule; seeds 1 (-3) per locule. (Gr. colla, gluten, from the seeds which are mucilaginous when wet.)

C. linearis Nutt. Annual to 4 dm high; leaves linear to oblong-lanceolate, 1-7 cm long; corolla pink to lilac to whitish, 8-15 mm long. Prairies and open disturbed ground, usually sandy or gravelly, throughout most of the state, not recorded from Lake and Cook counties.

PHLOX ----- PHLOX, SWEET WILLIAM

Perennial (ours) or less often annual herbs; leaves all or mostly opposite, entire; flowers in terminal or terminal and axillary cymes; calyx tubular or narrowly bell-shaped, 5-ribbed; corolla narrowly tubular below, abruptly wide-spreading above; stamens inserted at different levels in the corolla tube; ovules 1-4 per locule; capsule ovoid. (Gr. phlox, flame.)

A-Plants forming dense tufts or colonies; leaves 0.8-2 cm long; cultivated
     .... P. subulata
A-Plants mostly single or a few together, not colonial; leaves mostly
    3-8 cm long; native.
    B-Calyx glabrous; stems usually mottled or speckled with red-
        purple; corolla usually red-purple or purple .... P. maculata
    B-Calyx pubescent, the hairs often with globular tips; stems not
        mottled; corolla usually pink-magenta or blue.
        C-Corolla usually blue, glabrous; leaves oblong to lanceolate
         .... P. divaricata var. laphamii
        C-Corolla usually pink-magenta, the tube more or less pubescent
        on the outside; leaves lance-ovate to linear .. P. pilosa var. fulgida

P. divaricata var. laphamii Wood. Wild Blue Phlox. Leaves 2-4.5 times as long as wide, their tips obtuse to acute, not sharp-pointed; hairs of calyx and pedicel globular-tipped; corolla sometimes purplish or white; stigmas, style, and ovary in total 3-4 mm long. Mesic to moist open woods and rocky slopes, from Houston to Martin Co., w. and n. to Murray, Lac Qui Parle, Meeker, Hennepin, and Pine counties.

P. maculata L. Wild Sweet William, Meadow Phlox. Leaves linear to lanceolate or narrowly oblong; stigmas, style, and ovary in total 13-20 mm long. Moist meadows, thickets, and prairies, Wabasha and Olmsted to Dakota and Nicollet counties.

P. pilosa var. fulgida Wherry. Downy Phlox. Leaves 4-15 times as long as wide, their tips narrowed to sharp stiff points; hairs of calyx and pedicel without globular tips; stigmas, style, and ovary in total 2-4 mm long. Grasslands and open woods, Houston to Rock Co., n. to Pine, Crow Wing, Hubbard, Mahnomen, and Norman counties.

P. subulata L. Moss Pink, Moss Phlox, Rock Pink; cultivated. Leaves linear or awl-shaped, sharp-pointed; calyx pubescent; corolla pink, purplish, or white. E. N. America.

POLEMONIUM----- JACOB'S LADDER*

Perennial herbs; leaves alternate, pinnately compound or deeply cleft; flowers mostly blue, the inflorescence basically cymose, variously modified; calyx bell-shaped; corolla bell-shaped or funnel-shaped; stamens inserted at about equal levels on the corolla tube; seeds 1-10 per locule, sometimes becoming mucilaginous when wet; fruit a capsule. (Gr. name, of uncertain origin.)

P. reptans L. Leaves compound; leaflets of the main leaves 7-17, 2-4 (-7) cm long, ovate or lanceolate to elliptic; corolla blue, 8-15 mm long. Moist woods and bottomlands, Houston to Mower Co. and n. to Scott, Hennepin and Ramsey counties.

HYDROPHYLLACEAE ----- WATERLEAF FAMILY

Annual or perennial herbs (ours) or rarely shrubs, usually hairy; leaves alternate or opposite, simple or pinnately or rarely palmately divided; inflorescence cymose, often coiled, or the flowers solitary in the axils; flowers bisexual, regular; sepals 5, fused; petals 5, fused; stamens mostly 5, alternate with the petals, epipetalous; ovary superior (ours) or rarely 1/2 inferior, of 2 fused carpels, typically 1-locular with 2 parietal placentas, sometimes 2-locular; ovules 4-many; style 1, 2-cleft, or styles 2; fruit usually a loculicidal capsule opening by 2 or rarely 4 segments.

A-Flowers several to many in coiled cymes; filaments exserted
. . . . HYDROPHYLLUM
A-Flowers solitary at the nodes; filaments included in the corolla
tube . . . . ELLISIA

ELLISIA*

Annual herbs; leaves all or at least the lower ones opposite, the others alternate, the blades pinnately lobed or divided; flowers solitary in or opposite the leaf axils, and sometimes a few in a terminal inflorescence; calyx much enlarging in fruit; corolla bell-shaped to somewhat cylindric, about equalling or slightly exceeding the calyx, white to lavender, the tube with 5 minute appendages within; ovary 1-locular, 4-ovuled; style cleft up to 1/2 its length; capsule globose. (Named for John Ellis, British naturalist.)

E. nyctelea L. Leaf blades up to 8 cm long, deeply cut into 7-13 divisions; corolla 5-8 mm long; capsules pendulous. Moist shaded woods and disturbed soil, Houston to Rock counties, n. to Ramsey, Stearns, Grant, and Kittson counties, and in Aitkin Co.

HYDROPHYLLUM ----- WATERLEAF*

Biennial or perennial herbs; leaves alternate, variously lobed or cleft; flowers in more or less coiled cymes, white, blue, or purple; corolla bell-shaped to tubular, the tube with 5 lengthwise linear appendages opposite the lobes, each forming a nectar-bearing groove; stamens and style mostly exserted; filaments more or less hairy; ovary 1-locular, 4-ovuled; style shortly cleft; capsule globose, 1-4-seeded. (Gr. hydor, water, and phyllon, leaf.)

A-Middle and upper stem leaves pinnately cleft or divided; calyx without appendages . . . . H. virginianum
A-Middle and upper stem leaves shallowly palmately lobed; calyx appendaged with a reflexed lobe at each notch between the sepals
. . . . H. appendiculatum

H. appendiculatum Michx. Appendaged Waterleaf. Biennial; lower stem leaves and basal leaves pinnately divided; corolla violet, 9-13 mm long; stamens exserted 1-3 mm. Moist woods and river bottoms, Houston and Fillmore counties to Goodhue and Blue Earth counties.

H. virginianum L. Virginia Waterleaf. Perennial; leaves all pinnately cleft or divided; corolla lavender to white, 7-11 mm long; stamens exserted 2-7 mm. Mesic to damp woods and damp openings, Houston to Rock counties, n. as far as St. Louis, Clearwater, and Polk counties.

BORAGINACEAE ----- BORAGE FAMILY

Herbs (ours), shrubs, trees, or rarely vines; leaves alternate (rarely all or the lowermost opposite, not in ours), simple, usually entire; inflorescence basically cymose, usually coiled, uncoiling as the flowers open; flowers mostly bisexual, regular or nearly so, hypogynous; sepals 5, free or fused below; petals 5, fused, the corolla often with 5 swellings or outgrowths (scales) opposite the lobes that partly close the tube; stamens 5, alternate with the corolla lobes, rarely with outgrowths on their outer side; ovary 2-carpellate but mostly becoming 4-lobed and 4-locular through deep infolding of the walls, in most genera appearing as 4 ovaries with the single style arising in the center, each lobe containing 1 ovule and usually becoming a nutlet in fruit.

A-Corolla bright yellow to orange . . . . LITHOSPERMUM
A-Corolla all or mostly blue to white or greenish-white, sometimes slightly yellowish.
  B-Ovary developing small knobs or pin-points which become stout barb-tipped bristles in fruit.
    C-Leaves 1.5-10 cm long; flowers each regularly associated with a bract . . . . LAPPULA
    C-Leaves 10-30 cm long; flowers bractless or only a few bracted . . . . CYNOGLOSSUM
  B-Ovary smooth to wrinkled or pitted, without knobs or pin-points, the fruit without bristles.
    D-Corolla all or mostly blue or purple (sometimes pink when young).
      E-Corolla 3-8 mm long, its lobes usually wide-spreading.
        F-Leaves acute at base . . . . MYOSOTIS
        F-Lower leaves truncate to cordate at base . . . . BRUNNERA
      E-Corolla 10-26 mm long, its lobes only slightly spreading.
        G-Pedicels and calyx with appressed grayish hairs or glabrous . . . . MERTENSIA
        G-Pedicels and calyx with wide-spreading somewhat yellowish hairs or bristles . . . . SYMPHYTUM
    D-Corolla greenish-white to white or yellowish.
      H-Flowers in bractless inflorescences or sometimes the lowest flowers bracted.

I-Stem leaves 1-8 cm long . . . . MYOSOTIS
I-Stem leaves 10-30 cm long . . . . SYMPHYTUM
H-Flowers each with a conspicuous bract or the flowers in the
    leaf axils.
    J-Corolla 4-7 mm long; style 1-1.5 mm long; flowers in the
       axils of foliage leaves . . . . Lithospermum latifolium
    J-Corolla 8-16 mm long; style 10-20 mm long; at least the
       upper flowers with bracts less than 1/2 the size of the
       foliage leaves . . . . ONOSMODIUM

BRUNNERA

Leaves ovate, conspicuously veined; flowers blue, without bracts, in
coiled raceme-like cymes; corolla tube closed by scales, the lobes wide-
spreading; stamens included within the tube; nutlets with a short stalk-like
basal attachment which fits into a pit in the otherwise flattish receptacle, the
basal margin of each nutlet swollen downward and slightly outward to form a
ring around the stalk. (Named for S. Brunner, Swiss botanist.)

B. macrophylla Johnston (Anchusa myosotidiflora Lehm.). Cultivated.
Perennial; basal and lower stem leaves long-petioled, ovate, to 20 cm wide,
truncate to cordate at base; flowers 3-7 mm wide. Siberia and the Caucasus.

CYNOGLOSSUM ----- HOUND'S TONGUE*

Annual to perennial herbs; lower leaves petioled; flowers in raceme-
like cymes, bractless except sometimes at the base; corolla funnel-shaped
or the lobes abruptly wide-spreading, the short tube closed by scales; stamens
included in the tube; nutlets attached near their summits, bearing stout barb-
tipped bristles. (Gr. cynos, of a dog, and glossa, tongue.)

A-Plants leafy up to 3/4 of their height, bearing a single terminal
    inflorescence well above the leaves . . . . C. boreale
A-Plants leafy to the summit, bearing toward the top several to many
    axillary inflorescences or the inflorescences on short axillary
    branches . . . . C. officinale

C. boreale Fern. Northern Wild Comfrey. Perennial; upper leaves
clasping the stem by a deep cordate base; corolla blue-violet, 5-8 mm wide.
Mesic to dry woods, Cook to Clearwater, Morrison, and Hennepin counties.

C. officinale L. Common Hound's Tongue. Biennial; upper leaves sessile, the base rounded or slightly cordate; corolla red-purple, 8-11 mm
wide. From Eurasia, established in disturbed ground and open woods, recorded from Houston to Blue Earth and Hennepin counties and from Stearns,
s. St. Louis and Norman counties.

LAPPULA ----- STICKSEED, BEGGAR'S LICE

Hairy annuals; each branch ending in an elongate bracted raceme- or
spike-like coiled cyme; corolla blue or sometimes white, narrowly tubular
below, abruptly to gradually wide-spreading, the throat closed by scales;
stamens and style included; pedicels erect to horizontally spreading in fruit;
nutlets attached on their lower half or for up to their whole length along the

inner angle, bearing 1 or more rows of barb-tipped bristles. (Diminutive of
L. lappa, bur.)

A-Bristles in double rows on the angles of the nutlets, or sometimes
   3 in a row or irregularly distributed over most of the back. . L. echinata
A-Bristles in a single row on each angle . . . L. redowskii var. occidentalis

   L. echinata Gilib. Plants 2-8 dm high; leaves 2-10 cm long, linear to
linear-oblong or linear-oblanceolate, entire; corolla blue. From Eurasia,
established as a weed in disturbed ground over most of the state.

   L. redowskii var. occidentalis (Wats.) Rydb. Plants 1-3.5 dm high;
leaves 1.5-5 cm long, similar in shape to the above; corolla blue. From
Eurasia and w. N. America, in grasslands and disturbed ground, widely
scattered, sw. of a line through (and including) Houston to Kittson counties.

LITHOSPERMUM ----- PUCCOON; GROMWELL*

   Annual to perennial herbs; roots usually reddish; leaves in ours entire,
sessile or nearly so; flowers mostly yellow or orange to white or greenish-
white, in spike-like large-bracted coiled cymes or solitary in or near the upper
axils; corolla funnel-shaped or narrowly tubular below and abruptly wide-
spreading above, with or without scales; anthers almost sessile, included in
or partly exserted from the throat; nutlets smooth to pitted or wrinkled,
basally attached, sometimes only 1 of the 4 maturing. (Gr. lithos, stone,
and sperma, seed.)

A-Corolla greenish-white to pale yellow, 4-7 mm long; leaves narrowly
   elliptic to ovate, 10-35 mm wide . . . . L. latifolium
A-Corolla bright yellow to orange, 9-35 mm long; leaves linear to
   oblong or narrowly ovate, 1.5-15 mm wide.
   B-Corolla yellow, its lobes irregularly toothed or fringed . . L. incisum
   B-Corolla yellow-orange or orange, its lobes entire.
     C-Calyx lobes in flower 3-5.5 mm long; corolla 10-15 mm wide;
      foliage densely soft-hairy . . . . L. canescens
     C-Calyx lobes in flower 6.5-11 mm long; corolla 15-25 mm wide;
      foliage rough with stiff hairs . . . . L. caroliniense

   L. canescens (Michx.) Lehm. Hoary Puccoon. Leaves lanceolate or
narrowly ovate to oblong; flowers in bracted cymes; corolla light orange, its
tube 7-11 mm long. Prairies and dry open woods, Houston to Rock Co., n.
to Washington, Isanti, Crow Wing, Beltrami, Roseau, and Kittson counties,
and scattered ne. to Pine, St. Louis, and Koochiching counties.

   L. caroliniense (Walt.) MacMill.. (including L. croceum Fern.).
Carolina or Saffron Puccoon. Leaves linear to lanceolate; flowers in bracted
cymes; corolla yellow-orange, its tube 7-14 mm long. Dry prairies and open
woods and open disturbed ground, especially in sandy soil, Houston to Chisago,
Mille Lacs, Crow Wing, and Scott counties, and in Nicollet, Pine, and Itasca
counties.

   L. incisum Lehm. Narrow-leaved Puccoon. Leaves linear or linear-
oblong to narrowly lanceolate; flowers crowded in the upper axils; corolla
tube 15-30 mm long; smaller often closed and petal-less flowers usually produced later, lower on the stem. Dry prairies and dry disturbed ground,
Houston to Rock Co., n. to Ramsey, Stearns, Otter Tail, and Kittson counties.

L. latifolium Michx. Flowers single in the axils of the upper leaves; corolla tube 2-4 mm long. Mesic woods and thickets, Houston to Blue Earth counties, n. and w. to Hennepin, Wright, Swift, and Clay counties.

MERTENSIA ----- BLUEBELLS, LUNGWORT*

Perennials; leaves entire; flowers blue to blue-violet, sometimes pink in bud, in panicled or raceme-like cymes, without bracts except often for the lowest; corolla tubular, funnel-shaped, or bell-shaped, its scales small and inconspicuous or none; stamens included or slightly exserted from the throat; style long; nutlets smooth or wrinkled, obliquely attached at the inner angle. (Named for F. K. Mertens, a German botanist.)

A-Leaves and calyx pubescent; corolla 11-17 mm long . . . . . M. paniculata
A-Leaves and calyx glabrous; corolla 16-26 mm long . . . . . . M. virginica

M. paniculata (Ait.) G. Don. Tall Lungwort. Stem leaves lanceolate to ovate; corolla with swellings at the throat, the tube 4.5-7 mm long. Cool usually damp woods, thickets, and shores, Cook to Clearwater and Carlton counties and in one isolated stand in Fillmore Co.

M. virginica (L.) Pers. Virginia Cowslip, Bluebells. Stem leaves elliptic to obovate or oblanceolate; corolla almost or entirely without swellings at the throat, the tube 10-20 mm long. Moist woods, clearings, and bottomlands, Houston to Mower, Blue Earth, and Wabasha counties.

MYOSOTIS ----- FORGET-ME-NOT*

Annual to perennial herbs; leaves entire; flowers mostly small, mostly blue, sometimes white, pink, or yellow, in terminal raceme-like coiled cymes, without bracts except sometimes at the base or the basal ones in leaf axils; corolla narrowly tubular below and abruptly spreading above, to funnel-shaped, with small blunt swellings or outgrowths at the throat; stamens included in the throat; nutlets smooth, attached at base. (Gr. myos, mouse, and ous, ear, from the leaves of some.)

A-Hairs on calyx straight, closely appressed, without hooked tips.
  B-Calyx lobes usually shorter than the tube; corolla 5-11 mm wide;
    style 1.2-1.7 mm long, about equalling the calyx tube, extend-
    ing above the nutlets . . . . M. scorpiodes
  B-Calyx lobes about as long as the tube; corolla 2.5-6 mm wide;
    style ca. 0.5 mm long, much shorter than the calyx tube and
    nutlets . . . . M. laxa
A-Many of the hairs on the calyx spreading, some or all of these
  with hooked tips.
  C-Corolla 1-2 mm wide, white; calyx somewhat 2-lipped, 3 lobes
    shorter than the other 2 . . . . M. verna
  C-Corolla 1.8-8 mm wide, usually blue, rarely white; calyx lobes
    about equal.
    D-Corolla 1.8-4 mm wide, its lobes spreading-ascending; annual
      or biennial . . . . M. arvensis
    D-Corolla 5-8 (4-10) mm wide, its lobes abruptly spreading at
      right angles to the tube; biennial to perennial . . . . . . M. sylvatica

M. arvensis (L.) Hill. Field Forget-me-not. Flowers blue or occasionally white. From Eurasia, occasionally established as a weed in disturbed ground, recorded only from the Minneapolis and Duluth areas.

M. laxa Lehm. Bay Forget-me-not. Perennial to annual, not creeping nor with stolons; corolla pale blue. Moist ground and shallow water, Wadena, Crow Wing, and Morrison counties.

M. scorpioides L. Forget-me-not; cultivated. Perennial, often creeping at base, often with stolons; corolla blue (or pink or white) with a yellow center. From Europe, often escaped in shallow water or moist ground; recorded from Lake, St. Louis, Washington, Fillmore, and Houston counties. **M. s.** cv. Semperflorens is a dwarf, to 20 cm high, that blooms all summer.

M. sylvatica Hoffm. Garden Forget-me-not; cultivated. Flowers blue (or pink or white) with yellow center. From Eurasia, occasionally escaped, recorded only in Clearwater Co. and the Duluth area.

M. verna Nutt. Early Scorpion-grass. Annual or winter annual. Rock outcrops and edges of prairie swales, Big Stone, Chippewa, and Pipestone counties.

ONOSMODIUM ----- FALSE GROMWELL*

Perennial often rough-hairy herbs; leaves sessile or nearly so, entire, strongly veined; flowers greenish-white or white to yellow, in large-bracted raceme-like coiled cymes; corolla tubular or tubular-funnel-shaped, hairy outside; scales none; anthers dehiscent and the style exserted well before the corolla is full size, the anthers partly or wholly included in the throat, the style long; nutlets smooth or pitted, attached at the base. (From its likeness to the genus Onosma.)

O. molle Michx. Plants hairy; lower leaves deciduous, the middle and upper lanceolate to ovate, sessile; corolla 8-16 mm long, greenish-white to whitish or tinged with greenish-yellow; styles 10-20 mm long. Mesic to dry prairies and openings.

A-Nutlets convex to the base, without a constriction; Houston to
    Rock Co., n. to Hennepin, McLeod, Pope, Mahnomen, and
    Kittson counties . . . .
      . . . . . O. m. var. occidentale (Mack.) Johnst. (O. occidentale Mack.).
A-Nutlets with a very short neck or constriction at the base; Hennepin
    to Nicollet and Brown counties, Otter Tail to Mahnomen and
    Clearwater counties, and in Kittson Co. . . . .
     . . . O. m. var. hispidissimum (Mack.) Cronq. (O. hispidissimum Mack.).

SYMPHYTUM ----- COMFREY*

Perennial large-leaved herbs; flowers in raceme- or panicle-like cymes, bractless; corolla tubular to narrowly funnel-shaped; scales lanceolate to linear; stamens included; style long, shortly exserted; nutlets smooth to roughened, with a short stalk-like basal attachment which fits into a pit in the otherwise flattish receptacle, the basal margin of the nutlet with a downwardly toothed rim around the stalk. (Gr. symphyton, grown together, from the decurrent leaves of some species, hence supposed healing powers.)

A-Upper leaves decurrent 4-14 cm on the stem; hairs not broad-based
    and prickle-like, not flattened . . . . S. officinale

A-Leaves mostly decurrent less than 1 cm on the stem; many or all
    the hairs of stem and inflorescence broad-based and prickle-like,
    often flattened . . . . S. asperum

S. asperum Lepech. Prickly Comfrey. Leaves 10-35 cm long; corolla
11-19 mm long, blue (pink before anthesis). Russia to Iran; sometimes cultivated; occasional in disturbed ground; recorded from Goodhue Co.

S. officinale L. Common Comfrey. Leaves 10-30 cm long; corolla 10-17
mm long, whitish to yellowish or dull purple. Eurasia; sometimes cultivated;
occasional in disturbed ground; recorded from Hennepin Co.

LAMIACEAE (LABIATAE) ----- MINT FAMILY

Ours annual or perennial herbs or low shrubs, the herbage usually
aromatic; stems usually square in section; leaves opposite or sometimes
whorled, simple or compound; flowers bisexual, hypogynous, usually zygomorphic; sepals 5, variously fused, 5 lobes not always evident; petals 5,
fused, the corolla typically 2-lipped; stamens 2 or 4, epipetalous; ovary of
2 fused carpels, mostly becoming 4-lobed and 4-locular through deep infolding of the walls, in most genera appearing as 4 ovaries with a single style
arising in the center, each lobe containing 1 ovule and usually breaking off
as a nutlet in fruit; nectar gland around base of ovary sometimes producing
a conspicuous lobe simulating a 5th lobe of the ovary.

A-Leaves entire.
    B-Larger leaves 4-14 cm long including petioles . . . . PRUNELLA
    B-Larger leaves 0.5-2 cm long, including petiole if present.
        C-Leaves lanceolate to linear, 6-10 times as long as wide. . HEDEOMA
        C-Leaves ovate to ovate-oblong or roundish, 1.3-3 times as
            long as wide . . . . SCUTELLARIA
A-Leaves toothed or lobed.
    D-Upper leaves roundish with usually rounded teeth, about as wide
        as long . . . . GLECHOMA
    D-Upper leaves usually longer than wide, either sharp-toothed or
        acute at the apex or both.
        E-Lower leaves palmately lobed . . . . LEONURUS
        E-Lower leaves toothed to pinnately lobed.
            F-Flowers white, in the axils of foliage leaves . . . . LAMIUM
            F-Flowers light blue to purple or rarely white, in dense heads
                or spikes terminal on the main stem or its branches, the
                heads or spikes containing many bracts and occasionally a
                few small leaves.
                G-Leaves very sharply, regularly, and conspicuously toothed;
                    bracts of the inflorescence with several bristle-teeth
                    . . . . DRACOCEPHALUM
                G-Leaves with low irregular mostly blunt teeth; bracts with
                    a single short tooth . . . . PRUNELLA

DRACOCEPHALUM ----- DRAGONHEAD*

Erect annual to perennial herbs; leaves serrate; whorls of flowers forming leafy or bracted heads or spikes, these dense or interrupted; calyx 13-15-
nerved, 5-toothed, 2-lipped, the uppermost lobe much wider than the 4 lower
ones; corolla light blue to purple, in ours slightly 2-lipped, the upper lip

straight or slightly arched, 2-lobed, the lower curved down, 3-lobed, its
middle lobe notched; stamens 4, the upper pair slightly longer than the lower.
(Gr. dracon, dragon, and cephale, head, from the shape of the corolla in 1
species.)

D. parviflorum Nutt. Annual or biennial; leaves petioled, the blades mostly
lance-elliptic to lance-ovate, sharply toothed, 2.5-8 cm long; inflorescence
dense and spike-like, often interrupted below, its bracts each with several
bristle-teeth; corolla light blue to violet. Mostly in sandy to gravelly soil,
usually dry, often in recent clearings, throughout the state except sw. of a
line from Big Stone to Chippewa, Nicollet, and Olmsted counties.

GLECHOMA ----- GROUND IVY*

Perennial herbs, the stems mostly creeping, sometimes erect; leaf
blades roundish to kidney-shaped, toothed; flowers about 3 per leaf axil, blue
to blue-violet; calyx 15-nerved, its 5 lobes about equal and sharp-pointed;
upper lip of corolla shallowly 2-lobed, the lower lip much larger, with a
large middle lobe and 2 short side ones; stamens 4. (From Gr. glechon,
pennyroyal.)

G. hederacea L. Creeping Charlie; Gill-over-the-ground. Leaves petioled,
the blades cordate at base, 1-3 cm long; corolla blue-violet. Naturalized from
Europe in mesic to moist woods and various disturbed habitats, recorded from
St. Louis to Kittson Co., s. to Clay, Kandiyohi, Brown, Mower, and
Houston counties.

HEDEOMA

Ours small aromatic annuals with many axillary whorls of small pale
bluish flowers; calyx tubular, becoming enlarged below, 2-lipped, 13-nerved;
corolla moderately 2-lipped, the upper lip erect, notched, the lower spreading, 3-lobed; fertile stamens 2. (From hedyosmon, an ancient name for
mint, from Gr. hedys, sweet, and osme, scent.)

H. hispidum Pursh. Mock Pennyroyal. Leaves lanceolate to linear, entire, 10-21 mm long, mostly sessile or nearly so. Open dry sandy and gravelly places, often in disturbed ground, Houston to Rock Co., n. to Chisago,
Kanabec, Clearwater, and Clay counties, and in the Duluth area.

LAMIUM ----- DEAD NETTLE

Annual, biennial, or perennial herbs; leaves mostly cordate to triangular, toothed to pinnately cut; flowers in whorls in the axils of leaves or
large bracts, white to red or purple; calyx 5-nerved, the 5 lobes equal or the
upper largest; upper lip of corolla entire or 2-lobed, concave; lower lip with
a large middle notched or cleft lobe and 2 short broad pointed lobes; stamens
4, the lower pair longer than the upper. (Old Latin name of a nettle-like
plant mentioned by Pliny.)

L. album L. Snowflake. Perennial; leaves all petioled, the blades triangular to ovate, truncate to cordate at base, coarsely serrate, 3-10 cm long;
corolla white. From Eurasia, occasional in disturbed ground, recorded only
from Ramsey Co.

LEONURUS ----- MOTHERWORT*

Erect herbs; leaves toothed to cleft; flowers white to pink or purplish, in whorls in the axils of leaves or large bracts, forming a long widely interrupted terminal spike; calyx 5-10- nerved, the lower 2 lobes often slightly larger or turned down, all 5 spine-tipped; upper lip of corolla erect, concave, entire, hairy, the lower lip 3-lobed; stamens 4, nearly equal. (Gr. leon, lion, oura, tail.)

L. cardiaca L. Perennial; leaves all petioled, the lower ones palmately lobed and veined, 5-10 cm long, the upper ones successively smaller, narrower, and more shallowly cut; corolla pale pink to pale purple. From Asia, established as a weed from Houston to Pipestone Co., n. to Washington, Morrison, Clay, and Kittson counties.

PRUNELLA ----- SELFHEAL*

Perennial herbs; flowers blue or purple to white, in dense terminal heads or spikes with large bracts, the bracts sharply distinguished from the leaves; calyx irregularly 10-nerved, 2-lipped, the upper lip broad, shallowly 3-toothed, the lower deeply cut into 2 narrow divisions; corolla 2-lipped, the upper lip concave, entire, the lower reflexed-spreading, 3-cleft; stamens 4, the lower pair longer than the upper, the filaments more or less 2-toothed at the apex, with the anther borne on the lower tooth. (Name of uncertain origin.)

P. vulgaris var. lanceolata (Bart.) Fern. Heal-all, Carpenter-weed. Leaves all petioled, the blades entire or with low irregular mostly blunt teeth, lanceolate or wider, 2-9 cm long; bracts in the spike each with 1 short tooth; corolla blue-violet (or seldom pink or white). Open woods, thickets, and disturbed ground, Cook to Kittson Co., s. to Clay, Stearns, Blue Earth, and Houston counties.

SCUTELLARIA ----- SKULLCAP

Non-aromatic herbs, ours perennial; flowers single in the leaf axils or in axillary or terminal racemes, blue or violet or seldom pink or white; calyx 2-lipped, the lips entire, the upper one with a prominent bump or transverse ridge on top near the center which often enlarges greatly in fruit; upper corolla lip usually concave, the lower convex or nearly flat; stamens 4, the anthers of the upper pair 4-sporangiate, those of the lower pair 2-sporangiate. (L. scutella, a dish, from the shape of the most prominent calyx outgrowths.)

S. parvula var. leonardi (Epling) Fern. Middle and upper stem leaves with petioles 0-1.5 mm long, the blades ovate to ovate-oblong, ovate-triangular, or roundish, entire (rarely the lowest with a few irregular teeth), 9-16 mm long; corolla bluish. Sandy to gravelly dry to moist hillsides and prairies or dry open woods, Houston to Rock Co., n. to Chisago, Morrison, Clay, and Polk counties.

SOLANACEAE ----- NIGHTSHADE FAMILY

Herbs, shrubs, or trees; leaves alternate (rarely opposite at or near the inflorescence); flowers bisexual, regular or seldom slightly zygomorphic, hypogynous; sepals, petals, and stamens nearly always 5 each; sepals fused; petals fused; stamens epipetalous, alternate with the corolla lobes (sometimes 4 or very rarely 2 when the corolla is zygomorphic); ovary of 2 fused carpels, the locules usually as many; placentation axile, the ovules usually many;style 1; fruit a berry or septicidal capsule.

A-Anthers separated, opening by lengthwise slits; calyx tube 2.5-7
    mm long; corolla 10-25 mm long, whitish or yellowish . . . PHYSALIS
A-Anthers close together or fused around the style, opening by
    apical pores; calyx tube 0.5-1.5 mm long; corolla 5-10 mm
    long, white or purple . . . . SOLANUM

PHYSALIS ----- GROUND CHERRY*

    Annuals or perennials, ours herbs; flowers single or few at the nodes, white, greenish-yellow, or yellow, often with a darker center; calyx small in flower, its tube enlarging during fruit formation, nearly or completely enclosing the berry at maturity, usually appearing inflated; corolla wide-spreading to bell-shaped or funnel-shaped, shallowly lobed to entire; stamens separate, the anthers opening lengthwise; berry many-seeded. (Gr. physalis, bladder, from the calyx in fruit.)

A-Corolla yellow or yellowish.
  B-Upper stem with down-curved hairs less than 1 mm long or if
    occasionally with long spreading hairs then the anthers 2.5
    (2-3) mm long; leaf base narrowly to broadly acute; anthers
    2-4 mm long; corollas 15-25 mm long . . . . P. virginiana
  B-Upper stem with spreading hairs, usually some of them 1-2
    mm long; leaf base broadly rounded to truncate or cordate;
    anthers usually 3-4.5 mm long; corollas 10-18 mm long
    . . . . P. heterophylla var. heterophylla
A-Corolla white or whitish, sometimes with a yellow center.
  C-Flowers usually 2-4 at the same node; corolla wide-spreading,
    22-50 mm wide; calyx greenish in fruit; native . . . . . . P. grandiflora
  C-Flowers single at the nodes; corolla funnel-shaped, 10-15 mm
    wide; calyx bright red in fruit; cultivated . . . . P. alkekengi

P. alkekengi L. Chinese Lantern Plant, Winter-cherry, Strawberry Ground Cherry; cultivated. Perennial; leaves ovate or ovate-rhombic; corolla whitish, moderately lobed; calyx in fruit much larger than the fruit inside. From Eurasia, rarely escaped.

P. grandiflora Hook. (Chamaesaracha grandiflora (Hook.) Fern.). Large White Ground Cherry. Annual; stem hairy and sticky; leaves ovate to lance-ovate; corolla white with a pale yellow center; calyx in fruit rather close-fitting around the berry. Sandy or rocky dry to moist shores, clearings, and open woods, Cook to Roseau Co., s. to Clearwater, Wadena, and Anoka counties.

P. heterophylla Nees, var. heterophylla. Clammy Ground Cherry. Perennial; stem hairs often sticky; leaves usually broadly to narrowly ovate or ovate-rhombic; calyx in fruit greenish to brownish, much larger than the fruit inside. Open woods, prairies, hillsides, and disturbed habitats, Houston to Rock Co., n. to Chisago, Morrison, and Clay counties, and in s. St. Louis Co.

P. virginiana Mill. (Including our plants formerly placed in P. lanceolata Michx.) Virginia Ground Cherry. Perennial; stem hairs seldom sticky; leaves ovate to linear-lanceolate; calyx in fruit greenish to brownish, much larger than the fruit inside. Prairies and open woods, often sandy, and disturbed habitats, Houston to Rock Co., n. to Washington, Crow Wing, Beltrami, and Kittson counties, and in the Duluth area. Plants nearly glabrous except for some stiff spreading hairs ca. 1 mm long at least on the flower buds and leaf margins, usually growing in sand, are P. v. var. hispida Waterfall; our other plants fall in P. v. var. virginiana.

SOLANUM

Herbs (ours), shrubs, or small trees; inflorescences in ours usually opposite the leaves or above the leaf axils; corolla wide-spreading to broadly bell-shaped, its tube short; anthers close together, or fused, around the style, on very short filaments, in ours opening by apical pores or slits; fruit a many-seeded berry. (The classical Latin name.)

A-Corolla mostly purple to violet, rarely white; plants climbing or
   twining; leaves with 0-2 basal lobes or compound with 3 leaflets
   . . . . S. dulcamara
A-Corolla white; plants not climbing; leaves pinnately 5-11-lobed
   . . . . S. triflorum

S. dulcamara L. Bittersweet, Nightshade. Perennial, often woody below; leaves simple and entire or with 2 basal lobes or leaflets; berry red. From Eurasia, escaped in thickets, clearings, open woods, and disturbed ground, recorded at very wide intervals from Houston to Chippewa to s. St. Louis Co.

S. triflorum Nutt. Annual herb; berry green. Disturbed ground, Hennepin and Clay counties.

SCROPHULARIACEAE ----- FIGWORT FAMILY

Herbs (ours), shrubs, or trees; leaves alternate, opposite, or rarely whorled; inflorescence various; flowers bisexual, hypogynous, usually zygomorphic, rarely nearly regular; sepals usually 4-5, often fused; petals usually 4-5, fused, the corolla usually 2-lipped; stamens epipetalous, alternate with the corolla lobes, usually 4 or 2, sometimes 4 fertile and 1 sterile, rarely 5; ovary 2-locular, of 2 carpels; placentation axile, the ovules usually many; style 1; fruit usually a capsule.

A-Corolla with a prominent basal spur protruding between the 2 lower
   calyx lobes.
  B-Flowers in well-defined racemes; stems glabrous or nearly so
   . . . . LINARIA
  B-Flowers single in the leaf axils; stems hairy . . . . . . CHAENORRHINUM
A-Corolla not spurred.
  C-At least the lower stem leaves opposite, sometimes those sub-
    tending the flowers alternate.
    D-Leaves pinnately cut 1/2-7/8 of the way to the midrib, the lobes
      toothed . . . . PEDICULARIS
    D-Leaves entire or less deeply cut.
      E-Stamens 2.
        F-Sepals 4; corolla wide-spreading, nearly regular, 4-lobed
        . . . . VERONICA

  F-Sepals 5; corolla tubular to bell-shaped, 2-lipped, 5-
    toothed . . . . GRATIOLA
  E-Stamens 4 or 4 fertile and 1 sterile.
    G-Flowers white to violet, 15-50 mm long . . . . PENSTEMON
    G-Flowers greenish to yellowish to brownish, 7-11 mm
     long . . . . SCROPHULARIA
 C-Stem leaves alternate or the leaves all basal.
  H-Leaves all or most of them lobed or cleft 1/2 or more of the
   way to the midrib.
   I-Lobes of leaves entire; bracts subtending the flowers deeply
    3-5-cleft . . . . CASTILLEJA
   I-Lobes of leaves toothed; floral bracts toothed . . . . . PEDICULARIS
  H-Leaves entire to serrate.
   J-Corolla greenish-white to yellowish, 3.5-7 mm long. . . BESSEYA
   J-Corolla white to purple or red, 8-50 mm long.
    K-Corolla wide-spreading; stamens 5 . . . . VERBASCUM
    K-Corolla tubular; stamens 4 . . . . DIGITALIS

BESSEYA*

  Perennial herb; leaves mostly basal, the stem leaves reduced and
alternate; flowers small, in a terminal spike-like raceme; calyx deeply 4-
lobed, nearly regular; corolla strongly 2-lipped, the upper lip acute, the
lower shallowly or irregularly 3-lobed; stamens 2 (very rarely 4); capsule
loculicidal, slightly flattened. (Named for Charles E. Bessey, American
botanist.)

  B. bullii (Eat.) Rydb. (Wulfenia bullii (Eat.) Barnh.). Basal leaf blades
ovate, rounded to cordate at base, toothed; corolla greenish-white to yellow
or somewhat pinkish, 3.5-7 mm long. Prairies and bluffs, Washington to
Scott to ne. Goodhue Co.

CASTILLEJA

  Annual to perennial herbs, green but parasitic on roots of other plants;
leaves alternate, often deeply cleft; flowers in terminal spikes, the subtending
bracts entire to cleft, often brightly colored; calyx tubular, 2-cleft vertically;
corolla greenish-yellow to whitish or reddish, the tube elongate, narrow, the
upper lip small, triangular-acuminate, laterally compressed, the lower lip
much shorter, appressed or turned down, 3-lobed; stamens 4, the anther
halves unequally attached; capsule loculicidal. (Name for D. Castillejo, Span-
ish botanist.)

A-Bracts subtending the flowers red to yellow, or white . . . . C. coccinea
A-Bracts green . . . . C. sessiliflora

  C. coccinea (L.) Spreng. Painted Cup, Indian Paint Brush. Annual or
biennial; leaves variable, usually 3-5-cleft but the basal and lower stem ones
often entire, the floral bracts 3-5-cleft; calyx lobes sometimes notched;
corolla greenish-yellow. Meadows, moist prairies, and damp sandy or
gravelly soil, Lake to Kittson Co., s. to Clay, Stearns, Waseca, and Houston
counties.

  C. sessiliflora Pursh. Downy Painted Cup. Perennial; leaves mostly 3-
5-cleft, the lower ones sometimes entire, the floral bracts 3-5-cleft; the 2

calyx lobes each again cleft; corolla yellowish or white. Mesic to dry prairies, Houston to Jackson and Pipestone counties, n. to Washington, Brown, Pope, Mahnomen, and Kittson counties.

CHAENORRHINUM*

Annual or perennial herbs; leaves alternate or the lowest opposite, entire; flowers small, single in the leaf axils; calyx deeply 5-parted; corolla with a prominent basal spur protruding between the 2 lower calyx lobes, strongly 2-lipped; stamens 4; each locule of the capsule opening by an irregular terminal pore. (Gr. chainein, to gape, and rhis, snout.)

C. minus (L.) Lange. Dwarf Snapdragon. Annual with sticky hairs; leaves linear to lanceolate, 1-2 cm long; corolla blue-purple with yellow or white on the throat, the spur 1.5-2 mm long. European, established in disturbed ground, recorded from Blue Earth, Renville, and s. St. Louis counties.

DIGITALIS ----- FOXGLOVE

Biennial or perennial herbs; leaves alternate; flowers in racemes, white, purple, or yellowish; sepals 5; corolla slightly zygomorphic, tubular to bell-shaped; stamens 4; capsule primarily septicidally dehiscent. (L., of or belonging to the finger, as the finger of a glove, from the corolla form.)

D. purpurea L. Common Foxglove; cultivated. Biennial, sometimes perennial; corolla purple to white, more or less spotted with dark purple within, 4-5 cm long. From w. Europe.

GRATIOLA ----- HEDGE-HYSSOP*

Annual to perennial herbs; leaves opposite, sessile; flowers small, yellow or white, single in the leaf axils, each usually with a pair of bractlets just below the calyx; sepals 5, usually unequal; corolla tubular to bell-shaped, 2-lipped; stamens 2, the connective usually much broadened, a pair of minute staminodia sometimes present; capsule septicidal or also loculicidal. (Diminutive of L. gratia, grace or favor, from supposed therapeutic properties.)

G. neglecta Torr. Annual; leaves lanceolate to oblanceolate, 2-5.5 cm long; corolla 8-12 mm long, the lobes whitish, the tube yellowish. Wet soil throughout most of the state, unrecorded nw. of a line through St. Louis and Clay counties and from many other counties.

LINARIA ----- TOADFLAX

Annual to usually perennial herbs, usually glabrous; leaves entire, those of the stem mostly alternate, the lower ones and those on basal offshoots often opposite or whorled; flowers yellow, blue, or white, in terminal racemes or spikes; sepals 5; corolla with a prominent spur protruding between the 2 lower sepals, 2-lipped, the upper lip 2-lobed, the lower 3-lobed; stamens 4; each locule of the capsule opening irregularly at the top. (Name from Linum, the flax plant, from similarity of foliage.)

A-Corolla yellow to cream, 20-30 mm long including the spur . . L. vulgaris
A-Corolla blue-violet to white, 7-14 mm long. . . . . L. canadensis

L. canadensis (L.) Dumont. Old-field Toadflax. Annual or winter-annual, the stems glabrous or nearly so; leaves linear to oblong. Mostly in sandy soil, often as a weed, recorded from Houston, Washington, Hennepin, and Anoka counties.

L. vulgaris Hill. Butter-and-eggs. Perennials from spreading roots; stems glabrous or nearly so; leaves linear to lance-linear. From Europe, established as a weed in disturbed ground throughout the state.

PEDICULARIS ----- LOUSEWORT, WOOD BETONY

Annual to usually perennial herbs; leaves opposite or alternate, sharply toothed to bipinnatifid; flowers in terminal spikes or racemes, yellow to red or purple; calyx entire or lobed, usually longer on the upper side; corolla strongly 2-lipped, the upper lip arching, often laterally compressed, the lower lip 3-lobed with 2 lengthwise ridges; stamens 4; capsule compressed, loculicidal. (L. pediculus, louse, from the early belief that cattle became infested with lice from feeding where the plants were abundant.)

P. canadensis L. Perennial; stem leaves mostly alternate, sometimes opposite; leaves cut 1/2-7/8 of the way to the midrib, the lobes toothed; floral bracts toothed; flowers in spikes or spike-like racemes, yellow to red-purple. Woods and damp prairies, Houston to Rock Co., n. to Chisago, s. Itasca, s. Beltrami, and Kittson counties.

PENSTEMON ----- BEARD-TONGUE*

Perennial herbs (ours) or shrubs; leaves entire or toothed, the stem ones opposite (rarely whorled or the upper alternate); flowers showy, in raceme-like or panicle-like clusters, white to blue-violet or red-violet; calyx 5-lobed; corolla tubular or trumpet-shaped, 2-lipped; fertile stamens 4, a 5th stamen antherless, about as long as the others, usually yellow-bearded toward the tip; fruit a septicidal capsule. (Gr. pente, five, and stemon, in the sense of stamen, from the large staminode.)

A-Upper stem leaves ovate to roundish; corolla 35-50 mm long
. . . . P. grandiflorus
A-Upper stem leaves lance-oblong to linear; corolla 13-25 mm long.
  B-Corolla pale violet, its throat 2-ridged within at the lower lip,
     conspicuously hairy over and near the ridges with plain hairs,
     glabrous or nearly so elsewhere within . . . . P. gracilis
  B-Corolla white, sometimes tinged with pale pink-violet, not 2-
     ridged within, the throat and lobes minutely puberulent within
     with swollen-tipped hairs, a few longer plain hairs also present
     . . . . P. albidus

P. albidus Nutt. White-flowered Beard-tongue. Leaves glabrous to puberulent, entire or with a few small teeth; corolla lobes spreading. Dry sandy or gravelly prairies, Pipestone to Polk Co., e. to Chippewa and Otter Tail counties.

P. gracilis Nutt. Slender Beard-tongue. Leaves glabrous to pubescent, usually with small teeth; corolla lobes mostly directed forward. Prairies, dry open woods, and rock crevices, throughout the state except for Cook and Lake counties, the s. tier of counties e. of Rock Co., and a few other counties.

P. grandiflorus Nutt. Large-flowered or Shell-leaf Beard-tongue. Plants glabrous throughout; leaves entire; corolla pale purple. Sandy prairies, Rock to Polk Co., e. to Goodhue, Washington, Mille Lacs, Morrison, and Otter Tail counties, and in s. St. Louis Co.

SCROPHULARIA ----- FIGWORT

Perennial herbs with 4-angled stems; leaves mostly opposite, sharply toothed; flowers small, greenish to yellowish to brownish, in terminal panicle-like inflorescences; calyx regular, 5-lobed; corolla 2-lipped, the upper lip 2-lobed, directed forward, the lower lip with its 2 lateral lobes directed forward, the middle one turned down; stamens 4; staminode present; capsule septicidal. (Once thought to be a remedy for scrofula.)

S. lanceolata Pursh. Plants to 2 m high; leaf blades ovate to lance-ovate; corolla 7-11 mm long. Openings in woods, thickets, and roadsides, throughout the state.

VERBASCUM ----- MULLEIN

Biennial herbs, producing basal leaves the first year and an erect flowering stem the next; leaves alternate, entire or toothed; flowers in elongate often spike-like racemes, or in panicles, yellow, white, purple, or red; calyx regular, 5-lobed; corolla 5-lobed, wide-spreading or saucer-shaped, slightly zygomorphic; stamens 5; fruit a septicidal capsule. (The ancient L. name.)

V. phoeniceum L. Purple Mullein; cultivated. Plants to 1 1/2 m high; basal leaf blades ovate to oblong-rhombic, pubescent beneath; corolla 8-15 mm long, purple, red, or white. From Eurasia.

VERONICA ----- SPEEDWELL

Annual to perennial herbs; leaves opposite at least below, those subtending the flowers often alternate or irregularly arranged; flowers small, white to blue, rarely purple or pink, axillary or in lateral or terminal racemes; calyx in ours deeply 4-parted; corolla wide-spreading, nearly regular, 4-lobed (from the fusion of the upper 2 lobes), the tube usually very short; stamens 2; capsule often flattened, loculicidal and sometimes also septicidal, notched at the apex. (Named for St. Veronica.)

A-Flowers in axillary racemes, the foliage leaves all opposite.
  B-Leaves all short-petioled, lanceolate to lance-ovate ... V. americana
  B-Leaves sessile, lanceolate to linear.
    C-Ovary and fruit constricted lengthwise into 2 lobes, uncompressed, unnotched or slightly notched at the apex, the fruit shorter than to slightly exceeding the sepals; petals 1-1.5 times as long as the

    sepals; pedicels and rachis of inflorescence straight; leaves
    2.8-5.5 times as long as wide . . . . **V. comosa**
C-Ovary 2-lined or -creased lengthwise, not lobed, slightly com-
    pressed, the fruit strongly compressed, strongly notched at
    the apex, well exceeding the sepals; petals 1.5-2.2 times as
    long as the sepals; pedicels and rachis delicate and often zizag
    or curved; leaves 4-25 times as long as wide . . . . . . **V. scutellata**
A-Flowers single in the leaf axils or in a terminal raceme, the upper
    leaves or bracts usually alternate.
    D-Pedicels 8-15 mm long in flower, 15-35 mm long in fruit. . **V. persica**
    D-Pedicels 0-2 mm long in flower, 1-4 mm long in fruit.
      E-Principal leaf blades 3-7 times as long as wide . . . . . . **V. peregrina**
      E-Principal leaf blades 1-2 times as long as wide.
        F-Leaves, bracts, and sepals glabrous or nearly so; styles
        1.5-2.3 mm long . . . . **V. serpyllifolia**
        F-Leaves, bracts, and sepals hairy; styles 0.5-0.8 mm long
        . . . . **V. arvensis**

V. americana (Raf.) Schw. American Brooklime. Glabrous perennial
from a rhizome; leaves serrate to nearly entire, 1.5-8 cm long; corolla blue-
violet to lilac. Streambanks and swamps, Cook to Lake of the Woods Co., s.
to Clearwater, Pope, Kandiyohi, Rice, and Houston counties.

V. arvensis L. Corn Speedwell. Annual; leaves ovate to broadly elliptic,
toothed, 5-15 mm long; corolla blue-violet. From Eurasia, established
mostly in disturbed ground, recorded from Houston and Stearns counties.

V. comosa Richter (**V. catenata** Pennell). Water Speedwell. Perennial
from a rhizome, pubescent with globular-tipped hairs to sometimes glabrous;
leaves toothed to nearly entire, 1.5-10 cm long; sepals in flower 1.7-3.1
mm long; corolla white to pink or pale bluish. Stream edges, marshes, and
other wet places, Fillmore to Rock Co., n. to Wabasha, Morrison, Cass,
Koochiching, and Kittson counties, and at Knife River on the n. shore of
Lake Superior.

V. peregrina L. Neckweed, Purslane Speedwell. Annual; main leaves
oblong to linear-oblong to oblanceolate, toothed to entire, 5-35 mm long;
corolla whitish. Damp open places, often as a weed, throughout the state.
Glabrous plants fall in **V. p.** var. **peregrina;** those with the stem and usually
the sepals and fruits pubescent with short swollen-tipped hairs are in **V. p.**
var. **xalapensis** (HBK) St. John & Warren.

V. persica Poir. Bird's-eye. Annual; principal leaf blades roundish to
ovate, toothed, 1-2 cm long; corolla blue. From sw. Asia, established in
disturbed ground, recorded from Winona, Wabasha, and St. Louis counties.

V. scutellata L. Marsh Speedwell. Perennial from a rhizome, glabrous
or rarely with globule-tipped hairs; leaves entire or with a few teeth, 2-8 cm
long; sepals in flower 1.2-2 mm long; corolla bluish. Swamps, bogs, and
shores, Cook to Kittson Co., s. to Clay, Benton, and Chisago counties, and
in Winona and Mower counties.

V. serpyllifolia L. Thyme-leaved Speedwell. Perennial from a rhizome;
leaves ovate or broadly elliptic or oblong, slightly toothed or entire, 10-25
mm long; corolla whitish or pale blue. From Europe, established mostly in
damp disturbed ground, recorded from Lake to Carlton Co. and in Hennepin
and Houston counties.

OROBANCHACEAE ----- BROOM-RAPE FAMILY

Annual or perennial somewhat fleshy herbs, without chlorophyll or appearing so, parasitic on the roots of various plants; leaves alternate, reduced to scales; flowers mostly bisexual, hypogynous, zygomorphic; calyx usually 2-5-lobed; corolla 4-5-lobed, usually 2-lipped; stamens 4, epipetalous; ovary 1-locular with 2 or apparently 4 parietal placentas; ovules many; style 1, elongate; stigma usually 2-4-lobed; fruit a loculicidal capsule, usually with 2 divisions.

OROBANCHE ----- BROOM-RAPE

Plants brownish, purplish, or whitish; flowers blue, purple, or yellowish, in racemes or spikes or single, bisexual; calyx bell-shaped, variously lobed; corolla tubular, the tube usually down-curved, much longer than the lobes; stamens about as long as the corolla tube; placentas 4. (Gr. orobos, vetch, and anchein, to strangle.)

O. uniflora L. One-flowered Cancer Root. Flowers on pedicels 5-20 cm long, 1-3 from a stem, the true stem all or mostly underground; corolla creamy white to violet. Parasitic on various plants; mesic to moist woods, thickets and bluffs, Houston, Fillmore, Winona, Ramsey, and Hennepin counties.

PLANTAGINACEAE ----- PLANTAIN FAMILY

Herbs (ours) or rarely subshrubs; leaves mostly all basal or nearly so, the stem leaves when present usually alternate (rarely opposite); flowers small, in heads, spikes, or spike-like racemes, usually bisexual, hypogynous, regular or the calyx slightly zygomorphic; sepals mostly 4, free; petals mostly 4, fused; stamens 4 (rarely 1 or 2), epipetalous, alternate with the corolla lobes; ovary 2- (1-4-) locular, the ovules 1-many per locule, usually axile; style 1; fruit a circumscissile capsule or a bony nut.

PLANTAGO ----- PLANTAIN

Annuals to perennials, ours with only basal leaves; flowers sessile or subsessile, bisexual or sometimes polygamodioecious; sepals free, mostly 4, rarely 3 through the fusion of 2; corolla 4-lobed, whitish to pale straw-color or seldom brownish, persistent on the fruit, the fruit a 2-locular circumscissile capsule. (The L. name, from planta, footprint.)

A-Spike densely gray-woolly from long hairs on bracts and sepals
. . . . P. patagonica
A-Spike not woolly, the bracts and sepals glabrous or inconspicuously
    fringed.
    B-Leaves narrowly linear . . . . P. elongata
    B-Leaves narrowly elliptic or lance-elliptic to elliptic.
      C-Spikes densely flowered, the axis hidden; sepals 3 . . . P. lanceolata
      C-Spikes loosely flowered, the axis exposed at least in the lower
        half; sepals 4 . . . . P. eriopoda

P. elongata Pursh. Annual; leaves 2-5 cm long; spike loosely flowered, the axis exposed at least in the lower half. Wet places, often on rocks, Rock and Pipestone counties.

<u>P. eriopoda</u> Torr. Perennial; leaves 5-15 cm long. Damp to wet grass-lands, often alkaline, Kittson to Mahnomen, Wilkin and Stevens counties.

<u>P. lanceolata</u> L. Ribgrass, English Plantain. Perennial, but flowering the first year; leaves 10-40 cm long. From Eurasia, widely established in lawns and disturbed ground, recorded from Houston, Winona, Ramsey, Hennepin, and Clearwater counties.

<u>P. patagonica</u> Jacq. (<u>P. purshii</u> R. & S.). Annual; leaves linear to very narrowly elliptic, 3-12 cm long; spikes dense. Dry sandy or gravelly places and disturbed ground, Houston to Rock Co., n. to Washington, Morrison, Becker, and Clay counties, and in s. St. Louis Co. and near Lake Superior in Cook Co.

RUBIACEAE -----MADDER FAMILY

Herbs or more commonly shrubs or trees; leaves opposite, simple, entire or rarely toothed; opposing stipules of the leaf pair often united, some-times the united stipules or the individual stipules as large as the true leaf blades, the "leaves" thus whorled; flowers bisexual, mostly epigynous, mostly regular; sepals 4-5, free or fused; petals usually 4-5, fused; stamens epipeta-lous, as many as the corolla lobes (rarely fewer) and alternate with them; ovary mostly 2-locular; ovules usually many per locule, usually axile or basal; style 1, often 2-branched, or rarely styles 2; fruit various.

A-Leaves in whorls of 4 or more . . . . GALIUM
A-Leaves opposite.
  B-Stems erect; flowers several to many, separate . . . . . . HOUSTONIA
  B-Stems creeping; flowers in twos, their ovaries united . . . MITCHELLA

GALIUM ----- BEDSTRAW, CLEAVERS

Annual or perennial herbs; stems slender, 4-angled; leaves whorled; flowers mostly small, in cymes, 3-4-merous; calyx teeth none or vestigial; corolla in Minnesota species greenish-white to white, or yellow in one late-blooming species; corolla lobes wide-spreading; ovary 2-locular with 1 ovule per locule; styles 2; fruit a pair of globular, dry or fleshy, indehiscent divi-sions, sometimes bristly, separating when ripe. (From the Gr. <u>gala</u>, milk, which is curdled by some species.) The following treatment draws largely from that of Mr. John Seaholm in the Proc. Minn. Acad. Sci. 31: 99-104, 1964.

A-Ovaries and fruits bristly.
  B-At least the upper leaves with 3 main veins, pointed but not bristle-tipped, lanceolate, mostly in whorls of 4; bristles of fruit not hooked . . . . G. <u>boreale</u> var. <u>boreale</u>
  B-Leaves with 1 main vein, bristle-tipped, not lanceolate, mostly in whorls of 5-8; bristles of fruit hooked.
    C-Leaves narrowly oblanceolate, with back-turned bristles on the midveins beneath and on the margins, mostly in whorls of 8 (often 5-7); ribs of the stem with down-turned bristles along the internodes . . . . G. <u>aparine</u>
    C-Leaves elliptic-lanceolate (rarely to oblanceolate), with back-turned bristles only on the midveins beneath, the marginal bristles not turned back; leaves mostly in whorls of 6; ribs of the stem usually without bristles except for spreading

ones immediately above the nodes and sometimes on the upper
internodes . . . . G. triflorum
A-Ovaries and fruits glabrous.
    D-Flowers in compact terminal many-flowered panicles; plants erect
      with little branching of the main stem below the inflorescence
      . . . . G. boreale var. hyssopifolium
    D-Flowers single or in small cymes; plants matted, reclining, or
      weakly ascending.
      E-Corollas with 3 (rarely 4) obtuse lobes, the lobes about as long
        as wide . . . . G. tinctorium
      E-Corollas with 4 (rarely 3) acute lobes, the lobes obviously longer
        than wide.
        F-Leaves with bristles along the midvein beneath, narrowly
          elliptic, 1-8 mm wide, not angled downward, mostly in
          whorls of 5 or 6; cymes terminal on the lateral branches,
          the older ones rarely overtopped by younger ones . . . G. obtusum
        F-Leaves usually glabrous on the midveins beneath (rarely
          with a few bristles), narrowly oblanceolate, 1-3 mm wide,
          generally soon angled downward, mostly in whorls of 4;
          older cymes usually overtopped by younger ones or by new
          shoots . . . . G. labradoricum

G. aparine L. Cleavers, Goosegrass. Annual with weak stems; flowers
in 1-flowered cymes; corolla 4-lobed; bristles of fruit radiating outward.
Damp ground, usually in shade, Houston to Rock Co., n. to Chisago, Itasca,
Otter Tail, and Norman counties.

G. boreale L. Northern Bedstraw. Perennial; stems erect; leaves mostly
in whorls of 4, at least the upper ones with 3 main veins; flowers in compact
terminal panicles of cymes; corolla 4-lobed; bristles of fruit (when present)
more or less appressed. Open or lightly shaded mesic to damp ground,
throughout the state. Forms with bristly fruits are G. b. var. boreale; those
with glabrous fruits and sometimes with white bristles at the stem nodes have
been called G. b. var. hyssopifolium (Hoffm.) DC.

G. labradoricum Wieg. Perennial; leaves more or less inrolled below.
Bogs, swamps, and rarely in damp woods, St. Louis to Pennington Co., s.
to Otter Tail, Pope, Meeker, and Hennepin counties, and in Goodhue and
Waseca counties.

G. obtusum Bigel. Perennial; leaves more or less inrolled below. Wet
places and moist shaded soil, Pipestone to Nobles and Freeborn counties, n.
to Brown and Hennepin counties, and in St. Louis and Cook counties.

G. tinctorium L. (G. trifidum var. tinctorium (L.) T. & G.). Perennial;
leaves mostly in whorls of 5 or 6, not inrolled below, the midvein below with
bristles. Swamps and damp places, Cook to Kittson Co., s. to Clay, Stearns,
Carver, Blue Earth, and Wabasha counties. Forms with 3-flowered cymes
are G. t. var. tinctorium; those in which the flowers are usually borne singly
on separate axillary stalks have been named G. t. var. subbiflorum (Wieg.)
Fern.

G. triflorum Michx. Sweet-scented Bedstraw. Perennial with prostrate
or scrambling stems; flowers in 3-flowered cymes; corolla 4-lobed; bristles
of fruit radiating outward. Mesic to damp woods and thickets, throughout
most of the state, not recorded from several western counties nor s. of a
line from Lincoln to Blue Earth, Winona, and Houston counties.

HOUSTONIA*

Annual or perennial herbs; leaves opposite; flowers blue, purple, or nearly white, single and terminal or in terminal cymes, 4-merous; corolla funnel-shaped or abruptly wide-spreading above, the lobes often hairy within; ovary 1/2 or more inferior; style 1, stigmas 2; fruit a capsule, loculicidally dehiscent across the top; seeds 4-20 in each of the 2 locules. (Named for W. Houston, English botanist.)

H. longifolia Gaertn. Perennial with 1-several stems; leaves sessile, broadly linear to narrowly oblong, 10-30 mm long; flowers many, purplish to white. Open or lightly shaded sandy or rocky places, usually dry, Lake to Kittson Co., s. to Polk, Becker, Morrison, e. Stearns, Hennepin, Olmsted, and Houston counties, and along and near the Minnesota R. Valley, and in Pipestone Co.

MITCHELLA*

Creeping evergreen herbs; leaves opposite; flowers white, often tinged with purple, mostly 4-merous (rarely 3-6-merous), in axillary or terminal pairs, the ovaries of the two flowers united; corolla funnel-shaped, its lobes hairy on the inner side; ovary 4-locular, with 1 erect ovule per locule; style 1, stigmas 4; fruit a scarlet or rarely whitish twin berry-like drupe with 8 seed-like nutlets. (Named for J. Mitchell, American botanist.)

M. repens L. Partridge-berry. Stems rooting at the nodes, forming mats; leaf blades round-ovate, 1-2 cm long; flowers mostly terminal, fragrant. Dry to mesic woods, often on knolls, mostly infrequent, e. Cook Co., n. St. Louis Co., Pine and s. Aitkin to Anoka and Chisago counties, and in Houston Co.

CAPRIFOLIACEAE ----- HONEYSUCKLE FAMILY

Shrubs, vines, or seldom herbs; leaves opposite, mostly without stipules, usually simple, rarely pinnately compound; flowers mostly bisexual, regular or zygomorphic, epigynous; calyx 5-lobed or -toothed, often very small; petals typically 5, fused at least at base, the corolla wide-spreading to tubular; stamens epipetalous, usually as many as the corolla lobes and alternate with them (rarely 1 fewer than the lobes); ovary 3/4 to fully inferior, 1-5-locular, with 1 (many) ovules per locule, typically axile; style 1; fruit a capsule, berry, or drupe.

A-Herbs or creeping very slightly woody plants.
  B-Plants creeping; flowers in pairs on long stalks . . . . LINNAEA
  B-Plants erect; flowers sessile in the leaf axils . . . . TRIOSTEUM
A-Shrubs, erect or climbing.
  C-Leaves pinnately compound . . . . SAMBUCUS
  C-Leaves simple.
    D-Leaves entire to slightly wavy-edged . . . . LONICERA
    D-Leaves toothed to lobed.
      E-Flowers light yellow, often turning reddish in age . . . . DIERVILLA
      E-Flowers whitish to pink.
        F-Flowers many in compound cymes; corolla tube 1-10 mm
          long . . . . VIBURNUM
        F-Flowers in clusters of 1-4; corolla tube 15-25 mm long
          . . . . WEIGELA

DIERVILLA ----- BUSH-HONEYSUCKLE*

Low shrubs; leaves serrate; flowers yellow or greenish-yellow, in terminal or subterminal cymes; corolla funnel-shaped, nearly regular, 5-lobed; stamens 5; hypanthium prolonged above the ovary; ovary 2-locular; style elongate; fruit a slender pointed septicidal capsule. (Named for N. Dierville, a French surgeon.)

D. lonicera Mill. To 12 dm high; leaf blades oblong-lanceolate to oblong-ovate, 8-15 cm long, acuminate, glabrous to hairy beneath, usually fringed with hairs on the edges; flowers 3-7 together, light yellow, often turning reddish in age. Mesic to dry open woods, clearings, and rocky places, Cook to e. Roseau Co., s. to e. Becker, Morrison, Mille Lacs, e. Hennepin, e. Rice, Mower, and Houston counties, and in Pope Co.

LINNAEA ----- TWINFLOWER*

Evergreen creepers, the stems slightly woody, with ascending branchlets each typically with a 2-flowered stalk, the flowers nodding, fragrant; corolla white, tinged and striped with pink, funnel-shaped to bell-shaped, regular or nearly so, 5-lobed; stamens 4; ovary 3-locular with 1 fertile ovule; fruit dry, 1-seeded. (Named for Carolus Linnaeus.)

L. borealis var. americana (Forbes) Rehd. Leaf blades roundish to elliptic, crenate, 1-2 cm long; corolla 8-15 mm long, hairy inside. Cool moist to dry woods and bogs, Cook to Roseau Co., s. to Becker, Morrison, Anoka, e. Hennepin, and Chisago counties.

LONICERA ----- HONEYSUCKLE*

Erect shrubs or twining or trailing vines; leaves entire to slightly wavy-edged (ours) or rarely toothed or lobed; flowers in terminal clusters or in pairs on axillary stalks, each pair usually subtended by 2 bracts and 4 bractlets (2 bractlets per flower), the ovaries of the pair sometimes united; calyx teeth very short; corolla tubular to funnel-shaped, 5-lobed, often 2-lipped, the tube often pouched or short-spurred at base; stamens 5; ovary 2-3-locular with several ovules per locule; style elongate; fruit a few-seeded berry. (Named for A. Lonitzer, German botanist.)

A-Uppermost leaves of flowering shoots fused together around the stem; flowers terminal, in dense clusters or interrupted spikes; usually vines.
  B-Leaves fringed with hairs on the edges, all but the upper ones pubescent above . . . . L. hirsuta
  B-Leaves not fringed with hairs, all glabrous above.
    C-Leaves of the uppermost fused pair acute or drawn into a small point at the apex, green above, the pair 1.2-3 times as long as wide; flowers in 1-3 whorls, these usually crowded . . . . L. dioica
    C-Leaves of the uppermost fused pair rounded or notched at the apex, somewhat whitened above, the pair 1-1.2 (-1.4) times as long as wide; flowers in 2-6 whorls . . . . L. prolifera
A-All leaves separate; flowers in pairs on axillary stalks; shrubs.
  D-Branchlets of preceding years filled with white pith; ovaries of the flower pair separate to fully fused but if completely separate then the corolla cleft for only 1/4-1/3 of its length and the style glabrous; natives.

E-Peduncles 1-7 mm long . . . . L. villosa
E-Peduncles 15-40 mm long.
    F-Young twigs glabrous; leaves mostly widest below the middle;
        outside of corolla and the style glabrous . . . . . . L. canadensis
    F-Young twigs pubescent; leaves mostly widest at or above the
        middle; outside of corolla and style hairy . . . . . . L. oblongifolia
D-Branchlets of preceding years hollow in the internodes, the pith
    brown; ovaries completely separate; corolla cleft for more than
    1/2 its length; styles hairy; cultivated or escaped.
    G-Corolla tube glabrous on the outside . . . . L. tatarica
    G-Corolla tube pubescent on the outside.
        H-Filaments glabrous, or pubescent to 1/3 of the way up from
        the base; lobes of upper lip of corolla separate to the base
        of the lip . . . . L. morrowi
        H-Filaments pubescent 1/3 to all the way up; lobes of upper
        lip cut less than 1/2 way to the base . . . . L. xylosteum

L. canadensis Marsh. Fly Honeysuckle. Leaves triangular-ovate to
oblong, the edges irregularly fringed with hairs; bractlets none or up to 1/3
as long as the ovary, the ovaries separate; corolla yellowish, short-spurred
at base, cleft for 1/4-1/3 of its length; fruit red. Cool mesic to moist woods,
Cook to e. Marshall Co., s. to Clearwater, Wadena, Morrison, and
Carlton counties, and in Isanti Co.

L. dioica L. Wild Honeysuckle. Lower leaves ovate to obovate or oblong;
corolla pale yellow to maroon, 15-25 mm long; anthers 2.5-4.5 mm long; seeds
3-3.5 mm long. Mesic open woods and thickets and on bluffs, rocky banks,
grasslands, and sometimes in swamps.

A-Leaves pubescent beneath; corolla tube hairy and often with minute
    globules; style hairy; throughout the state except for the extreme
    sw. corner . . . . L. d. var. glaucescens (Rydb.) Butters.
A-Leaves glabrous beneath; corolla tube and style glabrous or nearly
    so; Houston to Mower, Waseca, Carver, and Anoka counties . L. d. var. dioica.

L. hirsuta Eat. Hairy Honeysuckle. Leaves green, the uppermost fused
ones each usually acuminate at the apex, the lower broadly elliptic to rhombic-
ovate; corolla yellow to orange, 20-25 mm long. Mesic to moist woods and
thickets, and in rocky places and swamps, Cook to Koochiching Co., w. and s.
to Clearwater, Otter Tail, Morrison, s. Mille Lacs, and Pine counties.

L. morrowi Gray. Cultivated. Young twigs pubescent; leaves ovate-oblong,
elliptic, or obovate-oblong, pubescent beneath, glabrous to pubescent above;
peduncles 5-15 mm long; bractlets pubescent; corolla white, turning yellow
in age; fruit red. From Japan. See under L. tatarica.

L. oblongifolia (Goldie) Hook. Swamp Fly Honeysuckle. Leaves ovate-
lanceolate to oblong or elliptic to oblanceolate, the edges pubescent but not
fringed; bracts and bractlets minute or none; ovaries fused for 1/3 to all of
their length; corolla light yellow, often streaked with purple, pouched on one
side at base, cleft for ca. 2/3 of its length; fruit red to orange-yellow. Bogs,
swamps, and wet woods, Cook to Kittson Co., s. to Norman, n. Cass, Isanti,
and Chisago counties.

L. prolifera (Kirchn.) Rehd. Grape Honeysuckle. Lower leaves obovate
to broadly elliptic or nearly round; corolla pale yellow, 20-30 mm long;
anthers 3.5-5 mm long; seeds 4.5-5 mm long. Moist woods and ravines
and on bluffs and rocky banks, Houston and Fillmore counties to Rice and
Goodhue counties.

L. tatarica L. Tartarian Honeysuckle; cultivated. Young twigs glabrous; leaves ovate to oblong, glabrous above, glabrous to pubescent beneath; peduncles 10-20 mm long; bractlets glabrous; corolla pink to white, the outer lobes of its upper lip cut more than 1/2 way to the base; fruit red or rarely yellow. From Eurasia, often escaped, so recorded at wide intervals from Houston to Pipestone, Kittson, and s. St. Louis counties. Some forms of the species are currently known incorrectly in the local trade as L. korolkowi Stapf. A common hybrid between L. tatarica and L. morrowi is L. X bella Zabel, which combines the pubescent twigs and yellowing corolla of L. morrowi with the glabrous corolla and longer peduncles of L. tatarica.

L. villosa (Michx.) R. & S. Mountain Fly Honeysuckle. Young twigs pubescent or rarely glabrous; leaves elliptic to oblong or obovate, more or less hairy at least beneath; bractlets all fused together around the ovaries, becoming fused to them, the ovaries separate from each other or becoming lightly adherent, concealed within the fused bracts and thus appearing fully fused, the whole ripening together; corolla pale yellow, pouched on one side at base, cleft for about 1/2 its length or a little less, glabrous to pubescent outside; style glabrous; fruit bluish-black. Our plants are usually placed in L. v. var. solonis (Eat.) Fern. Mostly in bogs, swamps, and wet woods, Cook to Lake of the Woods Co., s. to Clearwater, Morrison, Anoka, and Pine counties.

L. xylosteum L. European Fly Honeysuckle; cultivated. Young twigs glabrous or pubescent; leaves ovate to obovate, glabrous to pubescent above, pubescent below; peduncles 10-20 mm long; bractlets pubescent; corolla whitish or yellowish-white, often reddish-tinged; fruit dark red or sometimes yellow. From Eurasia. The cv. Clavey's Dwarf is apparently a low compact form of this species.

SAMBUCUS ----- ELDER

Shrubs (ours), small trees, or seldom large herbs; branchlets weak, the pith large; leaves pinnately compound, the leaflets serrate; flowers numerous, small, white to rarely pink, 5- (3-4-) merous, in terminal rounded to flat-topped compound cymes; calyx minute or none; corolla regular, wide-spreading to saucer-shaped; stamens as many as the corolla lobes; style very short; ovary 3- (-5-) locular with 1 ovule per locule; fruit a berry-like drupe with as many small seed-like stones as locules. (The ancient Latin name.)

S. pubens Michx. Red-berried Elder. Pith mostly orange-tan; leaflets 5-7, ovate-lanceolate or narrower; flowers yellowish-white, in rounded to pyramidal clusters; fruit red or rarely white or yellow. Mesic to moist woods and openings, often rocky, Cook to Lake of the Woods Co., s. to Becker, Chippewa, Blue Earth, Freeborn, and Houston counties.

TRIOSTEUM ----- FEVERWORT, HORSE GENTIAN[*]

Erect perennial herbs; leaves of each pair fused together at the base or joined by a ridge around the stem; flowers greenish-yellow to dull red or purplish, single or in small clusters in the leaf axils; sepals linear-lanceolate; corolla narrowly bell-shaped, pouched at the base on one side, unequally 5-lobed; stamens 5; ovary 3- (-5-) locular with 1 ovule per locule; fruit a few-stoned greenish, yellow, or red rather dry berry-like drupe. (From Gr. triosteospermum, referring to the 3 bony stones in the fruit.)

T. perfoliatum L. Tinker's Weed, Wild Coffee. Leaves obovate to ovate-oblong or somewhat 4-angled, broadly winged to the base and sometimes widened there, 10-22 cm long, usually hairy beneath; flowers 1-4 per axil; sepals 10-18 mm long; corolla 8-17 mm long. Mesic to moist open woods, clearings, or bluffs, Houston to Blue Earth Co., n. to Chisago, Kanabec, s. Cass, Mahnomen, Morrison, e. Stearns, and Carver counties.

A-Leaves (at least 3-5 middle pairs) fused at base around the stem, the bases of the larger ones 3-9 cm wide; hairs of the stem mostly less than 0.5 mm long; calyx lobes in flower 0.9-2 mm wide; corolla purplish to greenish-yellow, about equalling the stamens, its mouth 5-6 (-7) mm wide; style usually exserted 1.5-3 mm T. p. var. perfoliatum.
A-Leaves separate (rarely 1-3 pairs with fused bases 1-2 cm wide); hairs of the stem mostly more than 0.5 mm long; calyx lobes in flower 1.5-2.8 mm wide; corolla generally brighter and more purple, much exceeding the stamens, its mouth 7-9 mm wide and somewhat 2-lipped; style about equalling the corolla . . . .
. . T. p. var. aurantiacum (Bickn.) Wieg. (T. aurantiacum Bickn.).

VIBURNUM*

Shrubs or small trees; leaves toothed to lobed (ours) or entire, sometimes with stipules; flowers many in compound cymes, mostly small and white, rarely pink, the marginal ones of the cluster sometimes much larger than the others; corolla regular or sometimes the marginal ones zygomorphic, wide-spreading to broadly bell-shaped, 5-lobed; stamens 5; style none, the 3 stigmas sessile on a short projection on top the ovary; ovary 3-locular but only 1 locule contains an ovule; fruit a 1-seeded drupe. (The ancient Latin name.)

A-Some or all the leaves palmately 3-lobed, most or all of them palmately 3-5-veined.
   B-Marginal flowers of the cluster or all the flowers enlarged, their corollas 10-30 mm wide . . . . V. opulus
   B-Flowers all small, their corollas 4-7 mm wide . . . . V. edule
A-Leaves all unlobed, usually pinnately veined, sometimes 3-veined from the base.
   C-Upper leaf surfaces at flowering time glabrous or pubescent mostly with unbranched single hairs; stalk and branches of the inflorescence glabrous or pubescent with branched or unbranched hairs; native or cultivated.
      D-Leaf teeth 23-50 per side, 5-11 per cm; stalk of inflorescence 0-4 mm long; native . . . . V. lentago
      D-Leaf teeth 4-22 per side, 1-5 per cm; stalk of inflorescence 6-60 mm long; native or cultivated.
         E-Petioles of leaves subtending the inflorescence 2-6 mm long; projection on ovary top glabrous; petioles mostly with linear stipules; native . . . . V. rafinesquianum
         E-Petioles of leaves subtending the inflorescence 6-20 mm long; projection pubescent; stipules often absent; cultivated. V. dentatum
   C-Upper leaf surfaces at flowering time and stalk and branches of the inflorescence pubescent with star-like branched hairs or hair clusters; cultivated.
      F-Corolla wide-spreading, its tube 1-2 mm long . . . . . V. lantana
      F-Corolla narrowly tubular below, the tube 6-10 mm long. . V. carlesii

V. carlesii Hemsl. Cultivated. Shrub to 1.5 m high; leaves broadly ovate to elliptic, acute at apex, irregularly and rather finely toothed; flowers fragrant, the corolla 10-14 mm wide, changing from pinkish to white; fruit blue-black. Korea.

V. dentatum L. Arrow-wood; cultivated. Shrub 1-5 m high; leaves lance-ovate to round, short-acuminate to rounded, glabrous to pubescent; teeth 8-17 per side; stalk of inflorescence 3-6 cm long; fruit blue-black, its stone ellipsoid, deeply grooved on one side. E. United States, w. to Illinois, Missouri, and Texas.

V. edule (Michx.) Raf. Squashberry, Mooseberry. Shrub to 2 m high; leaves glabrous above, sharply serrate, some or all of them shallowly 3-lobed; inflorescence short-stalked; corolla wide-spreading; fruit red. Cool woods and thickets, Cook and e. Lake counties.

V. lantana L. Wayfaring Tree; cultivated. Shrub or small tree to 3 m high; leaves oblong to ovate, acute to obtuse at apex, usually finely toothed; inflorescence short-stalked; corolla ca. 4 mm wide; fruit red, turning blackish. Eurasia.

V. lentago L. Black Haw, Nannyberry. Shrub or small tree to 6 m high; leaves glabrous at least above, ovate to oblong or roundish, some or all abruptly acuminate; corolla 4-8 mm wide; fruit blue-black. Thickets, openings, and stream banks, throughout the state except for Cook and all but the nw. corner of Lake Co.

V. opulus L. Shrub 1-3 m high; leaves all or nearly all 3-lobed, coarsely toothed; inflorescences on stalks 2-5 cm long; enlarged flowers neutral, with neither functioning stamens nor pistils; fruit red.

A-"Glands" (short blunt outgrowths) at the upper end of the petiole on its upper side 0.3-0.8 mm wide (greatest width) when dry, 0.4-1 mm wide fresh, 1/3-2 times as high as wide; only the outer flowers of the cluster enlarged; native. Cool open woods and thickets, usually on damp soil, Cook to Kittson Co., s. to e. Clay, Pope, Blue Earth, Olmsted, and Houston counties . . . .
. . . . V. o. subsp. trilobum (Marsh.) Clausen (V. trilobum Marsh.; V. o. var. americanum Ait.). High-bush Cranberry.
A-Glands at upper end of petiole (0.7-) 1-2.4 mm wide when dry, 1-2.7 mm wide fresh, 1/4-3/4 as high as wide; only the outer flowers enlarged or more commonly all enlarged; cultivated. Eurasia and N. Africa. V. o. subsp. opulus. European Cranberry-bush. The form with all flowers enlarged is V. o. cv. Roseum, the Snowball or Guelder-rose.

V. rafinesquianum Schultes. Arrow-wood. Shrub to 1.4 m high; leaves ovate-lanceolate to ovate or roundish, acute to acuminate, pubescent to nearly glabrous beneath; teeth 6-12 per side; stalk of inflorescence 6-40 mm long; fruit blue-black, its stone flattened and shallowly grooved on both sides. Mesic to dry open woods and thickets, Cook to Kittson Co., s. to Clay, Todd, Meeker, Blue Earth, Fillmore, and Houston counties, and in Chippewa and Pipestone counties. Forms with the leaves soft-pubescent beneath are often distinguished as V. r. var. rafinesquianum, the Downy Arrow-wood; those with the pubescence restricted mainly to the veins and with slightly longer petioles on the average are then known as V. r. var. affine (Bush) House.

WEIGELA

Shrubs; leaves simple, serrate, without stipules; flowers 5-merous, 1-several in axillary cymes on new shoots, white to pink, purple, or crimson;

corolla slightly zygomorphic with a long tube; ovary 2-locular; fruit a many-seeded elongate capsule opening by 2 segments at the top, leaving a central column. (Named for C. E. von Weigel, German botanist.)

W. florida (Bunge) A. DC. To 2 m high; leaves elliptic to ovate-oblong or obovate, acuminate, glabrous above except for the midrib; flowers in clusters of 1-4; sepals fused for 1/3-1/2 of their length; corolla pink, funnel-shaped, 23-35 mm long. N. China, Korea.

ADOXACEAE ----- MOSCHATEL FAMILY

Perennial herbs; leaves compound, basal and in a single opposite pair on the stem, the basal ones 1-3 times ternate, the stem ones less divided; flowers in mostly 5-flowered head-like cymes, regular or nearly so, bisexual; petals fused, the corolla wide-spreading; terminal flower mostly with 2 sepals and 4 corolla lobes, the others mostly with 3 sepals and 5 corolla lobes; stamens in epipetalous pairs, the pairs alternating with the corolla lobes, each pair apparently representing a divided stamen; anthers 2-sporangiate; ovary about 1/2 inferior, the locules usually as many as the corolla lobes with 1 pendulous ovule per locule; style short; fruit a small dryish drupe with (1-) 4-5 stones.

ADOXA ----- MOSCHATEL*

Characters of the family. (Gr. adoxos, obscure or insignificant.)

A. moschatellina L. Glabrous herb with a musky odor; leaflets obovate, 3-cleft; corolla yellowish-green, 5-8 mm wide. Rich moist soil in woods, or in the north often in rocky or mossy places, Fillmore, Winona, Wabasha, and Goodhue counties, and in Carlton Co. and the s. 1/2 of St. Louis Co.

VALERIANACEAE ----- VALERIAN FAMILY

Ours herbs; plants often with an unpleasant odor especially when dry; leaves opposite or all basal, simple or compound; inflorescence diverse, basically cymose; flowers regular, zygomorphic, or asymmetric, bisexual or unisexual, epigynous; calyx divisions either inrolled at anthesis and later expanded, or reduced or none; corolla mostly 5-lobed, sometimes 2-lipped, the tube often spurred or pouched on one side at base; stamens 3 (1-4), epipetalous, alternate with the corolla lobes; pistil of 3 fused carpels, 1 fertile, the other 2 sterile or sometimes vestigial; style 1; ovule 1, pendulous; fruit dry, indehiscent.

VALERIANA ----- VALERIAN

Perennials (ours) or annuals; leaves entire to pinnately compound; flowers bisexual or unisexual; calyx of several to many divisions, inrolled at anthesis, in male flowers minute, in bisexual or female flowers later spreading and enlarged, dry and stiff, often feathery; corolla 5-lobed, regular or nearly so, the tube sometimes pouched on one side at base; stamens 3; the 2 sterile carpels vestigial; fruit an achene. (Perhaps from L. valere, to be strong.)

<u>V</u>. edulis var. ciliata (T. & G.) Cronquist. Dioecious or polygamo-dioecious; basal leaves linear-oblanceolate, entire or some or all pinnately cleft; stem leaves usually reduced in size, pinnately cleft or rarely simple; inflorescence panicle-like; corolla of bisexual and male flowers 2.5-3.5 mm long, of female flowers ca. 1 mm long. Wet meadows and swamps or sometimes on rock outcrops or bluffs, Houston to Mower Co., n. to Wabasha and Waseca counties and in Hennepin Co. and along the Minnesota River Valley in Dakota and Scott counties.

CAMPANULACEAE ----- BELLFLOWER FAMILY

Ours herbs, often with milky juice; leaves simple, alternate (ours) or rarely opposite or whorled; flowers bisexual, regular to zygomorphic; calyx lobes 5 (3-10); petals 5 (3-6), fused (ours) or rarely free, rarely absent ; stamens as many as the corolla lobes or petals and alternate with them, epipetalous or free from the corolla, the anthers separate or lightly fused together around the style; ovary 1/2 to fully inferior (ours) or rarely superior, typically 2-5-locular; ovules mostly numerous on axile placentas; style 1; fruit usually a capsule, usually opening by pores or slits.

A-Corolla bell-shaped; flowers 1-several in open raceme-like or
  panicle-like inflorescences . . . . CAMPANULA
A-Corolla wide-spreading; flowers sessile or nearly so in the leaf
  axils . . . . TRIODANIS

CAMPANULA ----- BELLFLOWER

Annuals or perennials; calyx 5-cleft; corolla bell-shaped to funnel-shaped to wide-spreading, 5-lobed, in ours blue, violet, or white; stamens attached at very base of corolla, the anthers separate; ovary fully inferior, in ours 3-locular, the ovules many; style elongate; capsule opening by 3 lateral pores. (Diminutive of L. campana, bell, from the corolla shape.)

C. rotundifolia L. Harebell, Bluebell. Perennial; basal leaf blades round-cordate to ovate or sometimes oblanceolate, mostly toothed, often withering early; stem leaves lanceolate to linear; flowers 1-several in open raceme-like or panicle-like inflorescences; corolla blue or rarely white. Open dry to wet locations, often sandy or rocky, Cook to Kittson Co., s. to Clay, Pope, Hennepin, Blue Earth, and Houston counties, and in Chippewa Co.

TRIODANIS*

Annuals; leaves toothed; flowers sessile or nearly so, 1-several together in the middle and upper leaf axils, the lower flowers closed with a reduced corolla or none, the upper ones normal with a wide-spreading corolla, its 5 lobes longer than its tube; calyx lobes 5 (-4 or 3 in the closed flowers); stamens free; ovary mostly 3-locular with axile placentation (varying to 1-locular with parietal placentation); capsules many-seeded, opening by pores above or less often at the middle. (Gr. combination said by Rafinesque to refer to the 3 unequal calyx teeth.)

A-Leaves or bracts subtending the flowers roundish to broadly ovate
  . . . . T. perfoliata

A-Leaves or bracts subtending the flowers lanceolate to linear. T. leptocarpa

   T. leptocarpa (Nutt.) Nieuwl. (Specularia leptocarpa (Nutt.) Gray).
Western Venus' Looking-glass. Corolla (of upper flowers) blue-violet; cap-
sules linear. Dry open places; small morainic hills in S. St. Paul, n. Dakota
Co.

   T. perfoliata (L.) Nieuwl. (Specularia perfoliata (L.) A. DC.). Clasping Venus' Looking-glass. Corolla (of upper flowers) deep purple to pale
lavender; capsules oblong, ellipsoid, or narrowly obovoid. Open mesic to dry
places, often sandy, Houston, Olmsted, Blue Earth, Nicollet, Redwood,
Hennepin, and Crow Wing counties.

ASTERACEAE (COMPOSITAE) ----- SUNFLOWER or COMPOSITE FAMILY

   Ours annual to perennial herbs, sometimes with milky juice; leaves
various; flowers in heads (fig. 71) or rarely short dense spikes, the head
nearly always closely surrounded by a series of bracts (involucral bracts);
outer flowers opening first; individual flowers (figs. 72 and 73) sometimes
each subtended by a small bract (receptacle bract), the flowers epigynous,
bisexual or unisexual; calyx represented (apparently) by a series of few to
many scales, bristles, or other appendages, collectively termed the pappus,
or the pappus a low crown or none; petals fused, the corolla in ours either
regular and tubular to trumpet-shaped with usually 5 short lobes (disk corollas, the flowers disk flowers, fig. 72) or split most of the way down one side
and spread flat, thus zygomorphic and appearing as one petal (ligulate corollas or ligules, the flowers ligulate, also termed ray flowers when the central
flowers are of the disk type; fig. 73); stamens epipetalous, as many as and
alternate with the corolla lobes, mostly with their elongate anthers united
into a tube around the style; ovary 1-locular (2-carpellate) with 1 basal ovule;
style 1, usually 2-cleft; fruit an achene, often bearing the pappus at its apex.

A-Ligules absent, the corollas all tubular.
   B-Leaves entire . . . . ANTENNARIA
   B-Leaves 1-3 times pinnately dissected . . . . MATRICARIA
A-Ligules present.
   C-Corollas all ligulate (when still immature the ligules are tubular and
      closed at the top).
      D-Flowers creamy white; foliage leaves appearing after the flowers,
         basal, the flowering stem with parallel-veined bracts; juice not
         milky . . . . PETASITES
      D-Flowers yellow to orange; foliage leaves present; juice milky.
         E-Leaves parallel-veined, entire, linear to lance-linear, basal
            and on the stem; pappus bristles branched, feather-like, with
            many fine lateral bristles along the central axis (lateral
            bristles appressed to the axis when young) . . . . . . TRAGOPOGON
         E-Leaves not parallel-veined, entire to toothed, linear or broader,
            sometimes only basal; pappus bristles unbranched.
            F-Flowers orange to yellow-orange; stem leaves and larger
               bracts 2/3 to fully clasped around the stem at base . . KRIGIA
            F-Flowers yellow; stem leaves and bracts if present not clasping.
               G-Heads 1-many, at least the upper stem with at least 1 or
                  2 small bracts; involucral bracts puberulent to pubescent
                  at least below; involucres 5-15 mm high . . . . . . CREPIS
               G-Heads single on leafless and bractless stalks; involucral
                  bracts usually glabrous; involucres 10-25 mm high.

H-Leaves normally cut 1/2 or more of the way to the midrib,
at least below the middle; achenes roughened with tiny
knobs or teeth at least at the top, (these plainly visible
at 3 X), drawn out at the top into a narrow stalk, the
"beak", 1/2-4 times as long as the main body . TARAXACUM
H-Leaves entire or rarely with a few teeth; achenes smooth,
beakless or tapering gradually into a beak 1/4-1/2 as
long as the main body . . . . AGOSERIS
C-Ligules present only around the edge of the head, the central flowers
with tubular corollas (closed at the top when immature).
I-Ligules yellow.
J-Heads several to many; stems leafy at least below, the leaves
present before flowering . . . . SENECIO
J-Heads each single on a stem bearing bracts; foliage leaves all
basal, appearing after the flowers . . . . TUSSILAGO
I-Ligules white to red, blue, or violet.
K-Leaves entire to coarsely lobed; pappus of hair-like bristles.
L-Foliage leaves present at time of flowering, with 0-3 length-
wise veins, usually less than 5 cm wide . . . . ERIGERON
L-Foliage leaves absent at flowering time, the flowering stem
with bracts only, the larger bracts with 5 or more length-
wise parallel veins; foliage leaves appearing after the
flowers, all basal, 5 cm wide or wider . . . . PETASITES
K-Leaves 2-3 times pinnately dissected into fine divisions; pappus
a low cup or none.
M-Heads numerous in a flat-topped or rounded inflorescence;
ligules about 5 . . . . ACHILLEA
M-Head single on the stem; ligules 20-40 . . . . . . CHRYSANTHEMUM

ACHILLEA

Perennials; leaves alternate, simple to compound; heads in a more or
less flat-topped or rounded cluster, each head with 3-13 marginal ligulate
flowers, these without stamens, fertile, the ligules white or sometimes pink
or pink-purple or rarely (not ours) yellow; involucral bracts with papery non-
green edges; receptacle bracts present; pappus none; achenes oblong, flattened.
(Its supposed healing powers said to have been discovered by Achilles.)

A. millefolium L. Yarrow, Milfoil. Aromatic; leaves 2-3 times pinnately dissected into fine divisions; ligules about 5, white to sometimes pink. Dry
to damp open places, especially in sandy, rocky, or disturbed sites.
A-Stem heavily woolly; finest leaf divisions tending to be narrowly
lanceolate or linear and congested, overlapping or turned at different
angles; native, throughout the state . . . .
. . . . A. m. subsp. lanulosa (Nutt.) Piper (A. lanulosa Nutt.).
A-Stem smoothish to cobwebby; finest leaf divisions tending to be lanceolate or ovate and flat-spreading; naturalized from Europe, occasional
from Cook to Kittson to Faribault to Houston Co. . . . .
. . . . A. m. subsp. millefolium.

AGOSERIS*

Herbs with milky juice; leaves all basal, entire to pinnately cut; heads
single on bractless stalks; flowers all ligulate and bisexual, yellow (ours) or

sometimes orange-red, often turning pinkish or purple in age or when dry; pappus of many hair-like bristles or these broadened at the base; receptacle bracts none; achenes oblong or linear, ca. 10-nerved, smooth, beakless or tapering at the top into a narrow "beak" up to 1/2 as long as the achene. (Gr. aix, goat, and seris, chicory.)

A-Leaves woolly along the edges, otherwise glabrous or nearly so;
    achenes tapering slightly above but not beaked, ca. 8 mm long;
    pappus of thread-like bristles mixed with slightly flattened
    bristles . . . . A. cuspidata
A-Leaves glabrous or nearly so, without marginal woolly strips;
    achenes tapering gradually above into a thick beak 1/4-1/2 as long
    as the main body, the whole 5-12 mm long; pappus of thread-like
    bristles only . . . . A. glauca

    A. cuspidata (Pursh) Raf. (Microseris cuspidata (Pursh) Schultz-Bip.). Wavy-leaf Agoseris. Perennial; leaves lanceolate, long-acuminate, entire. Mesic to dry prairies and open places, often in gravelly soil, Houston to Faribault and Pipestone counties, n. to Washington, Hennepin, Pope, and Clay counties.

    A. glauca (Pursh) Raf. Pale Agoseris. Perennial; leaves linear to oblanceolate, entire or sometimes with a few teeth or shallow lobes. Mesic to moist prairies and meadows, Kittson and w. Roseau counties s. to Mahnomen, Stevens, and Pipestone counties, and in s. Beltrami and Hubbard counties.

ANTENNARIA ----- EVERLASTING, PUSSY'S-TOES, LADIES'-TOBACCO*

    Dioecious perennials, often with overwintering leaves; leaves alternate, entire, white-woolly at least below; heads 1-many; involucral bracts papery, green at most below, whitish above, or sometimes colored; receptacle bracts none; corollas all tubular, those of the female plants very narrow, closely fitting around the style; style 2-cleft in female flowers, usually undivided in the male; pappus of hair-like bristles, thickened or minutely barbed in the male flowers; achenes cylindrical or slightly flattened. Staminate plants unknown in many species, these and often the other species reproducing apomictically. Name from the resemblance of the pappus of the male flowers to the antennae of certain insects.) The groupings of Antennaria are often obscured by polyploidy and by the development of apomictic races, frequently recognizable morphologically and difficult of taxonomic interpretation. The following conservative treatment is adapted primarily from that of Dr. A. J. Cronquist in Gleason's New Britton and Brown Illustrated Flora.

A-Largest basal leaves with 3-7 lengthwise nerves at base of blade,
    12-50 mm wide, 30-100 mm long; nerves prominent beneath, the
    2 (main) laterals nearest the midrib each nearly always 1/3-1/2
    of the way from the midrib to the margin at or just short of the
    widest point of the blade, usually extending past the widest point
    and converging toward and nearly reaching the leaf tip, secondary
    nerves if any branching mostly from the outer sides of the 2 main
    laterals; largest leaves tending to be widest 1/3-2/3 of the way to
    the tip; smaller leaves and those not fully expanded often with lateral
    nerves as described below . . . . A. plantaginifolia
A-Largest basal leaves with 1 (-3) lengthwise nerves at base of blade,
    3-15 (-21) mm wide, 5-55 mm long; nerves obscure to prominent
    beneath, when 3 then the 2 main laterals located from nearly 2/3

to 3/4 of the way from the midrib to the margin in the wider part
of the blade, usually extending at most shortly beyond the widest
point, rarely converging toward and nearly reaching the leaf tip,
rarely a faint additional nerve next one or both margins; secondary
nerves if any branching mostly from the midrib; largest leaves
tending to be widest 2/3-4/5 of the way to the tip.
B-Upper surfaces of basal leaves distinctly less pubescent than
the lower, sooner or later becoming glabrous or nearly so;
throughout the state . . . . A. neglecta
B-Upper surfaces of basal leaves nearly or quite as densely hairy
as the lower, becoming glabrous if at all only in extreme age;
Kittson to Clay Co.
C-Involucre 4.5-7 mm high; dry female corollas mostly 2.5-4.5
mm long . . . . A. rosea
C-Involucre 7-11 mm high; dry female corollas mostly 5-8 mm
long . . . . A. parvifolia

A. neglecta Greene. Fields, prairies, and open woods. Most of our plants
fall readily enough into one or another of the following varieties, but many are
borderlines. It should be noted that length of stolon, one of the distinguishing
characters, will depend partly on how late in the season the plant is collected.
It has been shown that the typical varieties of A. neglecta and A. plantaginifolia contain distinct diploid plants, but that these diploid groups are
joined by an intergrading series of polyploids represented in large part by
the other varieties.
A-Basal leaves and those at the ends of the stolons glabrous and bright
green above when new or immediately after; leaves on upper 1/3 of
flowering stem each with a thin flattened sometimes inrolled non-
green translucent ("scarious") tip 1.5-2.5 mm long by 0.4-0.9 mm
wide; basal leaves tending to have a straight even taper to the base;
stolons variable in length; often in Jack Pine woods; Cook to Kittson
Co., s. to ne. Todd and Ramsey counties . . . .
. . . . . . A. n. var. randii (Fern.) Cronq. (A. canadensis Greene).
A-Basal leaves and those at the ends of the stolons late in becoming
glabrous; leaves of flowering stem with or without scarious tips;
shape of basal leaves various; stolons long or short.
B-Stolons long, prostrate, with very small, sometimes scale-like,
often few lateral leaves; leaves on upper 1/3 of flowering stem
usually with scarious tips; basal leaves tending to have a straight
even taper to the base; Houston to Rock Co., n. to Chisago, s.
Beltrami, Roseau, and Kittson counties, and more widely scattered to Cook Co. . . . . A. n. var.
neglecta (incl. A. campestris Rydb., and A. petaloidea Fern.).
B-Stolons short, ascending at the ends, with abundant leaves of
medium size or larger at least towards the ends; leaves of
flowering stem blunt to bristle-tipped; basal leaf blades tending
to be more abruptly contracted toward the base with an inward
curve, often petioled; Cook to Kittson Co., s. to Clay, Stearns,
Blue Earth, Hennepin, and Washington counties . . . .
. . A. n. var. attenuata (Fern.) Cronq. (A. neodioica Greene).

A. parvifolia Nutt (A. aprica Greene). Leaves 10-35 mm long. Open
sandy places, Kittson and Polk counties.

A. plantaginifolia (L.) Richards. Leaves of flowering stem acute to
bristle-tipped. Mesic to dry fields, prairies, and open woods, often gravelly or rocky. Our herbarium collections divide fairly well into the 2 groups
shown below; however, the fact that an elongation of flower parts occurs dur-

ng maturation throws some doubt on the validity of the division, since specimens of the first and second varieties respectively average relatively young and relatively old in flowering stage. Fernald further subdivides the second group, but this division is not well supported by our material. See A. neglecta.

A-Involucre 5-7 mm high; mature pappus bristles 4-5 mm long; central
    corollas 3-4 mm long; Houston to Pipestone Co., n. to Pine, Morrison,
    Clearwater, and Kittson counties . . . . A. p. var. plantaginifolia.
A-Involucre 7-9 mm high; mature pappus bristles 6.5-8 mm long; central
    corollas 4.5-6 mm long; Cook to Itasca and Becker counties, s. to
    Morrison, Brown, Fillmore, and Houston counties . . . . A. p. var.
    ambigens (Greene) Cronq. (incl. A. fallax Greene and A. munda Fern.).

A. rosea Greene (A. microphylla Rydb.). Leaves 5-15 (-30) mm long.
Dry to wet prairies, Kittson to Clay Co.

CHRYSANTHEMUM

Annuals to perennials, often aromatic; leaves alternate, entire to compound; heads 1-many, usually (incl. ours) with a row of marginal ligulate flowers, these without stamens, fertile, the ligules white to red, purple, or yellow; involucral bracts with papery non-green translucent edges; receptacle bracts none; pappus a short crown or none; achenes 5-10-ribbed or those of the ligulate flowers with 2-3 winged angles. (Gr. chrysos, gold, and anthemon, flower.)

C. coccineum Willd. Common Pyrethrum; cultivated. Perennial; leaves 2-3 times pinnately dissected into fine divisions; head single; ligules 20-40, white to red or lilac. From sw. Asia.

CREPIS ----- HAWK'S BEARD*

Annuals to perennials with milky juice; leaves in ours entire to coarsely toothed or sometimes pinnately cleft, alternate or all basal; heads 1-many; receptacle bracts none; flowers all ligulate and bisexual, yellow; pappus of many white or whitish hair-like bristles; achenes 10-20-ribbed, smooth or roughened with minute teeth, often drawn out at the top into a narrow stalk, the "beak", supporting the pappus. (Gr. name of some plant, from crepis, foot.)

A-Stem leaves none or all but the lowest reduced to bracts; involucre
    8-15 mm high . . . . C. runcinata
A-Stem leaves several to many, reduced from the basal ones but only
    the uppermost bract-like; involucre 5-9 mm high . . . . C. tectorum

C. runcinata (James) T. & G. Perennial; heads 1-6 (-9); leaves mostly oblanceolate to narrowly elliptic; achenes 3.5-7.5 mm long, the ribs smooth or nearly so. Mesic to moist grasslands, often alkaline, Rock to Kittson Co., e. to Red Lake, Mahnomen, Stevens, Kandiyohi, and Cottonwood counties.

C. tectorum L. Annual; heads (1-) 3-50 or more; leaves mostly oblanceolate to narrowly elliptic to linear; achenes 2.5-4.5 mm long, the ribs rough with minute teeth at least above (visible at 15 X). From Eurasia, established in disturbed ground, recorded from Kittson and Roseau counties, from Clearwater to Clay and Otter Tail counties, and from s. St. Louis to Kanabec and Ramsey counties.

ERIGERON ----- DAISY, FLEABANE

Annuals to perennials; leaves alternate, entire or toothed; heads 1-many, usually with many marginal ligulate flowers, these without stamens, fertile, the ligules white to pink, blue, or purple; involucral bracts narrow, usually greenish; receptacle bracts none; disk corollas yellow; pappus of hair-like bristles with or without an outer series of minute bristles or scales; achenes in ours 0-4-nerved. (Gr. eri, early, and geron, old man, ancient name for a white-hairy early-blooming plant.)

A-Disk corollas ca. 1.5-3.2 mm high; involucres 2-6 mm high, if more
    than 5 mm high then the ligules 0.2-0.6 mm wide.
  B-Ligules 150 or more, 5-10 mm long; pappus of ligulate flowers like
    that of the disk flowers . . . . E. philadelphicus
  B-Ligules 50-100, 3-6 mm long; pappus of ligulate flowers much re-
    duced, less than 1 mm long . . . . E. strigosus
A-Disk corollas 4-6 mm high; involucres 5-9 mm high; ligules ca. 1-1.8
    mm wide.
  C-Ligules 125-175; plants without rhizomes or stolons; pappus double,
    with a ring of very short bristles outside the long ones . . . .
    . . . . E. glabellus var. pubescens
  C-Ligules 50-80 (-100); plants with superficial rhizomes or stolons;
    pappus not double. . . . . E. pulchellus

E. glabellus var. pubescens Hook. Biennial or perennial; leaves entire or seldom toothed, the basal ones oblanceolate, the stem ones lanceolate to linear; ligules blue to pink or seldom white, 8-15 mm long. Dry to wet prairies, meadows, and open woods, Kittson and Roseau to Clay and Hubbard counties, in Lincoln Co., and in Carlton and n. Pine counties.

E. philadelphicus L. Philadelphia Fleabane. Biennial or short-lived perennial; at least the larger leaves coarsely toothed, the basal ones narrowly oblanceolate to obovate, the stem ones to oblong or ovate and with broad bases clasping the stem; involucre 4-6 mm high; disk corollas 2.5-3.2 mm high; ligules pink to whitish, 0.2-0.6 mm wide. Mesic to wet open places, throughout the state.

E. pulchellus Michx. Poor-Robin's Plantain. Biennial or short-lived perennial; larger leaves usually toothed, the basal ones oblanceolate to roundish, the stem ones ovate to lanceolate or oblong, more or less clasping the stem at base; ligules blue to sometimes pink or white, 6-10 mm long. Woods, thickets, meadows, and stream banks, Houston and Fillmore counties n. to Carlton, Itasca, and Mahnomen counties.

E. strigosus Muhl. Daisy-fleabane; White-top. Annual or rarely biennial; larger leaves entire or toothed, the basal ones mostly oblanceolate to elliptic, the stem ones linear to lanceolate; involucre 2-5 mm high; disk corollas 1.5-2.6 mm high; ligules white or sometimes pinkish or bluish, 0.4-1.0 mm wide. Dry to wet fields and open woods, often in disturbed ground.

A-Hairs of the involucre not obviously flattened, less than 1 mm long;
    hairs of the stem mostly short and appressed except at the base;
    throughout the state. . . . . E. s. var. strigosus.
A-Hairs of the involucre flattened, more than 1 mm long; hairs of the
    stem mostly long and spreading; Cook to St. Louis Co. . . . .
    . . . . E. s. var. septentrionalis (Fern. & Wieg.) Fern.

One specimen from Anoka Co. has the much-branched, small-bracted inflorescence and small heads characteristic of E. s. var. beyrichii (Fisch. & Mey.) Gray, but is far out of the usual range of that variety.

KRIGIA ----- DWARF DANDELION*

Annuals or perennials with milky juice; leaves alternate to nearly opposite or all basal, entire to pinnately cut; heads 1-several; receptacle bracts none; flowers all ligulate and bisexual, orange (ours) to yellow; pappus usually of hair-like bristles and an outer row of 5 or more flat scales; achenes 10-20-nerved. (Named for D. Krig or Krieg, German physician.)

K. biflora (Walt.) Blake. Perennial; basal leaves oblanceolate to broadly elliptic, entire to pinnately cut, the stem leaves 1-3, alternate, they and the larger bracts of the inflorescence 2/3 to fully clasped around the stem at base; flowers orange to yellow-orange. Open woods, prairies, and fields in a band from se. to nw. across the state, Houston to Waseca Co., n. to Chisago and Morrison counties, to Wadena, s. Beltrami, and Polk counties, and in Kittson Co.

MATRICARIA ----- WILD CHAMOMILE

Ours annuals or short-lived perennials, often aromatic; leaves alternate, 1-3 times pinnately cleft into fine divisions; heads 1-many, with or without marginal ligulate flowers, these without stamens, usually fertile, the ligules white; involucral bracts with papery non-green translucent edges; receptacle bracts none; disk corollas yellow; pappus a short crown or none; achenes usually nerved on the edges and the inner face, nerveless on the outer face. (From L. mater, mother, for supposed medicinal properties.)

M. matricarioides (Less.) Porter. Pineapple-weed. Glabrous annual with pineapple odor; ligules none. Introduced from w. North America; disturbed ground throughout the state.

PETASITES ----- SWEET COLTSFOOT*

Functionally dioecious perennial herbs, spreading by rhizomes, more or less white-hairy; foliage leaves all basal, appearing after the flowers, the bracts of the stem alternate, parallel-veined; heads several to many, the flowers whitish (ours), purple, or rarely yellowish; receptacle bracts none; female heads all or nearly all of pistillate fertile flowers, these ligulate in ours, the heads usually with a few neuter tubular flowers in the center; male heads in ours with an outer row of ligulate neuter flowers and many inner tubular staminate ones; pappus of many hair-like bristles; achenes linear, 5-10-ribbed. (Gr. petasos, a broad-brimmed hat, from the large leaves.)

A-Leaves palmately veined and lobed, cut 1/2-9/10 of the way to the mid-point, round-heart-shaped or wider than long in overall outline . . . . P. palmatus
A-Leaves pinnately veined, toothed to nearly entire, cut up to 10 mm deep, 1/10 of the way to the midrib or less, heart-shaped to arrow-shaped in outline . . . . P. sagittatus

P. palmatus (Ait.) Gray (P. frigidus var. palmatus (Ait.) Cronq.). Leaves 5-25 cm wide. Moist woods, damp meadows, and swampy places, Cook to Roseau Co., s. to Mahnomen, Aitkin, and Carlton counties.

P. sagittatus (Pursh) Gray. Leaves 8-25 cm wide, to 35 cm long. Damp meadows, bogs, and low woods, Cook to Kittson Co., s. to Clay, Wadena, and Carlton counties.

Plants more or less intermediate between these two species occur occasionally in the state. In recent treatments these plants have been regarded as a separate species or variety which has been given various names, among them P. vitifolius Greene, P. frigidus var. nivalis (Greene) Cronq., and P. frigidus var. corymbosus (R. Br.) Cronq. However, according to Dr. A. L. Bogle, such plants are probably of hybrid derivation, the parental types being the two above. Plants of this kind are recorded from Lake to Carlton Co. and from Clearwater, Hubbard, and Morrison counties.

SENECIO ----- GROUNDSEL, RAGWORT, SQUAW-WEED, BUTTERWEED

Ours herbs; leaves alternate or all basal, entire to compound; heads 1-many, usually with marginal ligulate flowers, these without stamens, fertile the ligules yellow (ours) to orange or sometimes reddish; receptacle bracts none; disk corollas yellow to orange or reddish; pappus of many hair-like bristles; achenes 5-10-nerved. (L. senex, an old man, probably from the white pubescence of some species or from the white pappus.)

A-Basal leaf blades truncate to heart-shaped at base.
  B-Basal blades heart-shaped at base, typically the notch 3-30 mm
    deep, 1/8-1/4 or more the length of the blade; rootstock typi-
    cally 2-5 cm long . . . . S. aureus
  B-Basal blades truncate to slightly heart-shaped at base, typically
    the notch 0-5 mm deep, 0-1/8 the length of the blade; rootstock
    typically 0.5-2 cm long . . . . . S. pseudaureus var. semicordatus
A-Basal leaf blades narrowly to broadly acute at base, or none.
  C-Annual or biennial shore and marsh plants with hollow stems 2-11
    mm thick; stem leaves each overlapping the node above, to the
    inflorescence, the uppermost leaves mostly 1/3-2/3 as long as
    the lower stem ones, the broad base of the sessile stem leaves
    entire or rarely shallowly toothed . . . . S. congestus
  C-Perennials of prairies, open woods, rocky places, and sometimes
    bogs, the stems hollow or solid, 1.5-7 mm thick, the leaves
    various, if as above then the stems solid.
    D-Leaves entire to shallowly toothed, rarely the uppermost reduced
      ones cut up to 1/3 of the way to the midrib; basal leaf blades
      (5-) 7-16 cm long, acute at base with an included angle of 20-
      80°; rhizome short and erect, without tufted leafy offshoots
      . . . . S. integerrimus
    D-Leaves all toothed, at least some of the stem ones cut 1/2 or
      more of the way to the midrib or if rarely slightly less then
      some of the basal blades more broadly acute at base; basal
      blades (1-) 2-6 (-10) cm long; rhizome often producing tufts
      of leaves separate from the flowering stems.
      E-Plants glabrous or lightly white-woolly, especially in and
        near the axils of the basal leaves, usually becoming glabrous
        in age; achenes glabrous or sometimes minutely pubescent
        . . . . S. pauperculus
      E-Plants more or less persistently white-woolly, especially on
        the lower leaf surface, in and near the axils, and among the
        heads in the inflorescence; achenes normally minutely pubes-
        cent, sometimes glabrous . . . . S. plattensis

S. aureus L. Golden Ragwort, Squaw-weed. Perennial; glabrous, or scantily white-woolly in and near the axils of the basal leaves and sometimes among the heads; basal blades round-ovate to somewhat triangular-ovate, at least some of the stem leaves deeply pinnately cut. Meadows, swampy areas, and cool open woods, throughout the state.

S. congestus (R. Br.) DC. Marsh Groundsel, Marsh Fleabane. Pubescence of spreading usually long hairs; leaves linear to oblong-lanceolate, entire to pinnately cleft, the upper sessile with broad bases clasping the stem. Shores and marshes throughout the state except for Cook to n. St. Louis and Koochiching counties and the s. tier of counties.

S. integerrimus Nutt. Lambstongue Groundsel. Pubescent at first with straight non-woolly hairs, usually glabrous or nearly so by flowering time; basal leaves mostly elliptic to oblanceolate, middle and upper stem leaves sessile, sometimes with broad bases clasping the stem. Mesic to wet prairies and rocky places, rarely in open woods, Winona to Pipestone Co., n. to Goodhue, w. Stearns, and Clay counties.

S. pauperculus Michx. Basal leaf blades lanceolate to elliptic or oblanceolate. Meadows, bogs, streambanks, open woods, and rocky places throughout the state. Sometimes intergrading with S. plattensis, especially in the s. part of the state.

S. plattensis Nutt. Prairie Ragwort. Basal leaf blades elliptic-ovate to oblanceolate or sometimes roundish, rarely 1 or 2 of them truncate at base. Mesic to wet prairies, bluffs, and rocky places, throughout the state except for Cook, Lake, and Koochiching to Roseau counties. Sometimes intergrading with S. pauperculus, especially in the s. part of the state.

S. pseudaureus var. semicordatus (Mack. & Bush) Barkley. False Golden Ragwort. Perennial; glabrous, or lightly white-woolly when young; basal blades ovate to broadly lanceolate in outline, usually at least some of the stem leaves deeply pinnately cut. Low prairies, wet meadows, and sometimes low open woods, Rock to Kittson Co., e. to Nobles, Waseca, s. Pine, Stevens, Mahnomen, and Roseau counties.

TARAXACUM ----- DANDELION*

Perennials or biennials with milky juice; leaves all basal, entire to pinnately cut; heads single on bractless stalks; receptacle bracts none; flowers all ligulate and bisexual, yellow; pappus of numerous hair-like bristles; achenes grooved or ribbed lengthwise, roughened with tiny knobs or teeth at least at the top (these plainly visible at 3 X or less), usually drawn out at the top into a narrow stalk, the "beak", 1/2-4 times as long as the main body, topped by the pappus; fruit largely produced by apomixis. (Name perhaps a modification of the Arabic Tharakhchakon.)

A-Achenes brown, olive-brown, or straw-colored at maturity, the beak
    mostly 2.5-4 times as long as the body . . . . T. officinale
A-Achenes red, reddish-brown, or reddish-purple at maturity, the beak
    mostly 1-3 times as long as the body . . . . T. erythrospermum

T. erythrospermum Andrz. (T. laevigatum (Willd.) DC.). Red-seeded Dandelion. Leaves tending to be very deeply cut for their whole length, the terminal lobe seldom much larger than the lateral ones; at least some of the inner involucral bracts with a pronounced knob or ridge on the back 0.5-2.5 mm from the tip. From Eurasia, naturalized in disturbed and undisturbed open places over most of the state, unrecorded from Cook, Lake, and many other counties.

T. officinale Wiggers. Common Dandelion. Leaves sometimes as in the preceding but more often less deeply cut, the terminal lobe tending to be larger than the others; inner involucral bracts with or without knobs or ridges as above. From Eurasia, naturalized mostly in disturbed open ground throughout the state.

TRAGOPOGON ----- GOAT'S BEARD*

Annuals, biennials, or perennials with milky juice; leaves alternate, clasping the stem at base, linear to lance-linear, entire, more or less parallel-veined; heads single; receptacle bracts none; flowers all ligulate and bisexual, yellow or purple; pappus a single row of feathery bristles, each with many fine lateral bristles along a central axis (lateral bristles appressed to the axis when young); achenes 5-10-nerved, mostly drawn out at the top into a narrow "beak" supporting the pappus. (Gr. tragos, goat, and pogon, beard.)

A-Involucral bracts distinctly exceeding the ligules in flower, 24-40
    mm long, elongating in fruit to 40-70 mm; peduncle enlarged to
    ca. twice its diameter just below the heads, or thicker in fruit;
    achenes (including beak) mostly 25-35 mm long . . . . T. dubius
A-Involucral bracts shorter than to about equalling the ligules in
    flower, 12-24 mm long, elongating in fruit to 18-38 mm; pedun-
    cle not enlarged in flower, slightly so in fruit; achenes mostly
    12-25 mm long . . . . T. pratensis

T. dubius Scop. (T. major Jacq.). Biennial or sometimes annual; flowers yellow. From Europe, naturalized in open mostly disturbed ground, probably throughout the state, unrecorded from Cook and several other counties.

T. pratensis L. Mostly biennial; flowers yellow. From Europe, natura-lized in open mostly disturbed ground, recorded at very wide intervals from Houston to Rock Co. and n. to St. Louis, Clearwater, and Chippewa counties.

TUSSILAGO ----- COLTSFOOT*

Perennial herb; foliage leaves all basal, appearing after the flowers, the bracts of the stem alternate; head single, the outer several rows of flowers ligulate, without stamens, fertile, the ligules yellow; central flowers stam-inate with tubular corollas; receptacle bracts none; pappus of many hair-like bristles; achenes slender-cylindric or angled, 5-10-ribbed. (L. tussis, cough, the plant thought a remedy.)

T. farfara L. Plants with rhizomes; leaf blades heart-shaped to roundish, angled or shallowly toothed, 5-20 cm long and wide, gray- to white-woolly beneath. From Eurasia and n. Africa; recorded only from Wright Co., in disturbed ground.

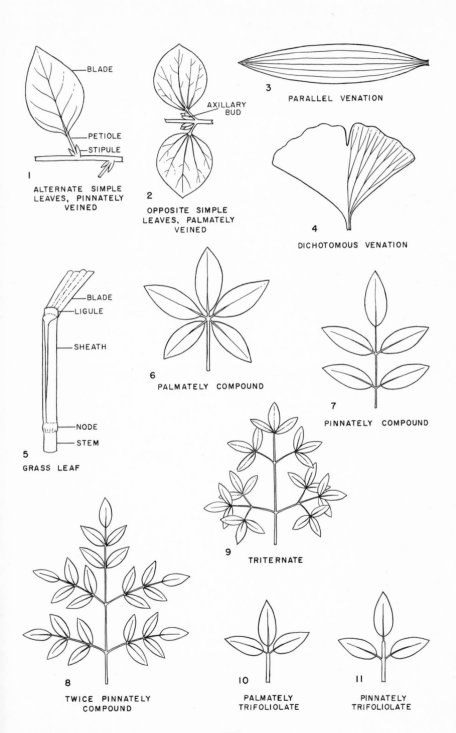

1

BLADE

PETIOLE

STIPULE

ALTERNATE SIMPLE
LEAVES, PINNATELY
VEINED

2

AXILLARY
BUD

OPPOSITE SIMPLE
LEAVES, PALMATELY
VEINED

3

PARALLEL VENATION

4

DICHOTOMOUS VENATION

5

BLADE

LIGULE

SHEATH

NODE

STEM

GRASS LEAF

6 PALMATELY COMPOUND

7

PINNATELY COMPOUND

9 TRITERNATE

8

TWICE PINNATELY
COMPOUND

10

PALMATELY
TRIFOLIOLATE

11

PINNATELY
TRIFOLIOLATE

257

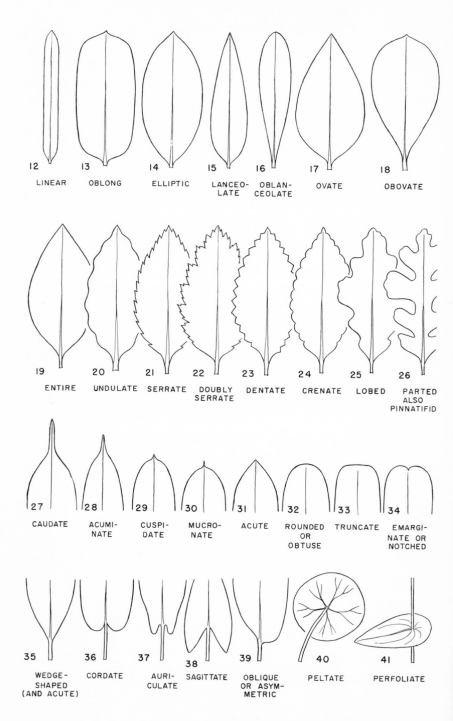

12	13	14	15	16	17	18
LINEAR	OBLONG	ELLIPTIC	LANCEO-LATE	OBLAN-CEOLATE	OVATE	OBOVATE

19	20	21	22	23	24	25	26
ENTIRE	UNDULATE	SERRATE	DOUBLY SERRATE	DENTATE	CRENATE	LOBED	PARTED ALSO PINNATIFID

27	28	29	30	31	32	33	34
CAUDATE	ACUMI-NATE	CUSPI-DATE	MUCRO-NATE	ACUTE	ROUNDED OR OBTUSE	TRUNCATE	EMARGI-NATE OR NOTCHED

35	36	37	38	39	40	41
WEDGE-SHAPED (AND ACUTE)	CORDATE	AURI-CULATE	SAGITTATE	OBLIQUE OR ASYM-METRIC	PELTATE	PERFOLIATE

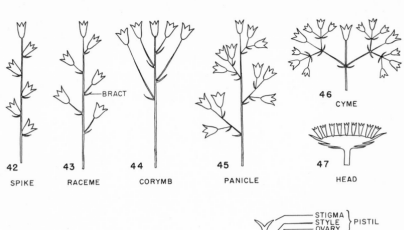

42 SPIKE 43 RACEME 44 CORYMB 45 PANICLE 46 CYME 47 HEAD

BRACT

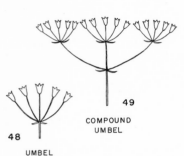

48 UMBEL 49 COMPOUND UMBEL

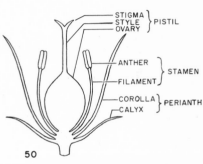

STIGMA ⎫
STYLE   ⎬ PISTIL
OVARY ⎭

ANTHER ⎫
FILAMENT ⎬ STAMEN

COROLLA ⎫
CALYX   ⎬ PERIANTH

50 HYPOGYNOUS PERIANTH AND STAMENS, SUPERIOR OVARY

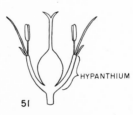

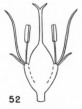

HYPANTHIUM

51 PERIGYNOUS PERIANTH AND STAMENS, SUPERIOR OVARY

52 ½ EPIGYNOUS PERIANTH AND STAMENS, ½ INFERIOR OVARY

53 EPIGYNOUS PERIANTH AND STAMENS, INFERIOR OVARY

54 EPIGYNOUS PERIANTH AND STAMENS, INFERIOR OVARY, PART OF HYPANTHIUM FREE

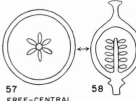

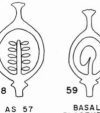

55 AXILE PLACENTATION

56 PARIETAL PLACENTATION

57 FREE-CENTRAL PLACENTATION

58 AS 57

59 BASAL PLACENTATION

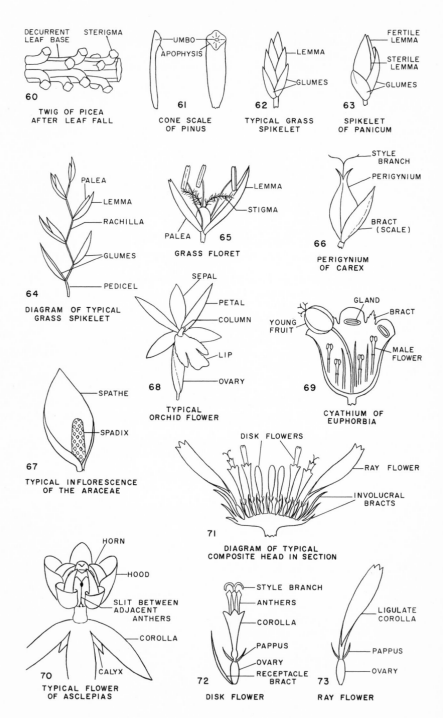

60 TWIG OF PICEA AFTER LEAF FALL

DECURRENT LEAF BASE · STERIGMA

61 CONE SCALE OF PINUS

UMBO · APOPHYSIS

62 TYPICAL GRASS SPIKELET

LEMMA · GLUMES

63 SPIKELET OF PANICUM

FERTILE LEMMA · STERILE LEMMA · GLUMES

64 DIAGRAM OF TYPICAL GRASS SPIKELET

PALEA · LEMMA · RACHILLA · GLUMES · PEDICEL

65 GRASS FLORET

LEMMA · STIGMA · PALEA

66 PERIGYNIUM OF CAREX

STYLE BRANCH · PERIGYNIUM · BRACT (SCALE)

67 TYPICAL INFLORESCENCE OF THE ARACEAE

SPATHE · SPADIX

68 TYPICAL ORCHID FLOWER

SEPAL · PETAL · COLUMN · LIP · OVARY

69 CYATHIUM OF EUPHORBIA

GLAND · BRACT · YOUNG FRUIT · MALE FLOWER

70 TYPICAL FLOWER OF ASCLEPIAS

HORN · HOOD · SLIT BETWEEN ADJACENT ANTHERS · COROLLA · CALYX

71 DIAGRAM OF TYPICAL COMPOSITE HEAD IN SECTION

DISK FLOWERS · RAY FLOWER · INVOLUCRAL BRACTS

72 DISK FLOWER

STYLE BRANCH · ANTHERS · COROLLA · PAPPUS · OVARY · RECEPTACLE BRACT

73 RAY FLOWER

LIGULATE COROLLA · PAPPUS · OVARY

GLOSSARY

Abrupt. Changing suddenly, as in a leaf in which the angle of taper of the edges changes abruptly.

Achene. A small dry indehiscent 1-seeded fruit with close-fitting thin ovary wall.

Acuminate. An apex drawn out into a gradually tapering point, the sides often somewhat concave. Fig. 28.

Acute. Forming an acute angle at base or apex, the included angle typically between 45° and 90°, the sides mostly straight or convex, the point not notably long drawn out. Figs. 31, 35.

Aggregate fruit. A fruit formed by the fusion or crowding of separate fleshy pistils within the same flower, as in the blackberry (Rubus).

Alternate. Placed singly at different heights on the axis or stem; any arrangement of leaves or other parts not opposite or whorled. Fig. 1.

Aneuploidy. A change in chromosome number of less than the whole haploid set, typically involving an increase or decrease of one chromosome at a time in the basic haploid number.

Annual. Of one season's duration from seed to maturity to death.

Anther. The pollen-bearing part of the stamen, typically borne at the apex of the filament. Fig. 50.

Anthesis. The period during which a flower is fully expanded and functional.

Apomixis. In general, reproduction without fertilization, usually referring to seed production without fertilization.

Apophysis. In Pinus, the thickened terminal part of a cone scale, exposed when the cone is closed. Fig. 61.

Appressed. Lying close to; pressed against.

Aril. An outgrowth from the base or the stalk of an ovule, partly or wholly covering the seed.

Articulate. In the grasses, with distinct joints, where separation may occur at maturity.

Ascending. Rising upward at an angle; above horizontal but not vertical.

Attenuate. Having a long very gradual taper; applied to bases or apexes of parts.

Auricle. A projecting lobe or appendage, typically at the base of an organ, commonly in pairs (fig. 37); in the grasses, projections at the base of the blade, one on each side of the stem.

Auriculate. Having one or more auricles. Fig. 37.

Awn. A bristle-like part or appendage.

Axil. The upper angle between an organ and the stem that bears it. Fig. 2.

Axile (placentation). The ovules attached to the central axis of an ovary with 2 or more locules, the ovary the product of the fusion of 2 or more carpels. Fig. 55.

Beak. Ending in a firm prolonged narrowed tip.

Berry. A fleshy fruit developed from a single ovary, containing 1-many seeds; loosely, any fleshy or juicy fruit. (Compare drupe.)

Biennial. Of 2 years' duration from seed to maturity to death.

Bilateral symmetry. See Zygomorphic.

Bisexual. Having organs of both sexes present and functional in one flower.

Biternate. Each of 3 divisions again divided into 3.

Blade. The broadened part of a flat organ such as a leaf or petal. Fig. 1.

Bract. A modified leaf, typically much reduced in size, such as often subtends a flower or a branch of an inflorescence. Figs. 42-49.

Bractlet. A small bract.

Broadly acute. The included angle greater than 90°.

Bud scale. A small protective much-reduced leaf, enclosing with others the bud itself.

Bulb. A short usually underground stem bearing thick fleshy overlapping modified leaves.

Bulblet. A little bulb; usually applied to the bulb-like structures produced by some plants in the leaf axils or in the inflorescence.

Bundle scar. Scar formed in the leaf scar by the breaking of the vascular bundles of the petiole.

Ca. L. circa, about, approximately.

Callus. A hard protuberance; in the grasses, usually the tough often hairy swelling at the base or point of attachment of the floret, visible when the floret is removed, morphologically a part of the rachilla.

Calyx. The outer series of perianth parts, when the perianth is differentiated into different outer and inner series. Fig. 50.

Capitate. Head-like; in a head. Fig. 47.

Capsule. A dry dehiscent fruit developed from a compound ovary (of more than 1 carpel) and almost always containing 2 or more seeds.

Carpel. The basic female structural unit of the flower, a simple pistil, in form like a very small leaf folded lengthwise with the edges touching and usually fused, bearing ovules inside usually only near the edges.

Carpellate. Having one or more carpels and no functional stamens; female.

Caryopsis. A small dry indehiscent 1-seeded fruit with the thin ovary wall fused to the seed.

Catkin. A spike or spike-like inflorescence of many small petalless unisexual flowers arranged around an elongate central axis, the whole falling as a unit, the inflorescence ordinarily of one sex, the flowers with a perianth of 1 whorl or none, the perianth never petal-like, the flowers usually subtended by bracts. Also called an "ament".

Ciliate. Fringed with hairs, usually on the edges.

Circumscissile. Opening by a transverse circular cleft around the fruit or anther, the top usually falling off as a lid.

Clasping. Partly or wholly surrounding another organ, usually at base.

Cleft. Divided to or shortly beyond the middle; not clearly distinguished from lobed or parted.

Cleistogamous. Referring to flowers which remain closed and which are automatically self-pollinated.

Cm. Centimeter, 1/100 of a meter, 10 millimeters.

Column. In the orchids, the structure formed by the fusion of the stamens, style, and stigmas. Fig. 68.

Compound. Composed of 2 or more similar parts; in an inflorescence or shoot, one which is branched. Figs. 45, 46, 49. See compound leaf.

Compound leaf. A leaf divided to the midrib or base into 2 or more separate divisions or leaflets. Figs. 6-11.

Compound pistil. One composed of 2 or more fused carpels.

Cone. A dense globose to cylindric aggregation of reproductive organs usually arranged along a central axis, each organ often subtended by a bract, the whole forming a detachable homogeneous often fruitlike body.

Connate. United together; said in particular of similar organs, as anthers connate into a tube.

Connective. The tissue of the anther between the pairs of sporangia or pollen sacs.

Convolute. Said of sepals, petals, or tepals in the bud when each member overlaps its neighbor on one edge and is overlapped on the other, regularly around the circle.

Cordate. Heart-shaped with the point apical; often only the base of the heart is referred to. Fig. 36.

Corm. A short thickened stem, usually underground, bulb-like but solid, with poorly developed scale-leaves or more commonly leafless.

Corolla. The inner series of perianth parts, when the perianth is differentiated into different outer and inner series. Fig. 50.

Corymb. A flat- or round-topped flower cluster, in the strict sense a type of raceme, the outer flowers opening first. Fig. 44.

Crenate. A toothed margin, the teeth rounded; scalloped. Fig. 24.

Crenulate. Diminutive of crenate.

Cultigen. Any plant or group of plants believed to have originated under cultivation.

Cultivar. A category in the nomenclature of cultivated plants, below the species level, referring to a distinguishable strain of plants developed in cultivation and capable of propagation without loss of its distinguishing features. The category can be used for plants of hybrid derivation; it is roughly equivalent in level to the "forma" used for wild plants.

Cuspidate. Tipped abruptly with a cusp or sharp firm point. Fig. 29.

Cv. Cultivar.

Cyathium. The inflorescence of Euphorbia, which see. Fig. 69.

Cyme. A type of inflorescence in which each flower is strictly terminal on the main axis or on a branch, the central flower in any group being the first-formed and thus the first to open. Fig. 46.

Cymose. Having the flowers in a cyme.

Deciduous. Leaves falling at the end of the growing season; generally, a structure falling after completion of its normal function.

Decurrent. Extending downward and along, as in the leaf bases of several conifers which run a short distance down the twig and merge into it. Fig. 60.

Decussate. The leaves opposite, each pair set at right angles to the next, so that if one pair is oriented east and west, the pairs above and below will be oriented north and south.

Dehiscent. Opening, as a fruit or an anther, to discharge the contents.

Deltoid. Broadly triangular.

Dentate. A toothed margin, the teeth sharp and directed outward at about right angles to the margin. Fig. 23.

Diadelphous. In 2 groups, referring especially to stamens when united in 2 sets, including the 9 and 1 arrangement common in the Fabaceae.

Dichotomous. Forking more or less regularly into 2 branches of about equal size. Fig. 4.

Dioecious. Having unisexual flowers, the male and female ones on different plants.

Disarticulate. In grasses, to separate at the joints at maturity.

Disk corolla. A regular tubular to trumpet-shaped corolla in the Asteraceae. Fig. 72.

Disk flower. In the Asteraceae, a flower with a regular tubular to trumpet-shaped corolla. Figs. 71, 72.

Distal. The apical part, away from the attached end.

Dm. Decimeter, 1/10 of a meter, 10 centimeters.

Double. Said of flowers with more than the usual number of perianth parts, especially petals.

Doubly crenate, dentate, serrate, and so on. With large teeth which are toothed in turn with smaller ones. Fig. 22.

Drupe. A fleshy fruit with the single seed enclosed in a hard inner layer of the ovary, the stone, or sometimes with several seeds, each separately enclosed in a stone.

Entire. The margin not indented in any way. Fig. 19.

Epigynous. The perianth and stamens attached at or near the top of the ovary, the ovary inferior, a condition derived from the fusion of the hypanthium to the ovary. Figs. 52, 53, 54.

Epipetalous. Attached to the petals or corolla.

Epiphyte. A plant growing on another plant or on some other elevated support, not parasitic.

Equitant. Astride, referring to leaves which are folded double lengthwise so as to clasp the stem at base.

Even-pinnate. A pinnately compound leaf with no terminal leaflet and an even number of leaflets.

Exserted. Projecting out or beyond, as stamens from a corolla.

Exstipulate. Without stipules.

F. Forma, a subspecific taxonomic category below the varietas.

Fascicle. A compact bundle or cluster.

Fertile. Capable of normal reproductive function; said of pollen-bearing stamens and seed-bearing fruits. Fertile flower, one capable of producing fruit, therefore one either bisexual or female. Fertile lemma, one subtending a fertile flower.

Filament. The stalk of the stamen, supporting the anther. Fig. 50.

Floral bract. A bract subtending a flower. Fig. 43.

Floret. A small flower; in the grasses, lemma plus palea plus the flower between. Fig. 65.

Floricane. The stem in flowering condition, as contrasted with the same stem in its earlier non-flowering condition, the primocane, in Rubus and similar genera; the primocane is usually the first year's growth, the flowers appearing the second year.

Flower. An axis bearing terminally 1 or more pistils or 1 or more stamens or both, commonly surrounded by protective or attractive structures or both.

-foliolate. With leaflets.

Follicle. A dry dehiscent fruit developed from a single carpel, usually opening along the edge toward the center of the flower.

Free-central placentation. A 1-locular ovary with the ovules attached to a central basally attached placenta which usually does not extend to the apex of the locule. Figs. 57, 58.

Fruit. Broadly, the seed-bearing organ; more narrowly, the ripened ovary with any other parts that become closely associated with it to form an integral unit.

Glabrate. Becoming glabrous or nearly so.

Glabrous. Without hairs or other surface appendages.

Gland. A secreting surface or structure, internal or external, in plants usually producing nectar or oils, often applied to any protuberance or rounded swelling or globular structure appearing gland-like; in Euphorbia, the outgrowths often produced between the bracts of the cyathium (see Euphorbia).

Glandular. Bearing (or containing) glands.

Glandular hairs. Hairs tipped with usually sticky globules.

Glaucous. The surface lightened with a whitish, grayish, or light blue-green coating that rubs off, often waxy in nature.

Glume. In the grasses, either of the two lowest bracts in a typical spikelet. Figs. 62-64.

Gynoecium. A collective term for all the carpels of a flower, whether free or fused.

Head. A dense cluster of sessile or nearly sessile flowers on a very short and often broadened axis. Fig. 47.

Herb. A plant whose stems die back to the ground at the end of the growing season, the stems relatively soft; herbs may be annual, biennial, or perennial.

Hirsute. With rather stiff spreading hairs.

Hood. In Asclepias, the prominent semi-cylindrical structures born on the
    stamen tube at the base of each anther. Fig. 70.

Horn. In Asclepias, the slender pointed structures often borne within the
    hoods, 1 in each. Fig. 70.

Hypanthium. A flat to cup-shaped or tubular structure originating beneath
    the ovary, to which are attached the perianth and stamens; of varying
    origins, in most cases apparently derived from the fusion of the lower
    parts of the perianth and stamens. Fig. 51.

Hypogynous. The perianth and stamens attached beneath the ovary, the
    ovary thus superior. Fig. 50.

Imbricate. With the edges overlapping.

Incised. Cut sharply and irregularly, more or less deeply.

Included. Not protruding from, not exserted.

Indehiscent. Not opening at maturity, usually applied to fruits.

Inferior ovary. One that has become fused to the hypanthium, the perianth
    and stamens thus attached at or near the top of the ovary, the ovary be-
    low them. Figs. 52, 53, 54.

Inflorescence. A flower cluster, including the stems and bracts.

Internode. The part of a stem between one node and the next.

Introrse. Facing the center of the flower.

Involucral bract. A bract of the involucre. Fig. 71.

Involucre. A series of bracts surrounding and closely associated with an in-
    florescence or a single flower.

Involute. The edges rolled inward, toward the upper surface.

Keel. A sharp or conspicuous lengthwise ridge; in the Fabaceae, the 2 lower
    petals together.

Lanceolate. Shaped like a narrow lance-head, several times longer than wide
    and broadest below the middle. Fig. 15.

Leaflet. One division of a compound leaf.

Leaf scar. A scar left on the twig when the leaf falls.

Lemma. Any of the primary bracts of a typical grass spikelet except the
    lower 2. Figs. 62-65.

Ligulate corolla. One form of corolla in the Asteraceae, tubular only at base,
    split most of the way up one side and spread flat. Fig. 73.

Ligule. In the grasses and similar plants, a small flat erect projection from
    the top of the sheath where it joins the blade; in the Asteraceae, a ligulate
    corolla. Figs. 5; 73.

Limb. The upper wide-spreading part of a corolla which is tubular below and
    widened above, or a similar part of some other structure.

Linear. Long and narrow, the sides parallel or nearly so. Fig. 12.

Lip. In the orchids, the distinctive member of the inner perianth whorl,
    morphologically uppermost but usually brought to a lowermost position
    through a twist in the ovary and pedicel. Fig. 68.

Lobed. Prominently cut, generally meaning cut less than half way to the mid-
    rib. Fig. 25.

Locule. A cavity or compartment in an ovary, fruit, or anther.

Loculicidal. Referring to a capsule which splits open opposite the locules
    rather than the partitions.

M. Meter, 3 feet 3.37 inches.

Mericarp. One of the divisions of a dry fruit that splits into separate segments
    at maturity, as in the Apiaceae.

-merous. With a numerical prefix, referring to the number of parts, parti-
    cularly the number in each whorl of the flower.

Mesic. Of medium moisture.

Mm. Millimeter, 1/1000 of a meter, 1/10 of a centimeter.

Monadelphous. In stamens, united into one group by fusion of the filaments.

Monoecious. The flowers unisexual, both sexes on the same plant.

Mucronate. Abruptly tipped with a short sharp almost spine-like point. Fig. 30.

Multiple fruit. A fruit formed from the tightly packed fruits of several to many separate but crowded flowers on a common axis, as in the mulberry or pineapple.

n. The haploid number of chromosomes, the number in the gametes, equal to the number of pairs of chromosomes in nuclei of the vegetative plant body (in seed plants).

Nectar gland or nectary. Any place or organ where nectar is secreted.

Net-veined. Forming a network; the veins running in various directions and often joining each other.

Neuter. Without functional stamens or pistils.

Node. A point on the stem where one or more leaves are or may be borne.

Nut. A hard dry indehiscent 1-seeded fruit.

Nutlet. A small nut, distinguished from an achene only by the relatively thick wall.

Ob-. A Latin prefix usually meaning inversion, as an obovate leaf blade, attached to the petiole at the small end. Figs. 16, 18.

Oblique. Unequal-sided or slanting; asymmetric at base. Fig. 39.

Obsolete. Rudimentary, vestigial, not evident or apparent.

Obtuse. Blunt or rounded at the end. Fig. 32.

Ocrea. A tubular sheath around the stem just above the leaf base formed by the fusion of the stipules.

Odd-pinnate. A pinnately compound leaf with a terminal leaflet and an odd number of leaflets.

Opposite. Two at a node, on opposite sides of the stem; or situated directly in front of another organ, as stamens opposite the petals. Fig. 2.

Ovary. The ovule-bearing part of the pistil. Fig. 50.

Ovate. In outline like a hen's egg, the widest point below the middle. Fig. 17.

Ovule. The body which, after fertilization, becomes the seed.

Palea. In the grass floret, the bract next the axis of the spikelet. Figs. 64, 65.

Palmate. With 3 or more nerves, lobes, leaflets, or other structures arising from one point, as the fingers of the hand. Figs. 2, 6, 10.

Panicle. A branched raceme, the flowers stalked, the youngest ones at the apex; often applied to any loosely branched inflorescence. Fig. 45.

Papillose. The surface bearing short, blunt or rounded, nipple-like projections.

Pappus. A series of few to many scales, bristles, or other appendages in the position of the calyx, in the Asteraceae. Figs. 72, 73.

Parallel venation. Fig. 3.

Parasitic. Growing on and deriving nourishment from another living organism.

Parietal placentation. The ovules borne on the inner surface of a compound ovary or on intrusions from the inner wall that do not reach the center, forming incomplete partitions. Fig. 56.

Parted. Cut more than half way but not quite to the base or midrib. Fig. 26.

Pedicel. The stalk of one flower in a cluster.

Peduncle. The stalk of a flower cluster, or of a single flower when it is the only one on the flowering stem.

Peltate. Attached to the stalk on the under surface away from the margin. Fig.40.

Pendulous ovule. One attached at or near the top of the locule, hanging downward.

Perennial. Living 3 or usually more years.

Perfect. A flower having both stamens and pistils present and functional; bisexual.

Perfoliate. The leaf or bract sessile with its base completely surrounding the stem, the stem seeming to pass through the leaf. Fig. 41.

Perianth. The non-reproductive flower parts surrounding the stamens, clos-
ing the flower in the bud, mostly protective or attractive in function or both,
undifferentiated or differentiated into calyx and corolla. Fig. 50.

Perigynium. The bract completely encircling the ovary in Carex, its edges
joined to make a structure open only at the apex. Fig. 66.

Perigynous. A flower with a hypanthium which is free from the ovary, the
ovary thus superior. Fig. 51.

Petal. One separate division of the corolla.

Petiole. The stalk of a leaf. Fig. 1.

Pilose. Rather sparsely hairy with soft spreading hairs.

Pinnate. Specifically, pinnately compound; generally, with veins, lobes,
leaflets, or branches arranged along opposite sides of an axis. Figs. 1,
7, 8, 11.

Pinnately compound. The leaflets arranged along both sides of an elongate
leaf axis. Figs. 7, 11. Twice pinnately compound, fig. 8.

Pinnatifid. Deeply cut pinnately. Fig. 26.

Pistil. An externally visible female (ovule-producing) organ of the flower,
1 or more being present in the center of the flower. This term takes no
account of internal structure when used without qualification. See simple
and compound pistil. Fig. 50.

Pistillate. Having one or more pistils and no functional stamens; female.

Placenta. A place or part inside the ovary where ovules are attached.

Placentation. The arrangement of the ovules within the ovary.

Plumose. Feathery; having fine and elongate hairs closely placed along an
axis.

Pod. Strictly, the fruit of the Fabaceae; loosely, a general term for any
dry dehiscent fruit.

Pollen sac. Properly, an individual microsporangium of the anther, but
sometimes applied to each pair of sporangia in a 4-sporangiate anther.

Polygamo-dioecious. The flowers on some plants partly bisexual and partly
pistillate, on others partly bisexual and partly staminate.

Polygamous. With bisexual and unisexual flowers on the same plant.

Polyploid. A plant with 3 or more full haploid sets of chromosomes per
nucleus.

Pome. A fleshy fruit formed from an inferior ovary, of which the apple is
typical, the ovary portion being relatively small, the fleshy part developed
largely from the hypanthium.

Primocane. The first year's stem of a biennial or rarely longer-lived somewhat woody plant such as Rubus and similar genera, vegetative only, the
flowers appearing later.

Puberulent. Minutely pubescent, the hairs scarcely visible to the unaided eye.

Pubescent. Bearing hairs on the surface, in particular short soft and down-
like hairs.

Raceme. An unbranched more or less elongate inflorescence with stalked
flowers, the lowest opening first. Fig. 43.

Rachilla. In the grasses, the axis of the spikelet above the lowest glume.
Fig. 64.

Rachis. The axis of a compound leaf or of an inflorescence.

Radial symmetry. See Regular.

Ray flower. In the head of the Asteraceae, an outer flower with a ligulate
corolla, when the central flowers have tubular corollas. Figs. 71, 72.

Receptacle. The end of the individual flower stalk, bearing the floral organs;
in the Asteraceae, the broadened end of the peduncle bearing the flowers
of the head.

Receptacle bract. A bract subtending an individual flower within the head, in the Asteraceae. Fig. 72.

Regular. Radially symmetrical, the different members of each whorl of parts similar in size and shape, the flower vertically divisible into equal halves in 2 or more planes.

Revolute. The edges rolled under toward the midrib; or any object rolled backward from the apex.

Rhizome. An underground stem, usually horizontal, short or elongate, usually sending off roots from the lower side and leafy stems from the upper, distinguished from a root by the presence of nodes, regularly spaced buds, or sometimes scale-like leaves, as well as by its internal structure.

Rhombic. Diamond-shaped; an oblique-angled equilateral parallelogram.

Rootstock. A rhizome, the term especially used when the rhizome is short and compact.

Samara. A dry indehiscent fruit with 1 or more well-developed wings, usually 1-seeded.

Saprophyte. A plant living on dead organic matter, usually without chlorophyll.

Savanna. Grassland with scattered trees.

Scabrous. Rough to the touch, due to the presence of very short stiff hairs or other projections.

Scale. Any small thin or flat structure; in the Boraginaceae, swellings or outgrowths of the corolla in its throat, opposite the lobes.

Scape. A leafless flowering stem rising directly from the ground or from a very short stem, with 1 or more flowers, with or without bracts but without foliage leaves.

Scarious. Thin, dry, not green, somewhat papery or membranaceous in texture, often more or less translucent.

Seed. A ripened ovule, consisting of the embryo and seed coat or coats, with or without additional storage tissues.

Sepal. One separate division of the calyx.

Septicidal. Referring to a capsule which splits open at the partitions rather than opposite the locules.

Serrate. Toothed along the margin, the teeth sharp and angled toward the leaf apex. Fig. 21.

Serrulate. Finely serrate.

Sessile. Without a stalk.

Sheath. A more or less tubular structure surrounding another organ, as the lower part of the grass leaf. Fig. 5.

Shrub. A woody plant, smaller than a tree, usually with several stems; not an exact term.

Simple. A leaf not divided to the midrib; an unbranched structure such as an inflorescence; the opposite of compound. Figs. 1, 2, 42-44, 48.

Simple pistil. A single carpel.

Sinus. The cleft or notch between two lobes or teeth.

Sp. Species.

Spadix. A very short to long spike with a thick or fleshy axis, the flowers usually closely crowded, as in the Araceae. Fig. 67.

Spathe. A large bract subtending and often enclosing an inflorescence, usually single, the term used only in the Monocotyledons. Fig. 67.

Spatulate. Oblanceolate with broadly rounded apex, or the wide part oblong.

Spike. An elongate unbranched inflorescence with sessile or very nearly sessile flowers, the lowest opening first, the term sometimes loosely applied. Fig. 42.

Spikelet. A small or secondary spike; see the Poaceae. Figs. 62-64.

Sporophyll. An organ bearing 1 or more sporangia, in many cases thought to be a modified leaf.

Spur. A hollow sac-like or tubular projection, usually from the corolla or calyx, usually nectar-producing.

Ssp. Subspecies, a taxonomic category below the species.

Stamen. A pollen-producing organ of the flower, typically consisting of anther and filament. Fig. 50.

Staminate. Having stamens and no functioning pistils; male.

Staminode, staminodium. A sterile stamen, often without an anther, often highly modified and judged to be a stamen only by its position.

Standard. In the Fabaceae, the uppermost petal, in a typical flower; in Iris, a member of the inner perianth whorl.

Sterigma (plural, sterigmata). As used here, a short hard stalk at the leaf base, persistent after leaf fall. Fig. 60.

Sterile. Incapable of normal reproductive function. Sterile flower, one incapable of producing fruit, therefore one either male or neuter. Sterile lemma, one subtending a sterile flower.

Stigma. The part of the pistil that receives the pollen, usually distinguished by a surface that is sticky, minutely papillose, or otherwise modified for reception. Figs. 50, 65.

Stipules. A pair of small structures at the base of the petiole of some leaves, one on each side, varying from minute to leaf-like, persistent or falling early. Fig. 1.

Stolon. A more or less horizontal above-ground stem arising at or near the base of the plant, touching ground and taking root and developing new plants at the nodes or apex.

Style. The narrowed more or less elongated upper part of many pistils, between the ovary and stigma, usually but not always present. Fig. 50.

Sub-. A Latin prefix, used in the sense of nearly, not quite, or somewhat.

Subsp. Subspecies, a taxonomic category below the species.

Subtend. Placed immediately below, as a bract subtends a flower in the axil of the bract.

Subulate. Awl-shaped, tapering from base to apex to a sharp point.

Superior ovary. One free to its base from perianth or hypanthium, these when present attached beside or below it. Figs. 50, 51.

Syncarp. A multiple or fleshy aggregate fruit, as the mulberry or Magnolia.

Tendril. A part of a stem or leaf modified into a slender twining thread-like holding organ.

Tepal. A member of a perianth not clearly differentiated into calyx and corolla.

Ternate. Generally, in 3's; specifically, ternately compound: once ternate, with three leaflets.

Throat. In a calyx or corolla with a tubular lower part and a wide-spreading upper part, the region of the junction of the two parts.

Tomentose. Woolly, densely covered with curly matted hairs.

Tomentum. A dense covering of curly matted hairs.

Tree. A relatively tall woody plant with one main trunk.

Trifoliolate. Having 3 leaflets. Figs. 10, 11.

Triternate. The leaflets of a biternate leaf each again divided into 3. Fig. 9.

Truncate. The apex or base straight transversely or nearly so, as if cut off at right angles to the length. Fig. 33.

Tuber. A short thickened stem, usually subterranean, beset with buds or "eyes", serving for food storage; sometimes also applied to similar organs developed from roots.

Umbel. A flat-topped or rounded inflorescence with flowers whose stalks arise from a common point, resembling the stays of an umbrella, the outer flowers typically blooming first. In a compound umbel each of the stalks terminates not in a flower but in another smaller umbel, an umbellet. Figs. 48, 49.

Umbellate. Arranged in umbels.

Umbellet. One of the small umbels terminating the branches of a compound umbel. Fig. 49.

Umbo. In Pinus, a small differentiated area of the apophysis, usually raised, often rhombic in outline, often bearing a prickle. Fig. 61.

Undulate. Wavy-edged. Fig. 20.

Unisexual. Of 1 sex; bearing functional stamens or pistils but not both.

Valvate. With the edges meeting and not overlapping (referring to the perianth);opening by valves, as in a capsule.

Valve. A portion of the wall of a fruit or other part that separates from the rest at maturity, or one of the partial segments into which the object splits.

Var. Varietas, a taxonomic category below the subspecies.

Villous. Bearing fine long hairs, not matted or interwoven or only obscurely so.

Whorl. A circle of 3 or more leaves or other parts arising from the same node.

Wing. Any thin dry flat often membranous appendage or border of an organ; in the Fabaceae, the lateral petals.

Winter annual. A plant which begins growth in fall and completes its life cycle the following year.

Zygomorphic. Having bilateral symmetry; divisible into equal halves in one plane only, as in humans.

INDEX

INDEX TO COUNTIES

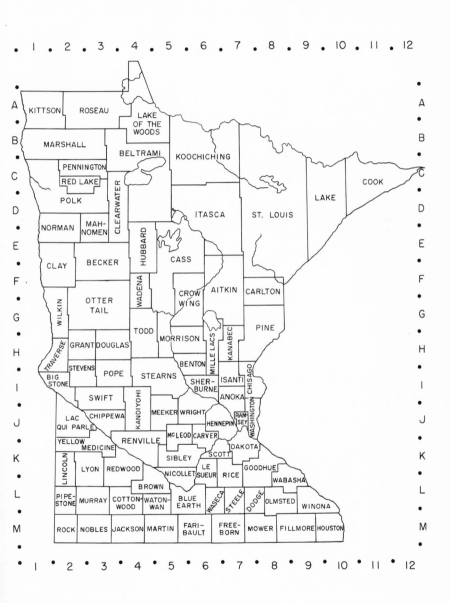